D1256452

NARCOTIC ADDICTS IN KENTUCKY

BY JOHN A. O'DONNELL, Ph.D.

Chief, Research Branch, NIMH Clinical Research Center
Lexington, Kentucky

DEPARTMENT OF
HEALTH, EDUCATION, AND WELFARE
PUBLIC HEALTH SERVICE
HEALTH SERVICES AND MENTAL HEALTH ADMINISTRATION
NATIONAL INSTITUTE OF MENTAL HEALTH
5454 WISCONSIN AVENUE
CHEVY CHASE, MARYLAND 20015

Public Health Service Publication No. 1881

PRINTED 1969

For sale by the Superintendent of Documents, U.S. Government Printing Office
Washington, D.C. 20402 - Price $3

Contents

LIST OF TABLES

Table Page

Author's Preface

The planning for this study, and the administrative arrangements which made it possible, were facilitated by Murray A. Diamond, M.D. and Robert W. Rasor, M.D., Medical Officers in Charge of the United States Public Health Service Hospital, Lexington, Kentucky, and by James V. Lowry, M.D., former Chief, Bureau of Medical Services, U.S. Public Health Service. Technical consultation in the design of the study, and in sample selection, were provided by Robert Straus, Ph.D. and Alan Ross, Ph.D., Department of Behavioral Science, University of Kentucky Medical Center, Lexington, Kentucky.

At various times the following staff of the Social Science Section, Addiction Research Center, assisted in the analysis of data: Mrs. Emily Cottrell, Mr. Dennis Dedrick, Miss Darjeel Heffelfinger, Mrs. Judith Jones, Mr. Robert L. Whitten and Mrs. Dona Wilson. Mrs. Doris Giannasio typed the several drafts of the report, with the assistance of Mrs. Evelyn Marshall. Mrs. Patricia Burton handled all of the clerical work involved in the data-collection stage of the study, much of the abstracting of hospital records, and was invaluable in coordinating the various activities of other staff. In later stages similar services were performed by Mrs. Doris Cash, Mrs. Betty Tuttle, Mrs. Helen Mull and Mrs. Marge Phillips.

Mr. William F. Owsley, Chief of General Services at the Lexington hospital, participated in the planning of the study and conducted some of the field interviews. The bulk of the field work was done by Mr. Karst J. Besteman, then on the Social Service staff of the hospital. Without his ingenuity, patience and perseverance in tracing subjects, and his unusual ability to obtain their cooperation and that of their relatives and other informants, the study could not have been successful.

Anna J. Eisenman, Ph.D. and Charles R. Brown, Jr., of the Biochemistry Unit of the Addiction Research Center, tested for opiates and barbiturates the urine specimens obtained from subjects.

Many physicians, County Health Department staff, police and other local officials provided information about subjects which was invaluable. They cannot be named, because identifying them would mean identifying the counties in the sample, and the subjects in the study, but I would like to express my appreciation for all the help they gave. Russell E. Teague, M.D., Commisisoner of Health in Kentucky, Mr. Strawn Taylor and Mr. Martin Niswonger of his staff, supplied information about subjects, traced death certificates, coded causes of deaths in other states, and furnished statistical data needed.

Records on veterans were obtained through the courtesy of Aaron S. Mason, M.D., Superintendent, and W. Arthur Theobald, Chief Social Worker, of the Veterans Administration Hospital, Lexington. Commissioner Henry Giordano, of the Bureau of Narcotics, opened the Bureau's files for checking, and Mr. H. Emmett Corrick and Mr. Charles Rhodes of his staff spent several days each in facilitating the search for files on subjects. Similar record searches were arranged in the files of the Kentucky Department of Prisons by Mr. Harold Black, and of the Kentucky Probation and Parole files by Mr. James Wells.

I am also indebted to James F. Maddux, M.D., Medical Officer in Charge of the U.S. Public Health Service Hospital at Fort Worth, Texas, and to Sherman N. Kieffer, M.D. and Arthur K. Berliner of his staff for supplying data on subjects from the hospital files. Drs. Maddux and Kieffer also reviewed the first draft of this report, as did Drs. Rasor and Warren P. Jurgensen of the Lexington hospital, and my colleagues at the Addiction Research Center, William M. Bates, Ph.D., B. E. Jones, Ph.D. and William R. Martin, M.D. The final draft profited greatly from their suggestions. I owe another debt of thanks particularly to another colleague, John C. Ball, Ph.D. who was conducting a similar study in Puerto Rico, for regular consultation, many helpful suggestions, and for his careful review of the report.

Above all, I am grateful to the addicts who were subjects in this study, and their relatives, whose readiness to supply information, sometimes at inconvenient times, occasionally at the cost of re-awakening painful memories, and at the risk that the information might harm them, made the study possible. The study could not be beneficial to them, but most of them hoped it might be helpful to others, and cooperated fully.

The study was initially supported by grant (M-4014) from the National Institute of Mental Health, when the writer was on the Social Service staff of the Lexington hospital.

Parts of several chapters have been reported before in the following papers:

1. "A Post-Hospital Study of Kentucky Addicts—A Preliminary Report," *Journal of Kentucky Medical Association,* Vol. 61 (July, 1963), pp. 573–577, 604.
2. "A Follow-up of Narcotic Addicts—Mortality, Relapse, and Abstinence," *American Journal of Orthopsychiatry,* Vol. 34 (October, 1964), pp. 948–954.
3. "Narcotic Addiction and Crime," *Social Problems,* Vol. 13 (Spring, 1966), pp. 374–385.

4. "Marital History of Narcotics Addicts," *International Journal of the Addictions,* Vol. 2, No. 1 (Spring, 1967).
5. "The Rise and Decline of a Subculture," *Social Problems,* Vol. 15, No. 1 (Summer, 1967), pp. 73–84.
6. "The Relapse Rate in Narcotic Addiction: A Critique of Follow-up Studies," *Narcotics,* ed. Daniel M. Wilner and Gene G. Kassebaum (New York: McGraw-Hill, Inc., 1965), pp. 226–246.
7. "Research Problems in Follow-up Studies of Addicts," *Rehabilitating the Narcotic Addict,* ed. S. B. Sells (Washington, D.C.: U.S. Government Printing Office, 1967), pp. 321–334.

CHAPTER 1

Aims and Methods

The United States Public Health Service Hospital in Lexington, Kentucky, was established in May, 1935 for the treatment of narcotic addicts. By December, 1965 about 45,000 addicts had been admitted for a total of about 75,000 admissions. Most were voluntary patients, admitted on their own application, with about one-fourth of the admissions representing Federal prisoners or probationers sent to the hospital for treatment. The hospital treatment program included withdrawal of narcotics, treatment of general medical and surgical problems, psychotherapy to the extent that staff limitations and patients' motivation permitted, vocational training, and maintenance of a drug-free therapeutic environment in which patients' attitudes and personalities might be modified.[1]

The hospital staff and others have long recognized that hospitalization alone is usually not sufficient for the rehabilitation of addicts. They have advocated posthospital services for patients in their communities, to maintain the benefits of hospitalization and prevent relapse, but such services have rarely been available to or used by discharged patients, except for the relatively small number of prisoners and probationers discharged under the supervision of Federal Probation officers.

Some followup studies have been done to discover how patients adjusted after discharge from the hospital, with emphasis on their use of or abstinence from narcotics. Such studies are potentially valuable in several ways. To the extent that some patients are found to remain abstinent after release, while others relapse, it may be possible to identify some parts of the hospital treatment program as more effective than others. Relapse and abstinence are associated with posthospital variables too; as these are identified, the hospital may be better able to prepare patients for the posthospital problems they will face, and community programs can perhaps be designed to assist in their solution. Finally, in the United States today, and for at least the past few generations, the natural history of addiction has consisted largely in cyclical patterns of treatment, abstinence and relapse; studies which cover some period of time after any point in the cycle can contribute to knowledge of that natural history.

Previous Followup Studies

Other followup studies will be discussed, and their findings compared with those of this study, at several points in this report. At this time these studies will be discussed only in relation to those aspects which had some influence on the design of this study.

The first followup of Lexington patients was done by Pescor, who collected data on 4,766 male patients discharged from the hospital between January 1, 1936 and December 31, 1940.[2] Data were obtained, from 6 months to 6 years after release, from four sources: the records of readmitted patients; Federal Bureau of Investigation reports on subsequent arrests of those patients who had been prisoners or probationers; reports of Probation Officers on those patients who were or had been under their supervision; and replies to letters of inquiry sent periodically to former patients or to their relatives. Pescor reported that 7 percent of the former patients were dead, 14 percent abstinent, 40 percent relapsed, and 40 percent were classed as unknown (percentages rounded).[3]

Kuznesof reports a study of 83 persons discharged from Lexington in the period 1949–53.[4] They had been placed on probation by the Federal Court of the Southern District of New York, with treatment at Lexington ordered as one of the conditions of probation. While the focus of the report is on the success or failure of probation (most were declared violators of probation), it is clear that most of this group relapsed to drug use.

Hunt and Odoroff report a more recent study of 1,912 patients discharged from the Lexington hospital between July 17, 1952 and December 31, 1955, after completing detoxification.[5] All subjects were residents of New York City. Data were obtained from official records of arrests and treatment and, in a large but unspecified proportion of cases, from interviews with the former patients or their relatives. Of the 1,881 patients on whom data were secured, 90.1 percent were judged to be readdicted and 6.6 percent abstinent; 3.3 percent used narcotics irregularly, or their addiction status could not be determined.

Duvall, Locke, and Brill have reported a continuation of the Hunt-Odoroff study, in which a subsample of 453 subjects was followed to a date 5 years after discharge for each subject.[6] Among their findings was an increase in abstinence with the passage of time. At 6 months after discharge, only 9 percent of the patients were voluntarily abstinent; at 2 years 17 percent, and at 5 years 25 percent were voluntarily abstinent.

Vaillant also did a followup study of 100 patients from New York City who were first admitted to Lexington in 1952.[7] In 1965 he reported that, while almost all had relapsed at one time or another after release, the proportion free of drugs increased steadily with time, so that 12 years after release almost half were drug free.

These are the only previous followup studies on Lexington patients. Similar studies have, however, been done on addicts released from other institutions.[8] In general, these other studies also found high relapse rates.

The followup studies suggest that a number of factors may be associated with relapse and abstinence. Prisoners, or perhaps only prisoners released on parole, seem to be abstinent more often than voluntary patients. Age seems to be related to relapse, with higher abstinence rates among older subjects. Several studies suggest a relationship, albeit a weak one, between length of hospitalization and relapse, with very short and also, possibly, very long periods of treatment associated with higher relapse rates. The relationship of sex and race to relapse is not clear or consistent in those studies which report on these variables.[9]

Three findings seem reasonably well established by these studies. Relapse, if it does occur, tends to occur quickly after release from the institution. Second, the Duvall and Vaillant studies suggest that even when relapse occurs, abstinence increases with time. Third, though most of the studies mention deaths only briefly, the death rate among their subjects is high.

It is difficult to compare the different followup studies. They collected data from different sources and by different methods, and most do not describe their methodology. Even if the reader could assume that the data were comparable, he could not be sure that the procedures by which the data are combined into the classifications used were equally careful and rigorous from one study to another.

None of the studies discusses in detail the problems of classifying a subject as relapsed or abstinent. Addiction status is, however, not a visible characteristic which the investigator simply observes and records, but rather is a judgment he makes on the basis of different kinds of evidence. The quality of his judgment and the weight of the evidence on which it is based are clearly factors to be considered before the findings of the study are accepted.

It is clear in some studies that classification as relapsed is based most often on subjects' statements that they relapsed. This is reasonable enough. But it is evident that a subject's denial of relapse could not be accepted as sufficient evidence to classify him as abstinent, and most of the studies do not specify what confirmation of this denial was required before subjects were so classified. This lack of concern as to what evidence is sufficient to classify subjects as abstinent probably is related to the fact that high relapse rates were commonly found. If the finding is that the vast majority relapsed, it does not matter much if errors exist in the classification of the few remaining subjects as abstinent.

That few factors have been established to be associated with relapse and abstinence is also explained partly by high relapse rates. The key method of identifying such factors is comparison of the relapsed subjects with the abstinent. If almost all subjects fall in the relapsed category and almost none in the abstinent, statistical comparisons of the two groups are not likely to identify significant differences on other variables.

The procedures and definitions used in most studies were such as to minimize the group classed as abstinent, and maximize the number of relapsed. This bias toward relapse arises from two causes. First, in some studies the percentage of unlocated subjects is high. Since relapsed addicts are likely to return to the institution where the study is conducted, or to go to other institutions voluntarily or after arrests, they are relatively easy to locate; those who are difficult to locate, because they have not been arrested or reinstitutionalized, are likely to include many of the abstinent. This plausible hypothesis is supported by the finding of Trussell and his associates, that those patients whom they had most difficulty in locating showed a higher percentage abstinent. To ensure that abstinent patients have an equal chance of being represented, therefore, requires that close to 100 percent of the subjects be located.

The second cause is that many studies define as relapsed those subjects who used narcotics at any point in the time period covered by the followup, and for any portion of that period. They define as abstinent only those who did not use narcotics during the entire followup period. As an example, in the Hunt-Odoroff study relapse was defined as daily drug use for 2 weeks or more, during a followup period of up to 5 years. If subjects were followed for 5 years, only those were counted as abstinent who used no drugs in the entire 5 years. Grouped together as readdicted could be: some who used drugs the entire 5 years; some who were abstinent up to the last 2 weeks, and then relapsed; some who used drugs for the first 2 weeks, and then were abstinent for the remainder of the 5 years; and a large number of subgroups who were abstinent for varying periods, between the extremes described.

Such grouping of widely diverse patterns of drug behavior into a single category is inevitable if only two categories, relapse and abstinence, are used. It would clearly be preferable, if feasible, to use intermediate categories too, and to conceive of relapse behavior along a continuum ranging from spending all of the followup period using narcotics to spending none of it in drug use.

Goals of the Study

A major goal of this study was methodological, to contribute to the development of feasible followup methods. It was intended to answer such questions as: Can patients discharged many years earlier, as well as recent discharges, be located; what kinds of data can be obtained, and from what sources; can these data be combined into reliable and valid measures of posthospital behavior, in more detail than the simple relapse-abstinence dichotomy; would it be possible to obtain objective evidence of relapse and abstinence for one point in time by getting urine specimens from subjects?

Assuming that a good measure of posthospital drug behavior could be devised, it could be related to the variables used in other studies, and additional variables which might be abstracted from hospital records, to see to what extent these predict posthospital behavior. Merely to know the percentage of patients who relapse is of trivial scientific value; what is needed is an understanding of the determinants of relapse and abstinence.

In this connection, there were four questions of theoretical importance the study might answer. One relates to urban-rural differences. Most previous studies, and particularly the more recent and better designed studies, were restricted to metropolitan areas. Those which included nonmetropolitan addicts did not report on urban-rural differences. But such differences have been found with respect to other kinds of behavior, and might exist with respect to relapse after treatment for addiction.

Another relates to the self concept of the addict. Most addicts admitted to the hospital from large metropolitan areas perceive themselves as essentially healthy persons who use narcotics—usually heroin—for "kicks." Many addicts admitted from the Southern States perceive themselves as being ill, and as using narcotics—rarely heroin—as medicine. Again, it is conceivable that relapse after treatment might vary with such a difference in self concept.

In metropolitan areas, the source of narcotics is primarily an illicit market. Such a market could not exist where there are only a few addicts, and it is known that many Southern addicts receive their drugs only from legal sources. This difference in the source of drugs might be related to relapse behavior.

Finally, most addicts from metropolitan areas are part of a drug subculture, and frequently such addicts attribute relapse to the influence of old associates whom they meet again. In rural areas there might be so few addicts that this cause of relapse would be absent.

The variables in these questions—urban *vs.* rural, kicks *vs.* medicine, illicit *vs.* legal source, and presence *vs.* absence of addict associates—might be stated as hypotheses, in the form that one of each pair would be associated with relapse and the other with abstinence. A case could be made for predicting that the first in each pair would be more closely associated with relapse, but with the exception of the last, it was easy to conceive of possible situations which would reverse the relationship. For example, addicts who depended on illicit sources might be more likely than users of legally obtained narcotics to relapse, but if illicit narcotics were blocked more effectively than legal drugs, they might be forced into abstinence more often. Further, it seemed probable that the sets of variables would be empirically related, and their interaction might be more important than their individual effect. The second major goal of the study, therefore, was to determine how such variables were related to relapse, but the directions of individual relationships were not stated in hypothetical form.

335-199—69——2

The third goal was to study the death rate in the sample. The study would determine how many subjects had died and whether this number was greater than would be expected. If so, it would try to discover what factors accounted for the high death rate.

Two of these goals required that some subjects in the sample be selected from the early admissions to Lexington, as much as 25 years before the study could start. Their inclusion would make possible a test of how long after discharge data could be obtained, and would increase the number of deaths to be studied. If early admissions were included, many in the sample would be dead, and the living subjects would be fairly old. The data would then cover the entire life span of part of the sample, and almost the full life span for the remainder. This would make possible a fourth goal, the description of the natural history of addiction in the sample. This goal, it will be seen, took on major importance, and most of this report deals with the natural history of addiction in the sample.

The goals, therefore, required that a long time span be covered in the followup. All could be achieved if the sample were chosen from Kentucky residents. Kentucky includes a range from some of the most isolated and rural areas in the United States to several metropolitan areas. It was known that many Kentucky addicts used narcotics obtained legally, while others used illicit narcotics. For these variables Kentucky would be preferable to other possible locations, and for other purposes it would serve as well as any other location. Since Kentucky offered the additional advantage that it would be easier and cheaper, working from the hospital, to locate ex-patients who lived nearby, it was decided to restrict the sample to Kentucky patients.

Methods

The sample. A sample of 266 white patients from Kentucky was selected by a stratified random procedure, which is described in detail in Appendix A. Counties rather than individuals were the sampling units, except that individual patients were selected from the two largest metropolitan counties. The sampling procedure was designed to overrepresent the more rural counties, and those which had sent only one or a few patients to the hospital, because such overrepresentation was needed to provide enough cases for the study of urban-rural and subculture differences.

Since a stratified procedure was used, and some patients had a greater chance than others to be selected into the sample, estimates of percentages in the sampling universe from findings in the study should employ weights. This will not be done in following chapters, because the primary interest of the study is not in such estimates, but in the relations between variables within the sample.

Strictly speaking, generalizations from findings are statistically justified only to white patients who were residents of Kentucky on their first admission to Lexington. There is no statistical justification to generalize from this sample to addicts in general. The sample subjects are largely rural, white, and Anglo-Saxon; the typical addict of today is metropolitan and nonwhite, or a member of an ethnic minority group. Even subjects from the metropolitan areas of Kentucky cannot be assumed to be typical of white addicts from New York, Chicago, and Los Angeles.

On the other hand, it is reasonable to believe that the sample studied here is representative of a still fairly large number of addicts from the southern and midwestern states, and quite possibly of a fair number of addicts even in such states as New York, Illinois, and California. The current emphasis on the urban addict who obtains heroin on the illicit market may well have masked the continued existence of other addicts who obtain legal narcotics by means similar to those found in this sample.

It is also reasonable to believe that this sample may shed some light on the history of the addiction problem in the United States. Those who are familiar with the description of addicts in the older literature will be struck by the similarities between the subjects in this study and those described a generation or two ago. Such similarities are found in the high proportion whose drug use began in the context of medical treatment, or treatment of alcoholism, who used morphine rather than heroin, and who obtained it from legal sources. Indeed, the sample includes some subjects whose drug use began before the passage of the Harrison Narcotic Act, and before the public attitudes toward drug use had become strongly negative.

In the opinion of the writer, the resemblances between these subjects and some other addicts living today, and between them and the addicts of several generations ago, are strong enough to warrant some extrapolation of findings to those groups. The primary interest of the study, however, is not in making such extrapolations. It is rather to relate the relapse and abstinence behavior of these subjects to such factors as self-concept, involvement in a drug subculture, the source of drugs, and the reasons for beginning drug use. Inferences about the behavior of other individuals or groups will then be justified to the extent that the individuals, their histories, and the circumstances they face after treatment resemble those described here. The statistical procedures followed in the selection of the sample have their major importance in the fact that, with respect to the variables studied here, findings will not be biased by the selection of cases studied. Generalizing these findings to other groups must be based on specific evidence or plausible assumption that the other groups resemble this sample.

Specific Goals. The study aimed to locate and interview all of the subjects who were still alive, and to obtain a urine specimen from each subject who was not in a hospital or a prison. The urine test for opiates is the most objective and most reliable basis for a conclusion that a person is or is not currently using narcotics. It is even preferable to observation in a drug-free institution for detection of infrequent use or of regular doses so small that cessation would not produce withdrawal symptoms.

Urine specimens would supply part of the needed evidence of narcotics use or abstinence at the time the specimen was produced. For past periods of time, however, no equally objective evidence could be obtained. If a subject admitted addiction for some or all of the period between his first admission to Lexington and the time of the interview, this might be accepted as sufficient evidence. Even for such admissions, confirmation would be desirable. Several Lexington patients who had been subjects in followup studies in New York later claimed they had admitted relapse to interviewers long before it actually occurred, as the quickest and easiest way of terminating the interviews.

But when subjects claimed periods of abstinence, their statements alone could not be accepted as sufficient evidence. Interviews therefore were to be sought with close relatives, and with family physicians if at all possible, as the persons who might be able to confirm or deny the claim. Information was also to be sought in these interviews on other aspects of adjustment, particularly on employment, criminal record, and other behavior which might furnish a basis for inferences about the truth or falsity of their claims, as well as for the inherent value of this information. All official records which might furnish useful information were to be checked, if this could be done without identifying subjects as ex-addicts to other persons.

For those subjects who were dead, a copy of the death certificate was to be obtained. With respect to past drug use or abstinence, the interviews and record checks were to be the same as for the living subjects.

Locating Subjects and Informants. The field trips to locate subjects and other informants began in March 1961 and were ended in October 1963. Of the 266 subjects, 144 had died before the attempt to locate them. Of the remaining 122, 118 had been interviewed by October 1963.

Table 1.1 shows where subjects were located, or where they had died. Almost two-thirds of the subjects were found, or had died, in the same county from which they were first admitted. Three-quarters were located or had died in Kentucky. Since a few residents of Kentucky were interviewed in other States, and more had died in hospitals outside of Ken-

Table 1.1. Places where subjects were located, or died, by sex

	Male		Female		Total
	Living	Dead	Living	Dead	
Kentucky county of first admission	53	72	22	13	160
Other Kentucky county	14	22	4	2	42
Indiana	6	7	5	--	18
Ohio	1	4	1	2	8
Florida	2	4	--	1	7
Tennessee	2	4	--	1	7
West Virginia	1	5	--	--	6
California	2	2	--	--	4
Georgia	1	1	--	--	2
Michigan	--	1	--	1	2
Mississippi	--	1	1	--	2
Missouri	1	--	--	--	1
North Carolina	1	--	--	--	1
Virginia	1	--	--	--	1
Texas	--	1	--	--	1
Not located	3	--	1	--	4
Total	88	124	34	20	266

tucky, the geographical mobility of the sample was even less than indicated by the table.

Twenty-two percent of the subjects had left the State and continued to reside in another State up to the time of interview or death. Since the mean period from first admission to that time was 11.25 years, the outmigration in the sample averaged about 2 percent per year. It is known that the outmigration from Kentucky is greater than from most other States, and that, in the 5-year period 1955–1960, 9.2 percent of the white population of the United States had moved from one State to another, almost 2 percent per year. Further, the Kentucky counties represented in the sample included many whose outmigration was above the average for the State; 17 of the 36 counties had lost over 20 percent of their 1950 population by migration between 1950 and 1960.[10] It may be inferred, therefore, that outmigration in the sample was not appreciably greater than would be expected for comparable nonaddicts in Kentucky.

While only 24 percent of the 122 living subjects had to be sought in other States, table 1.1 shows that the migrants were widely distributed. Subjects were located in 13 States, in addition to Kentucky, and field trips were necessary to cities as distant as Key West, Florida, and Los Angeles, California.

Locating a subject began with a visit to the community from which he had first been admitted. The county health department and Chief of Police were usually visited first. Particularly in rural areas, the health department was a valuable source of information on the adjustment of patients, including their drug use, and could often direct the interviewer to the subject's current address or could locate his death certificate. The police were less valuable mainly because the interviewers felt less free to discuss individual subjects with them.

There was little difficulty in locating those subjects who had remained in the county from which they were originally admitted. In rural counties two or three inquiries would suffice to produce an informant who could direct the interviewer to the subject, or say approximately when he had died. In larger cities more persistence was needed, because neighbors did not know each other as well, and frequently were less ready than in small towns to help a stranger find someone they knew. But in the larger cities the addicts usually knew each other, so that when one subject was found, he could help to locate others.

When subjects had left the county and the State, even many years before, field staff were often helped by the fact that family ties were strong enough so that local informants could say where and when they had died, or in what city they were still living. Only a few had moved to rural areas; in one case it was known only that a subject had moved to a farm in north central Tennessee, and the interviewer spent 2 days driving through several counties, checking with postmasters and crossroads stores, until he found someone who could direct him to the subject. When subjects had moved to large cities, telephone and city directories were useful for those who had made some kind of stable adjustment, and police and local hospital records for the skidrow residents.

Two groups, women and skidrow men, posed particular problems of location. Women married and remarried, changing their names and usually their addresses with each marriage. It was sometimes easy enough to locate a woman after the new community and name were known, but it could take weeks of correspondence and of locating relatives or friends before the new name and city were discovered. Those women who were prostitutes tended to move frequently. When the city of her current residence was established, the interviewer's problem was to locate someone in contact with the subject, who could take him to her. In one case a vice squad officer picked the interviewer up in an unmarked car, drove him to the brothel where she worked, and waited outside while he conducted the interview.

The other difficult group was those men who had become alcoholics, and who lived in skidrow areas of large cities. One of the three unlocated men, for example, was a subject who moved from one room to another every few days. He had a history of being picked up as drunk at one street corner in Chicago almost every week for years. Two interviewers each spent a couple of days and nights in Chicago, visiting the bars and checking with the local police station and the patrol car police, but were not lucky enough to choose one of the nights on which he was arrested. But similar methods worked in other cases.

In one case, the subject had left his home community 20 years earlier. Through the Federal Bureau of Narcotics it was discovered that he had recently been arrested in California for drunkenness, and an arrest record obtained from California showed a regular pattern of arrests in Los Angeles. An interviewer spent 12 hours one day in Los Angeles, checking with police, jails, clinics, and missions run by religious organizations for skidrow alcoholics. Finally the address of an old employer, obtained from the county jail, led to locating the subject because he happened to be working there again.

When field trips were ended in October 1963, interviewers had seen, or obtained a death certificate for, 262 of the 266 subjects. Of the remaining four, the only woman was later readmitted to Lexington, and interviewed then. One of the men, the alcoholic in Chicago, was never interviewed, but it is almost certain he could have been located if it had been worth the time and money to visit Chicago again. He eventually died in 1965, and his death certificate was obtained.[11] Another man, with a similar pattern of frequent arrests for drunkenness in another city, also could probably have been located. In these three cases, however, the search for the subjects had produced so much information about them that little more could have been added by an interview.

In only one case in the sample, therefore, were all possible leads checked, and the search given up as hopeless. Even for this man, who left the hospital in 1939, it was possible to account for part of his time up to 1952, since in the interval he was arrested four times and served sentences of 2 and 4 years.

Locating subjects required an interviewer with patience, persistence, imagination, and an ability to establish quick relationships with all kinds of people. Given these qualities, however, the experience in this project suggests that locating subjects is mainly a function of the amount of time and money that can be invested in the search. It should also be noted that verifying a death by locating the death certificate can be as difficult, as time-consuming and as expensive as locating and interviewing a living subject. Similarly, the search for relatives of deceased subjects posed as many problems as locating the living subjects.

Sources of Information. Table 1.2 reports on the number of interviews obtained with informants other than the subject, separately for living and deceased subjects. This table includes only informants who were able to furnish information about the subject's addiction history or other

Table 1.2. Number of interviews, and number of cases in which at least one interview was obtained, by types of informants and survival status of subjects

	Living Subjects		Deceased Subjects		All Subjects	
	Cases	Interviews	Cases	Interviews	Cases	Interviews
Spouse, ex-spouse, etc	40	41	37	37	77	78
Children, children-in-law	8	8	24	27	32	35
Parents, foster-parents, etc	22	26	19	22	41	48
Siblings	34	43	47	61	81	104
Police, local officials	27	38	24	29	51	67
Health Dept. officials	7	8	9	13	16	21
Physicians	48	58	42	53	90	111
Other subjects	21	28	17	19	38	47
Others	36	44	31	38	67	82
Total	243	294	250	299	493	593
Number of subjects	122		144		266	

history; it does not include the hundreds of interviews which served only to help locate the subject. The table shows both the number of interviews and the number of cases to which the interviews applied. Thus 104 brothers and sisters of subjects were interviewed, but sometimes two or three siblings of the same subject were interviewed, so the table also shows that there were 81 subjects for whom at least one sibling was interviewed.

The table reflects to only a small degree the fact that it was more difficult to obtain information on deceased subjects. For the 122 living subjects, the number of interviews with other informants is almost identical with that for the larger group of deceased subjects. The interviews on the living subjects were, however, usually easier to obtain and the informants tended to be somewhat closer to the subject. For example, the number of interviews with spouses and parents is less for the deceased subjects; they were more likely to be dead too. Another factor was that after the death of a subject, his relatives sometimes had moved to another State, and were not easily available.

For a living subject, the interviewer might obtain interviews with him, his wife, another relative, and a physician, and determine that no further information was needed. Children and siblings were then not sought for interview. For a deceased subject, the interviewer might learn of his death, seek his widow and learn that she was also dead, and then look for children and siblings as the only possible source of information.

A special attempt was made to obtain information from medical sources, and that this was largely successful is seen in the fact that more interviews were obtained with physicians than with other types of informants. One hundred and eleven such interviews were obtained, and at least one physician was interviewed in 90 cases, or one-third of the sample.

There were 593 interviews with informants other than the subject, slightly over two such interviews per subject. No informant was located for 13 percent of the deceased subjects, and none, other than the subject himself, for 8 percent of the living. But two or more informants were interviewed for 63 percent of the subjects, ranging up to as many as 8 interviews in two cases.

In addition to information from interviews, much data were obtained from various records. The most valuable of these were the case records of the Lexington hospital. At the minimum, even for patients who left the hospital within a day or two after admission, these records would contain a brief history of drug use, a physical examination and objective observations on signs of withdrawal illness, plus current information on residence, employment and family ties, and identifying data. If the patient remained for any length of time, there would be histories by social workers and psychiatrists, and for prisoners and probationers copies of the FBI arrest record, presentence reports by probation officers, and abstracts of previous periods of imprisonment.

There was such a record on each subject, and much of the historical data on subjects, described in part II of this report, comes from the Lexington hospital records. In addition, 45 percent of the subjects had at least one readmission to Lexington, and their records normally contained interval histories, from one discharge to the next admission. Information therefore was already on hand on part of the followup period for almost half of the subjects; in a few cases, where there had been several readmissions up to the early 1960's, there was hardly any need for additional data from interviews with the subject or other informants.

Four additional sets of records were checked on all subjects. These were:

1. The Federal Bureau of Narcotics.
2. Kentucky State Hospitals.
3. Kentucky Department of Corrections (including prison, probation and parole records.)
4. County Court records, in those counties in which subjects had lived.

This does not imply that a record was found on each patient, but that for these sources, the absence of a record constituted useful information.

If a subject claimed abstinence and no criminal behavior, the fact that he was not known to any of these agencies furnished some corroboration. When he was known, the records supplied detailed information. For example, 46 subjects had been hospitalized in Kentucky State Hospitals, mostly for addiction or alcoholism, and the psychiatric records contained details on their adjustment for varying parts of the posthospital period. Forty had served sentences in Kentucky prisons. More than half were known to the Bureau of Narcotics, and many of these had been reported on repeated occasions. When a subject gave a history of addiction up to some date, and abstinence thereafter, a pattern of reports to the Bureau to that time, and none after it, supplied part of the confirmation that was desired.

In addition, records were obtained from other sources. Local police records gave information on 81 subjects, community hospitals on 30, prisons in other States on 15, and Federal probation offices on 5. Veterans Administration Claims files, which usually included detailed reports of repeated hospitalizations, were found on 39 of the male subjects. For these types of records, of course, the fact that no record was found did not furnish the same kind of negative information obtained from the first group of records described.

Between the interviews and records, information was available on some subjects from more than a dozen different sources. In no case was information obtained from less than two sources, plus the Lexington hospital record and the positive or negative information from the four agencies whose records were checked for all subjects.

Medical information, subsequent to the subject's first discharge from Lexington, and therefore relevant to at least part of the followup period, was available from seven sources. These were: interviews with physicians; interviews with county health department officials; State psychiatric and tuberculosis hospital records; city and county hospital records; Veterans Administration Hospital records; correspondence with medical agencies; and records of readmissions to the Lexington hospital. Information was obtained from at least one of these medical sources on 211 cases, 79 percent of the sample.

Interviewing Procedures. No attempt was made to arrange for interviews by letter or telephone call. The practice was to call on subjects or other informants with no prior notice. In the course of the study no subject refused to be interviewed, and indeed only 3 of 104 who were asked to furnish a urine specimen refused to do so. There were two refusals of interviews among the hundreds of potential informants other than subjects who were approached. Interviewers were surprised to find subjects and others as accepting and cooperative as they proved to be, but found that this acceptance had to be achieved in the first few minutes of the interview.

Some subjects and others were reluctant, and interviews were obtained only because they found it difficult to refuse in a face-to-face situation.

In one case there was verbal refusal to be interviewed, but the interviewer's persistence led to a useable interview.[12] It is impossible to know what would have happened with different procedures, but all three of the staff who conducted interviews were convinced that an approach by letter or telephone would have elicited some refusals, and that subsequent attempts to overcome a definite refusal would probably have failed. Whether correct or not, this conclusion was accepted on the basis of experience in the counties used for a pilot study, and the procedure became one of locating the subject or other informant by whatever means were available, and then calling on him, preferably at his home but sometimes at his place of work. Interviews were also conducted in prisons, jails, hospitals, stores, hotel rooms, parked cars, brothels, restaurants, bars, and outdoors in fields and on street corners.

With few exceptions, the subject knew nothing of the study prior to the appearance of the interviewer. A brief explanation of the purpose of the study naturally led to a discussion of the subject's use of or abstinence from narcotics since his last discharge. In many cases, the subject was soon talking freely, and the interviewer simply guided the interview into the areas of interest. In others, direct questioning was used.

Interview schedules were tested and found to be impractical. One reason was that, when the interview was obtained with no prior notice, the subject might have only a limited time available. Sometimes the interviewer could make an appointment to continue the interview, but he might not feel sure it would be kept; it was then essential to obtain the most important data in the brief time he could be sure of.

Some subjects, and some of their relatives, were senile. A few were intoxicated when interviewed. In either case a fixed order of questions was impossible. Interviews were sometimes conducted in places where other people were nearby, and occasionally, when subjects so chose, in the presence of other family members. Then the interviewer might avoid some questions, and phrase others so as not to give information the relative might not possess. Subjects and others might be willing to discuss areas they recognized to be relevant to the study, such as drug history, while they were unwilling to discuss other areas, like family background or early history.

The nature of the data sought also required a flexible interviewing procedure. If a subject had been addicted all of the time since his first admission to Lexington, the posthospital drug history might require only a few minutes. If he claimed abstinence for the entire time, the interviewer searched for possible sources of confirmation for various parts of the period, and this part of the interview was somewhat longer. But if the subject described a pattern of alternating periods of abstinence and relapse, it could require a long time to date the periods with some precision, and search for confirming sources. Then many other questions, for example on employment, would relate the data sought to the different periods in the drug history. For all of these reasons, interviews could not be standardized, but were modified to fit the situation the interviewer faced.

A one-page check list which fitted into a notebook was used to remind the interviewer of all the areas on which information was desired. Spaces on the form, and the opposite page in the notebook, were used during the interview to record factual data such as dates, numbers, and occupations. Notes on other data were recorded during the interview, or immediately after it, as seemed better to the interviewer. He then reconstructed the interview by dictating it to a tape recorder.

A tape recorder was used for interviews with subjects in the hospital, and for about half a dozen on the early field interviews. These were used to check the adequacy of the interviewers' notes, and had some extra value in that they furnished verbatim material which will be used in this report to illustrate points of interest. There were no objections from those subjects who were asked if the interview could be recorded, but there were several who would have refused if asked. Not infrequently the interview took place in a situation where the use of a tape recorder would have been impossible, as in a public place where it would have attracted attention. Even when the subject was interviewed at home, sometimes he wanted to conceal from his family the purpose of the interview, and the recorder could have been seen and difficult for him to explain.

For such reasons, it would have been impractical to tape interviews in more than about half of the cases. In addition, it was time-consuming and expensive to transcribe the tapes, and it was found to require much more time to code data from transcribed interviews than from a few pages of notes dictated after the interview. Comparison of the early taped interviews with notes found the latter to be sufficiently accurate and complete, so the tentative idea of taping all possible interviews was abandoned.

The major interests of the study dictated the priorities in the interview. First in importance was the use of narcotics, barbiturates, and alcohol since last discharge. Next came the filling in of data missing from the hospital record, or a check on the accuracy of the data in the record, with respect to early drug use. Then information on family background, more details of pre- and post-hospital adjustment, and information on employment and criminal record were sought.

The interview always ended with two points. One was an attempt to identify informants who knew the subject well, and obtain permission to see them. Whenever a significant period of abstinence from narcotics was claimed, the interviewer specifically checked to see if a physician or other medical source could confirm this. Finally, the subject was asked to furnish a urine specimen, with the explanation that it would be tested for narcotics and barbiturates, to confirm his account of current use or abstinence.

Protection of Subjects. In interviews with persons other than the subject, the major purposes were to confirm the subject's drug use or abstinence, to corroborate other information he gave, and, for deceased subjects, to obtain and confirm whatever data were available on his adjustment. A major concern was that such interviews might have effects damaging to the subject.

Most of the subjects in the study had been voluntary patients, and the law which authorizes the hospital to admit them specifically forbids releasing any information about their hospitalization to anyone. This law does not apply to those patients who were prisoners or probationers, but the ethical limitations are identical. A basic operating rule was that no injury to an ex-patient, by divulging the fact of his past addiction, would be risked. When the subject was dead, it might seem that he could no longer be injured, but his relatives might be, so the rule was not relaxed for the deceased. It was initially feared that this might mean the loss of data in so many cases that the findings of the study would be of dubious value.

This fear was quickly dispelled for the rural counties. In those counties, addicts seemed to be known to the whole community, or at least to its officials and physicians. These did not hesitate to talk about addicts to the project interviewers. Such knowledge about addicts was not as widespread in the larger cities, but by the time the interviewers visited these cities, they had developed techniques, or more accurately attitudes, which made it possible to make inquiries without violating confidentiality.

Interviewers often assume that they must explain why they want the information they seek. Experience showed that explanations were not needed at all, or could be extremely sketchy. In early contacts, a satisfactory explanation was found to be that the interviewer was with the Public Health Service, and was doing a followup study of patients who had been under treatment some years before. The interviewer was rarely asked for what illness the subject had been treated, though in some cases it was evident that the informant had asked and answered the question in his own mind, in terms of his knowledge of the subject. Some, for example, thought it was a followup of tubercular or alcoholic patients. Most, particularly close relatives, associated the Public Health Service with the treatment of narcotic addiction, because they knew of the subject's addiction and his treatment by the Service. In such cases, they opened the subject of his addiction, and the interviewer did not need to fear he was divulging any information.

No matter what the informant's idea of the purpose of the interview, questions on health and medical treatment could include some about medications, with no particular emphasis. If the subject was dead, questions on the cause of death, treatment prior to it, pain and medication for it, made mention of narcotics easy. If these approaches produced no result, it meant that the informant knew nothing of the subject's use of drugs, or intended to say nothing about it, and in either case the interviewer had to be satisfied with what information he had obtained in other areas.

More frequently, since the interviewers were seeking informants who were or had been close to the subject, and who knew something about him, the informant did mention the use of narcotics. By tying this mention to something else, as an indicator of the severity and length of illness, or as affecting the subject's ability to work, the interviewer could ask direct questions about the use of drugs without suggesting that this was his major interest, or that he had any prior knowledge of the drug use. A factor which helped in this was that most people find addiction interesting to discuss, so that informants tended to expand on it, and the interviewer's interest could be regarded as normal curiosity.

The above considerations applied only when the interviewer was trying to obtain information on the subject's adjustment without first having obtained his permission to see the informant. This situation occurred most frequently when the subject was deceased, and then usually when the interviewer knew he was dead. When, however, the subject had not been seen, and was not yet known to be dead, the interviewer's focus was on obtaining information about his whereabouts, and no information was sought on his adjustment unless the hospital record contained the patient's consent to release information to the informant or unless information was spontaneously offered. To locate subjects, the interviewer frequently needed to offer no identification or explanation at all. In the rural counties of Kentucky, it was enough to say that one was looking for the subject. Anyone so approached would give the address if he knew it, and often would offer to show the way to the home of the subject, or of some "kinfolk" who would be able to help the interviewer find him.

This was less true in the larger cities, particularly when the subject had moved to such cities as Chicago, Los Angeles, or Detroit. Even there the need was not to explain why the interviewer wanted to see the subject, but to rule out possible explanations which might make the potential informant deny knowledge he actually had. Ordinarily, the approach was, "I'm from Kentucky, up here on a trip. I'm looking for Joe Smith. He came up here from————a few years ago." Most people accepted the implied assertion that this was just a friendly visit. In skid row areas it was helpful to be directly reassuring: "Look, I'm not a cop or a social worker, or anything like that. I'm from Kentucky and . . . ."

Cost of Study

When this study was planned, it was difficult to estimate costs, because few comparable studies had been done, and these had not reported their costs. The experience in this followup may be of value to future investigators. Salary levels and costs of data analysis will vary from one research center to another, and will not be discussed here. Time and travel costs, however, would presumably be about the same for any similar data-collection.

The total expenses for data collection in this study were just under $40,000, for an average cost of about $150 per subject. Progress was twice delayed by illness of staff; if these delays had been avoidable, the work could have been completed about 6 months earlier, and the savings in salaries would have brought the average cost per subject to about $130.

Data-collection required about 225 man-days in the field. Only one interviewer was used at any given time, and the field work was spread over 2½ years. It would have had to be spread over a minimum of 2 years, to allow the interviewer reasonable time at home, and allow time for reviewing the work of one field trip and preparing for the next. Increasing the number of interviewers could, of course, reduce the time needed for a comparable study, but probably not in proportion to the increase in number; several trips might have to be made to the same distant place, if a subject was traced there by a second interviewer after the first had visited it.

The bulk of the data collection cost was attributable to salaries. Travel costs were $5,500, of which about $1,300 provided air travel to a few distant cities. The remainder was for automobile travel, about $1,700 reimbursement for 24,000 miles at 7 cents per mile, and $2,500 per diem allowances in lieu of reimbursement for meals and lodging.

Organization of the Report

The report falls into three parts. In chapters 2 through 4 the strictly followup findings are presented. These cover the mortality in the sample, the current addiction status of living subjects, the overall posthospital drug patterns for all subjects, and the evidence on which these classifications are based.

Chapters 5 through 11 cover the individual histories of subjects: family background, education, military and employment histories; the onset and continuation of narcotics use; criminal record; marital history; use of alcohol; and data on their hospital treatment in Lexington. The data in these chapters are of interest in their own right, as a description of the careers of addicts in Kentucky. The findings are also examined to see to what extent they are predictive of the major followup classification, posthospital drug pattern.

Finally, chapters 12 through 16 examine the addiction in these subjects as behavior which was part of a structure of relationships. Urban-rural differences are examined, and the reasons for posthospital patterns of relapse and abstinence are shown to include structural changes in Kentucky society as well as personal characteristics of subjects. One chapter is devoted to relations between addiction and medical practice. The last chapters summarize the changes in the addiction pattern in Kentucky over several generations, and suggest some implications of the findings for the theory of addiction and deviant behavior, and for public policies with respect to the addiction problem.

Summary

The major aims of the project were to study the mortality in a sample of addicts, the factors associated with their posthospital drug use and abstinence, and the natural history of narcotic addiction. The sample consisted of 266 white addicts who were residents of Kentucky when first admitted to the U.S. Public Health Service Hospital in Lexington, Kentucky. Their first admissions took place over the first 25 years of the hospital's existence, from 1935 to 1959. The sample was selected by a stratified random procedure in which counties, rather than individuals, were the major sampling units. The sampling procedure was designed to ensure adequate representation of both urban and rural addicts, and of addicts who came from counties with few and many admissions.

The data collection procedures were successful in that an interview or a death certificate was eventually obtained for all but two subjects. In addition, two other informants per subject were interviewed, on the average, and police and medical records were checked. The procedures were especially successful in locating some information on posthospital histories of subjects from medical sources, for over three-fourths of the subjects.

While field trips to 14 States, scattered widely over the United States, were necessary, the mobility in the sample did not exceed that for the Kentucky population in general. Almost 80 percent of the subjects had continued to be residents of Kentucky, and nine out of 10 of these were still residents of the county from which they were first admitted to the hospital, or had died there.

Footnotes, Chapter 1

[1] LOWRY, JAMES V. Hospital treatment of the narcotic addict. *Federal Probation,* 20:42–51, December 1956.

O'DONNELL, JOHN A. The Lexington program for narcotic addicts. *Federal Probation,* 26:55–60, March 1962.

[2] PESCOR, MICHAEL J. Follow-up study of treated narcotic drug addicts. *Public Health Reports,* Supplement No. 170, pp. 1–18, 1943.

[3] See Table 4, p. 16 in Pescor, *op. cit.*

[4] KUZNESOF, MORRIS. *Probation for a Cure: An Analysis of 85 Drug Addict Cases Committed to the United States Public Health Hospital for Treatment as Part of Probation.* U.S. Probation Office, Southern District of New York, September 1955. (mimeo.) Reprinted in U.S. Senate, Committee on the Judiciary, *Hearings Before the Subcommittee on Improvements in the Federal Criminal Code, September 19, 20, and 21, 1955,* Part 5, Exhibit No. 30, pp. 2091–2110.

[5] HUNT, G. H.; AND ODOROFF, M. E. Follow-up study of narcotic drug addicts after hospitalization. *Public Health Reports,* 77:41–54, January 1962.

[6] DUVALL, HENRIETTA J.; LOCKE, BEN Z.; AND BRILL, LEON. Follow-up study of narcotic drug addicts five years after hospitalization. *Public Health Reports,* 78:185–193, March 1963.

[7] VAILLANT, GEORGE E. A twelve year follow-up of New York City addicts: I. The relation of treatment to outcome. *American Journal of Psychiatry,* 122:727–737, January 1966.

[8] DISKIND, MEYER H.; AND KLONSKY, GEORGE. *Recent Developments in the Treatment of Paroled Offenders Addicted to Narcotic Drugs.* New York State Division of Parole, 1964.

GERARD, D. L.; LEE, R. S.; ROSENFELD, E.; AND CHEIN, I. *Post-hospitalization Adjustment: A Follow-up Study of Adolescent Opiate Addicts.* Research Center for Human Relations, New York University, October 1956. (Ditto.)

KNIGHT, ROBERT G.; AND PROUT, CURTIS T. A study of results in hospital treatment of drug addiction. *American Journal of Psychiatry,* 108:303–308, October 1951.

Senate Interim Narcotic Committee. A critical analysis of eight years operation at Spadra. *Report on Drug Addiction in California.* Sacramento: State Printing Office, 1936, pp. 57–60, 77–78.

TRUSSELL, R. E.; ALKSNE, H.; ELINSON, J.; AND PATRICK, S. *A Follow-up Study of Treated Adolescent Narcotic Users.* School of Public Health and Administrative Medicine, New York: Columbia Univ. May 1959. (mimeo.)

Studies which were not available when this one was planned include:

BAGANZ, PAUL C.; AND MADDUX, JAMES F. Employment status of narcotic addicts one year after hospital discharge. *Public Health Reports,* 80: 615–621, July 1965.

BALL, JOHN C.; AND PABON, DELIA O. Locating and interviewing narcotic addicts in Puerto Rico. *Sociology and Social Research,* 49:401–411, July 1965.

BEECH, C. E.; AND GREGERSEN, A. I. Three-year follow-up study drug addiction clinic, Mimico. *Canadian Journal of Corrections,* 6:211–224, April 1964.

335-199—69——3

Clark, John A. The prognosis in drug addiction. *Journal of Mental Science,* 108:411–418, July 1962.

Richman, Alex. Follow-up of criminal narcotic addicts. Paper read at Annual Meeting Canadian Psychiatric Association, Vancouver, June 1964.

[9] The findings and methods of the studies cited in footnotes 2–6 and the first five studies of footnote 8 are discussed in more detail in the writer's "The relapse rate in narcotic addiction: A critique of follow-up studies." In: Wilner, Daniel M.; and Kassebaum, Gene G., eds. *Narcotics.* New York: McGraw-Hill, 1965. pp. 226–246.

[10] Ford, Thomas R. *Health and Demography in Kentucky.* University of Kentucky Press, 1964. pp. 8–10.

[11] Locating subjects is a fascinating game, and everyone connected with the study celebrated when the unlocated woman was re-admitted and interviewed. The score became three unlocated out of 266, instead of four. It was then reduced to two, when the death certificate was obtained for this unlocated man. The fascination with problems of locating subjects was valuable, because it motivated field staff to explore every possible lead. It had a negative side, however, in that it could emphasize locating subjects at the expense of getting data on those located. Particularly in early field trips, when it was not yet known how many could be located, interviewers found themselves cutting interviews short, and "forgetting" to ask some questions of a subject they had located, in their eagerness to get started on the search for the next subject.

[12] One action was found to be so useful that it was adopted as a technique With his first words to the subject (or other informant) the interviewer handed him an identification card in laminated plastic. People invariably took this, looked it over, and perhaps compared the picture with the interviewer. They could not get rid of the interviewer without returning the card, but by the time they were finished with it the interviewer was inside the door, had elicited some remarks, and the interview was under way.

CHAPTER 2

Mortality

The mortality rate among narcotic addicts is high. In Formosa, from 1901 to 1935, the mortality rate was about 2.5 times higher for addicts than for the general population.[1] In Bavaria, the death rate of morphine addicts was three times as high as in the general population.[2] Chopra reports early deaths among addicts in Calcutta.[3]

Followup studies of addicts in the United States also indicate a high death rate. Pescor reports that of 4,700 male patients discharged from the Lexington hospital, who had been released from 6 months to over 5 years before the followup data were collected, 7 percent were dead.[4] In a later study of 453 Lexington patients, each followed for 5 years, 52 were reported dead, and 20 of these deaths were "directly attributable to drug usage—overdose of narcotics, tetanus due to unsterile needle, addiction, and such causes." [5]

Among 83 addicts placed on probation, Kuznesof reports one death from an overdose of narcotics.[6] The followup period could not have averaged more than 1 year for the group. Knight and Prout report that among 75 patients, two-thirds of whom were addicted to narcotics and one-third to barbiturates, there were 14 deaths, two of them suicides. The period observed ranged from a short time up to 20 years.[7] California reported 9 deaths among 661 addicts during a period of observation of 16 months.[8] In a followup of Riverside patients, 11 of 247 subjects died within a 3-year period, a very high death rate for the young age group treated there, and most of these deaths were caused by overdoses of narcotics.[9]

The data obtained in this study permit a more detailed analysis of mortality, but some prefatory notes are required. In the previous chapter, tables reported data for living and dead subjects, identifying 122 as living and 144 as dead. The distinction relevant there was between those who were living and were interviewed and those who had died before they could be interviewed.

The subjects who were located living outside of Kentucky were interviewed in 1963; some of those still in Kentucky had been interviewed in 1961 and 1962. In July 1963, the death records for Kentucky were checked and it was found that six of those who had been interviewed—all men—had died in the interim. This chapter deals with all subjects who died before July 1963. The total is 150, consisting of the 144 who had died before they could be interviewed and the six who died after being interviewed. It will be recalled that one subject could not be located, and could not be traced after 1952. Death records were searched in all states for him, under his name and the only known alias, without result. For the purposes of this chapter, he is assumed to have been alive in July 1963.

Copies of the death certificate were obtained on 149 subjects. In one case no death certificate was ever filed. The fact of death was established by interviews with several relatives, the funeral director, and a health department official, and by an entry in the family Bible. The cause of death was taken as that given by the family, an overdose of narcotics. Causes of death as given on the death certificates were coded for the study by the Kentucky Health Department personnel who do such coding for the official statistics.

Age-sex-race-specific death rates in Kentucky were used to compute, for each subject in the study, the probability of his being alive in July 1963. A detailed description of the procedure will be found in appendix B. These probabilities also give the expected number of deaths in the sample by July 1963.

Table 2.1 shows that, for both sexes, the number of observed deaths is much greater than expected. The differences are significant beyond the .001 level. The ratio of observed to expected deaths is 2.50 for the men, and 2.86 for the women. While over half of the men were dead, and less than half of the women, deaths exceed expectations even more for women than for men. This apparently paradoxical finding is due to two facts. The mean age at first admission was almost the same for the sexes, and at any age the death rate is lower for women than for men. For this reason, the proportion of expected deaths is lower for the women than for the men. In addition, the men were admitted to the hospital earlier than the women, on the average, and were exposed to the risk of death longer, thus increasing the number of expected deaths for men. In this sample, 13 percent of the 54 women, and 24 percent of the 212 men, would have been expected to die before July 1963. Thirty-seven percent of the women and 61 percent of the men did die, so the excess in deaths is proportionately greater for the women.

Appendix C lists all of the causes of death reported in the sample; these are summarized, and divided into natural and nonnatural causes

Table 2.1. Observed and expected deaths, by sex

	Male	Female	Total
Number of Subjects	212	54	266
Observed Deaths	130 (61%)	20 (37%)	150 (56%)
Expected Deaths	52 (24%)	7 (13%)	59 (22%)
Ratio, Observed to expected Deaths	2.50	2.86	2.54

in table 2.2. "Psychoses" and "Psychoneuroses" are grouped with non-natural causes because such deaths in this sample were due to delirium tremens, overdoses, and in one case to morphine withdrawal. Two death certificates had "unknown" given as the cause of death, but both were actually due to overdoses, according to statements made in one case by the family, and in the other by the physician who had signed the certificate. These are also counted with the nonnatural causes. With "non-natural" so defined, 28 percent of the deaths of men, and 5 percent of the deaths of women, were due to nonnatural causes.

Table 2.3 compares the frequency of nonnatural deaths in the sample with the frequency of such deaths in Kentucky in 1960. The choice of the 1960 mortality figures as the basis of comparison is arbitrary, and some differences might appear if a different year were chosen for comparison, but variations in death rates from year to year could not account for the excessive rate of nonnatural deaths in the sample. It is to be noted

Table 2.2. Causes of death, classified as natural or non-natural, by sex

Cause	Male	Female
Natural Causes		
Tuberculosis	12	1
Malignant neoplasms	6	2
Diabetes mellitus	4	1
Vascular lesions affecting CNS	9	4
Heart diseases	36	6
Cirrhosis of liver	7	0
Nephritis	5	0
All other natural	15	5
Sub-total	94	19
Non-Natural Causes		
Accidents	16	1
Suicide	7	0
Homicide	2	0
Psychoses	1	0
Psychoneuroses	8	0
Unknown	2	0
Sub-total	36	1
Total	130	20

Table 2.3. Percentage of sample deaths due to non-natural causes, compared with percentage of all deaths due to the same causes, of whites, 25 years and older, in Kentucky in 1960

Cause of death	Male		Female	
	Percent of Sample	Percent in Kentucky [1]	Percent of Sample	Percent in Kentucky [1]
Accidents	12. 3	6. 3	5. 0	3. 4
Suicides	5. 4	1. 7	---	. 4
Homicides	1. 5	. 6	---	. 1
Psychoses	. 8	. 1	---	. 1
Psychoneuroses	6. 2	. 2	---	. 1
Unknown	1. 5	. 6	---	. 6
All non-natural	27. 7	9. 4	5. 0	4. 7
Number of deaths	130	13, 778	20	10, 192
Number of non-natural deaths	36	1, 302	1	481

[1] Source is Kentucky State Department of Health, *1960 Vital Statistics Report*, Table 6.

that the frequency of such deaths was about three times the expected frequency for men, but was not higher than expected for women.

The tables, however, almost certainly underestimate the frequency of nonnatural deaths in the sample. Since psychoses, psychoneuroses and unknowns are regarded as nonnatural causes in the sample, they are also so counted for Kentucky deaths in 1960. But there is a specific reason for regarding each of these sample deaths as nonnatural, while for the State many such deaths may be due to natural causes. Further, in eight sample cases, listed as deaths from natural causes, statements made by the families of subjects give reason to believe that the true cause was not natural. One was almost certainly a suicide, and in the remaining seven an overdose or acute alcoholism was probably—with varying degrees of probability—the immediate cause of death. All were men.

The facts that an excessive number of these subjects have died, and that so many died of nonnatural causes, suggest that their life expectancy was appreciably shortened. The extent to which this is true is estimated in table 2.4.

Table 2.4 shows that the 212 men would have been expected to live a total of 6,305 years after their first admissions. Those who were dead in 1963 had lived only 1,149 years, and since their expectancy had been 3,610 years, there was a loss of 2,461 years for male subjects.

Table 2.4. Loss of life expectancy in years, by sex

	Male			Female		
	Dead	Living	Total	Dead	Living	Total
a. Expected Years of Life, at First Admission	3, 610	2, 695	6, 305	593	1, 220	1, 813
b. Years Lived, First Admission to Death	1, 149			148		
c. Years Lost (a minus b)	2, 461		2, 461	445		445
d. Correction for Life Expectancy in 1963			322			98
e. Net Loss (c minus d)			2, 139			347
Number of subjects	130	82	212	20	34	54
Mean Age at First Admission	43. 8	38. 0		47. 1	40. 1	
Mean Age at Death, or in 1963	52. 7	54. 3		54. 5	52. 2	

A correction factor, however, is needed. The men still alive in 1963 had lived a total of 1,333 years from first admission to 1963, and their life expectancy computed as of 1963 was 1,684 years. These figures total to 3,017 years, 322 more than their original life expectancy. It could be assumed that to this extent they will make up for some of the years lost by men who have already died. This figure therefore is subtracted from the years lost by the dead, to arrive at an estimate of 2,139 years as the net loss of life for all of the men. This is a loss of about one-third of their original life expectancy.

Parallel computations for the women show that those who have died have lost 445 of their expected 593 years. The correction factor for the living women is 98 years, so the estimated net loss for women is 347 years, one-fifth of their original life expectancy, 1,813 years.

Since some subjects are still alive, it is conceivable that they could live long enough to offset the years lost by those who have already died. In 1963, the living men were 54 years old, on the average; they might be expected to live to about age 74, but would have to live to 100 to make up for the loss that has already occurred. The living women, 52 years old on the average, would have to live to 89, rather than the expected 79. These are, of course, unlikely events.

Even the assumption in the correction factors of table 2.4, that subjects alive in 1963 would live for their full life expectancy, is extremely conservative. One was not expected to live more than a few weeks after the date she was interviewed. Several others were bedfast and seriously ill.

Still others were skidrow alcoholics, leading lives not conducive to longevity.[10] It is probable that the living subjects will also fall short of their life expectancy, and add to rather than counterbalance the loss of years estimated in the tables.

The fact and the extent of this loss can be established with certainty only by another followup of the living subjects in 5 to 10 years, when many of them will have died. But for practical purposes it may be regarded as a finding of this study that the men lost about one-third of the years of life expected at the time of their first admission to Lexington.

The differences between men and women in table 2.4 do not indicate that the loss will be much less for women. Differences this large could appear, as of 1963, even if the eventual loss for women will equal that for men. Men were admitted to the hospital in 1935, but no women until 1941. This is reflected in the fact that table 2.4 shows the men alive in 1963 as 16 years older than at first admission, while the women living were only 12 years older. The women were under observation a shorter time, and their life expectancy was somewhat greater; premature deaths had not had as much chance of appearing for women as for men.

That the loss will eventually approach that of the men is suggested by two facts. One is the finding of table 2.1, that the number of deaths has exceeded expectations more for women than for men. The second may be seen in the cumulative survival tables of appendix D. The cumulative survival rate of women exceeds that of men by only about 5 percentage points for the first 8 years after first admission; it seems to exceed the male rate more in later years, but the later rates are based on smaller numbers and may be less reliable .

Table 2.4, then, indicates if it does not establish an appreciable loss of life expectancy in addicts, but it may be asked to what specific aspects of addiction this loss is due.

The table estimates life expectancy at time of first admission on the basis of age at that time. This may be unrealistic to the extent that some subjects were suffering from serious illnesses at the time of first admission, so that their life expectancy would have been less than age alone would indicate. One possible measure of the extent to which such illnesses may have shortened life is the number of subjects whose death was eventually caused by an illness diagnosed on first admission.

The 25 men who died of an illness diagnosed on first admission lived only one-fifth of the years expected for them (126 of 596), as against two-fifths of expected years for all other natural deaths (737 of 1,861). The finding is even more marked for the women. The seven who died of an illness diagnosed on first admission lived only 13 percent of expected years (32 of 240), against 31 percent of expected years for all other natural deaths (102 of 328).

Some of the loss of expected years of life, therefore, is accounted for by illnesses existing at time of first admission. This does not indicate, however, that these subjects were moribund or even seriously ill, except in a few cases, at time of first admission. While subjects in this subgroup died earlier than others, almost half of them lived at least 5 years after first admission, a few 10 years or more, and one more than 20 years.

The second factor which accounted for an appreciable part of the loss, though only for men, was death from nonnatural causes. The men who died from such causes lived one-fourth of their expected years (287 of 1,153) slightly more than the one-fifth for those who died of diagnosed causes and less than the two-fifths for those who died from all other causes.

Two factors, therefore, can be identified as causing much of the loss, preadmission illness and nonnatural deaths. These, however, account for only a little over half of the loss for men, and just under a half for women. It was pointed out above that the causes of death given on death certificates almost certainly conceal some nonnatural causes, and it may well be that life expectancy was reduced by illness to a greater extent than indicated by the measure used here. These two factors, then, if more accurately measured, might account for well over half of the loss of expected years of life. But it seems unlikely that they could account for all of it, so other factors must also have been operating.

If there were other factors, the available data do not suggest what they were. Some possible factors, however, can be ruled out. The use of narcotics did not directly cause death earlier than expected, since there were numerous subjects who used narcotics for several decades or more—the total length of addiction in the sample ranged up to more than 50 years—and are still alive or died at an advanced age. Posthospital abstinence and drug use, it will be seen in the next chapter, do not explain the high death rate.

Summary

As in previous studies which mention mortality, it was found that the death rate of subjects was high. Observed deaths exceeded the expected number by a ratio of 2.5 to 1 for men, and almost 3 to 1 for women. Among the men, but not the women, about three times the expected percentage died from nonnatural causes—accidents, suicide, homicide, and overdoses of or withdrawal from narcotics, barbiturates and alcohol.

Only a later followup, when more subjects have died, can determine how many expected years of life will have been lost by this sample, but the findings as of 1963 make it seem highly probable that the men will have lost one-third or more of the years expected at time of first admission. The corresponding estimated loss for women would be about one-fifth of their expected years. But there are several indications that this may be an underestimate, and that their loss will eventually approach that of the men.

Two factors can be identified as accounting for much of this loss, deaths from nonnatural causes and illnesses which existed prior to first admission and made the true life expectancy of some subjects less than that estimated from their age alone. Some of the loss, however, remains to be accounted for. This study is not able to identify the additional factors which probably exist, but does indicate that they do not include any direct effect of use of narcotics, nor the posthospital pattern of drug use or abstinence.

Footnotes, Chapter 2

[1] Tu, Tsungming. Statistical studies on the mortality rates and the causes of death among the opium addicts in Formosa. *Bulletin on Narcotics,* 3:9–11, April 1951.

[2] Rudin, Edith. Zur sterblichkeit der morphinisten. *Archiv fur Psychiatrie und Zeitschrift Neurologie,* 193: 98–116, 1955.

[3] Chopra, G. S.; and Chopra, P. S. Studies on 300 Indian drug addicts with special reference to psychological aspects, etiology and treatment. *Bulletin on Narcotics.* 17:1–9, April–June 1965.

[4] Pescor, Michael G. Follow-up study of treated narcotic drug addicts. *Public Health Reports,* Supplement No. 170. p. 8, 1943.

[5] Duvall, Henrietta J.; Locke, Ben Z.; and Brill, Leon. Follow-up study of narcotic drug addicts five years after hospitalization. *Public Health Reports* 78:185–186, March 1963.

[6] Kuznesof, Morris. *Probation for a Cure: An Analysis of 85 Drug Addict Cases Committed to the United States Public Health Hospital for Treatment as Part of Probation.* U.S. Probation Office, Southern District of New York, September 1955. (mimeo.) Reprinted in U.S. Senate, Committee on the Judiciary, *Hearings Before the Subcommittee on Improvements in the Federal Criminal Code, September 19, 20, and 21, 1955,* Part 5, Exhibit No. 30, p. 4.

[7] Knight, Robert G.; and Prout, C. T. A study of results in hospital treatment of drug addiction. *American Journal of Psychiatry,* Volume 108. p. 306.

[8] Senate Interim Narcotic Committee. A critical analysis of eight years operation at Spadra. *Report on Drug Addiction in California,* Sacramento: State Printing Office, 1936, p. 77.

[9] Trussell, R. E.; Alksne, H.; Elinson, J.; and Patrick, *S. A. Follow-up Study of Treated Adolescent Narcotic Users.* School of Public Health and Administrative Medicine, New York: Columbia Univ. May 1959. (mimeo.) pp. 8, 39.

[10] Bogue, Donald J. *Skid Row in American Cities.* Community and Family Study Center, University of Chicago, 1963. pp. 225–230.

CHAPTER 3

Posthospital Drug Use

This chapter will report on the drug use of subjects after their first admission to the Lexington hospital. Several measures will be employed. The next chapter will describe the evidence on which these measures are based.

Current Addiction Status

The first measure applies only to the 119 [1] subjects who were interviewed and to the three subjects who were not located. Two of these three were known to be alive in 1963, and sufficient information was obtained to classify them with respect to current and past use of drugs. Information was obtained on the third subject only up to 1952, and it is not known that he lived after that year. For brevity, these 122 subjects are referred to in this chapter as the "living" subjects, though six of them died before July 1963, and at least one more has died since then.

Addiction status can be reported as of the dates of the interviews. On those dates 14 subjects were institutionalized, 21 were addicted to narcotics, four to barbiturates, and two were intoxicated on alcohol. Three must be classified as unknown. The remainder (78) could be classed as abstinent, as of the date of the interview.

This, however, would be misleading in that it suggests a higher rate of complete abstinence than actually existed. It counts as abstinent some known to have been alcoholic for years, but who were sober on the date they were interviewed. It also includes among the abstinent some known to use drugs occasionally, but who had not used them for weeks or months before the interview.

"Current addiction status" is therefore here defined as referring to the date of the interview for those subjects who were then institutionalized or addicted to some drug, and as referring to a short period of time, ending on the date of the interview and beginning up to a few months before that date, for all others. The purpose of this definition is to make it possible to classify some subjects as alcoholics or as occasional users of drugs on the basis of their prevailing patterns of behavior. In one case this period was 6 months long, and in a few, 2 or 3 months, since the last documented spree preceded the interview by that much time; in most cases it refers to a few weeks or a month.

This definition also makes it possible to classify one of the men who was never interviewed as of October 1963, when field work ended, on the basis of arrests for drunkenness up to and after that month. The woman who had not then been located, but was later interviewed, is also coded as of October 1963, on the basis of her later statement that she had then been addicted to narcotics, and on other evidence of this.

Using this definition, table 3.1 gives a more accurate picture of the addiction status of living subjects at the time they were located and interviewed. Only 17 percent were addicted to narcotics, but another 11 percent were in institutions, most of them for the treatment of addiction. Another 17 percent were not using narcotics, but were alcoholics or, in a few cases, addicted to barbiturates. Eleven percent were not addicted to any drug, but were not completely abstinent either. But 31 percent of the men, and 74 percent of the women, were completely abstinent. It may be noted that while many more women were abstinent, the percentage of women who were addicted is practically identical with that of the men. The difference is that many men, but few women, were in institutions or were alcoholics, barbiturate addicts, or occasional users of drugs.

The classification on current addiction status might be regarded as an ordinal scale of success and failure, with the classifications at the top representing failures, and those at the bottom increasing degrees of success. Some combinations of the classes might be used as legitimate success-failure scales for specific purposes, but they will be avoided here because no combinations would be legitimate for general purposes. A therapist who had treated an addict would hardly consider his treatment successful if his patient gives up narcotics solely because he cannot obtain them, and shifts to alcohol or barbiturates. The same alcoholic would clearly represent success, however, for law enforcement officers who are trying to end or reduce addiction by making the drug unobtainable.

Table 3.1. Current addiction status of living subjects, by sex

	Male		Female		Total	
	Number	Percent	Number	Percent	Number	Percent
Institutionalized	13	15	1	3	14	11
Addicted to narcotics	15	17	6	18	21	17
Addicted to barbiturates, or alcoholic	20	23	1	3	21	17
Occasional narcotic or barbiturate use, or alcoholic excess	12	14	1	3	13	11
Abstinent	27	31	25	74	52	43
Unknown	1	1	--	--	1	1
Total	88	[1] 100	34	[1] 100	122	100

[1] Figures do not add to 100 due to rounding.

Posthospital Drug History

Current addiction status reflects the status of living subjects as of a point in time, or of a brief period of time. Much more significant is the amount of time spent by subjects in each status from first admission to the time of the interview, or, for the deceased subjects, to the time of death. This status is shown in table 3.2.

Subjects lived about 3,000 man-years from first admission to death or interview. Only one-third of these years were spent addicted to narcotics. Male subjects spent much of the remaining time in the Lexington hospital or in other institutions, or in the use of alcohol or barbiturates, so that only 18 percent of the total man-years for men can be classed as completely abstinent. The women spent slightly more time than the men on narcotics, but 43 percent of their years were completely abstinent. As in the classification on current addiction status, the women were much less likely to have been in institutions, or to have substituted alcohol or barbiturates for narcotics.

Looking at man-years from a slightly different viewpoint, the mean time from first admission to death, or to interview, for the 212 men was 11.6 years. Of this time, they averaged 2.2 years in Lexington or other institutions, and 3.7 years addicted to narcotics. For the remaining 5.7 years they were free to use drugs, but were not addicted to narcotics.

Table 3.2. Drug history from first admission to end of followup, or to death, by sex and survival status (percentages)

	Percent of Man-Years in Various Addiction Statuses						
	Male			Female			Total
	Living	Dead	Total	Living	Dead	Total	
In Lexington Hospital	6	10	8	3	6	3	7
In Other Institutions	12	10	11	3	6	4	9
Addicted to Narcotics	31	34	32	34	40	36	33
Alcoholic, or addicted to barbiturates	23	18	21	6	1	5	18
Occasional Use	7	6	6	4	22	9	7
Completely Abstinennt	18	18	18	50	25	43	23
Unknown	4	4	4	--	--	--	3
Total	[1] 100	100	100	100	100	100	100
Number of Subjects	88	124	212	34	20	54	266
Number of Man-Years	1, 394	1, 056	2, 450	393	149	542	2, 992

[1] Figures do not add to 100 due to rounding.

They averaged only 2.1 years, however, of complete abstinence. The remainder was accounted for by use of substitutes, or by occasional use.

The mean time from first admission to death or interview was 10 years for the women, of which 0.7 years were spent in institutions, and 3.6 years addicted to narcotics. For 5.7 years, therefore, they were free to use drugs, but were not addicted to narcotics. This is exactly the same figure as for the men, but the women averaged 4.4 years, as against 2.1 for the men, of complete abstinence.

The differences between living and dead male subjects in table 3.2 are minor and negligible. But among the women, the percentage of completely abstinent years is twice as high for the living women as for the dead. This difference is significant beyond the .001 level, by chi-square on the number of man-years in the various statuses. A possible explanation of the difference might be that becoming abstinent was conducive to longevity, and that continued addiction was a third factor, in addition to deaths from nonnatural causes and from illnesses diagnosed on first admission, which explains the high death rate in the sample.

But the explanation is not supported by similar findings for the men, nor even by an appreciably lower percentage of man-years addicted to narcotics for living women as compared with the dead. The difference among the women in man-years of complete abstinence is almost balanced by an opposite difference in years of occasional use. It will be seen later that occasional use, in this sample, most often indicated continued efforts to use narcotics, but difficulty in obtaining them, so that the use was irregular. It may be that as it became difficult to obtain narcotics, the illnesses which led to death furnished reasons or pretexts for drug use, so the dead women were able to continue occasional use while the living women were forced into complete abstinence. This alternative explanation can only be advanced as a possibility on the basis of the data presented up to this point, but it will find support in later chapters. The later data will also show why the same explanation would not be expected to produce a similar difference between living and dead men.

Status on Anniversaries of First Admission

The construction of table 3.2 involved assigning post-hospital years to the different statuses, and this assignment makes it possible to examine changes over time. This change is depicted in figure 3.1; for clarity of presentation this figure uses only the 117 men and 28 women who were alive for at least 10 years after first admission, and is restricted to the first 10 anniversaries of the first admission. The inferences to be drawn are also, however, supported by similar figures on larger numbers for shorter periods of time, and on smaller numbers for longer periods of time.

FIGURE 3.1
PERCENT IN VARIOUS DRUG STATUSES ON FIRST TEN ANNIVERSARIES OF FIRST ADMISSION, BY SEX, (BASED ON SUBJECTS WHO WERE ALIVE AND FOLLOWED FOR AT LEAST TEN YEARS AFTER FIRST ADMISSION.)

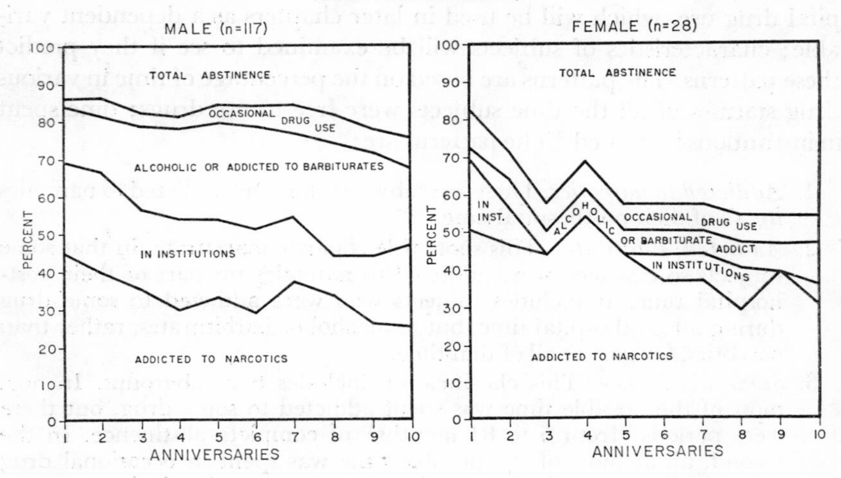

The differences between the sexes discussed in the previous sections are visible in figure 3.1. The women show much larger percentages of abstinence for any anniversary except the first, much smaller percentages of alcoholism or barbiturate addiction, and approximately equal percentages in institutions or addiction to narcotics.

For the men, a decrease in institutionalization and narcotic addiction is clear, and fairly steady over time. It is equally clear that only a minor part of this decrease is accounted for by an increase in the proportion who are abstinent, and most is accounted for by a shift to alcohol or barbiturates. The pattern is somewhat different for the women, but the number of women is too small to warrant much confidence in the difference. The decrease in institutionalization and narcotic addiction is marked in the first few years, and is balanced by an increase in abstinence, but the curves then level off.

From the graph it is evident that a large proportion of the men who were still alive could be expected to be in an institution, or addicted to some drug, at any given point in time for 10 years after first admission. This proportion is about four-fifths of the sample for the first 5 years, and decreases to about two-thirds by the 10th year. Data not included in figure 3.1, and based on smaller numbers of cases, suggest it holds steady at about two-thirds for the next 10 years.

As for the women, after the first couple of years about half would be expected to be in institutions or addicted to narcotics, and most of the remainder to be completely abstinent.

Patterns of Posthospital Drug Use

This section will describe a measure of individual patterns of posthospital drug use, which will be used in later chapters as a dependent variable; characteristics of subjects will be examined to see if they predict these patterns. The patterns are based on the percentage of time in various drug statuses of all the time subjects were free to use drugs; time spent in institutions is ignored.[2] The patterns are:

1. *Addicted to narcotics.* These are subjects who were addicted to narcotics for all of their posthospital time.
2. *Addicted, substitutes.* This short title is partly inaccurate, in that some subjects so classified were addicted to narcotics for part of their posthospital time. It includes subjects who were addicted to some drug during all posthospital time, but to alcohol or barbiturates, rather than narcotics, for part or all of that time.
3. *Some abstinence.* This classification includes two subgroups. In one, most of the possible time was spent addicted to some drug, but there were periods (from 6 to 84 months) of complete abstinence. In the second, all or most of the possible time was spent in occasional drug use, and little or none in an addiction status, or in abstinent status.
4. *Much abstinence.* Over half of the time of these subjects, but not all of it, was completely abstinent.
5. *Complete abstinence.* All posthospital time was completely free of use of narcotics and barbiturates and of alcoholic excesses.
6. *Unknown.* This classification includes those cases in which it was not possible to determine drug status for half or more of the time when subjects could have been using drugs.
7. *No posthospital time.* This includes subjects who died in the Lexington hospital, or very soon after discharge, or whose post-Lexington time was in other institutions.

There is, of course, a loss of much detail in reducing to so small a number of patterns the wide variations that exist among the 266 subjects. But table 3.3 makes it clear that the patterns identify significant differences in behavior. The 76 subjects classified as addicted to narcotics averaged 78 months of posthospital time out of institutions, and all but one of these months were addicted to narcotics. In the next pattern, again all but 1 month spent out of institutions was in an addiction status, but 88 months to alcohol or barbiturates as against only 33 months to narcotics.

In the "Some abstinence" pattern, 62 of 144 months, on the average, were addicted to narcotics, 33 to alcohol or barbiturates, but 15 months were completely abstinent and in 34 more the use of drugs was too irregular to constitute addiction. In the next two patterns, 78 percent and 100 percent of all posthospital time were completely abstinent.

Twenty cases will not contribute to the analysis; 8 had no posthospital time and 12 must be classed as unknown. An interesting figure in table

Table 3.3. Mean months in each addiction status for the different patterns of posthospital drug use

Pattern of Posthospital Drug Use	No. of Subj.	Months					
		Out of Institution	Addicted to Narcotics	Addicted to Barbiturates or Alcohol	Occasional Use	Abstinent	Unknown
Addicted, narcotics	76	78	77	--	--	(1)	1
Addicted, substitutes	45	122	33	88	--	--	1
Some abstinence	65	144	62	33	34	15	(1)
Much abstinence	32	155 [2]	13	10	7	121	5
Complete abstinence	28	118	--	--	--	118	--
Unknown	12	74	6	--	--	2	66
No posthospital time	8	--	--	--	--	--	--
Total	266	113 [2]	44	24	9	31	4

[1] Less than one month.
[2] The remaining figures on this line do not sum to this figure due to rounding.

3.3 is that for 28 subjects addiction ended with the first admission to the Lexington hospital, since they had patterns of complete abstinence for the posthospital period. These 28 subjects are slightly more than 10 percent of the sample, and the length of abstinence averaged almost exactly 10 years for this group.

Table 3.4 presents these patterns of posthospital drug use for the living and deceased subjects by sex. Since this table is based on the same data presented in table 3.2, the inferences to be drawn from it are the same as those drawn from the earlier table. Again, women show much less substitution of alcohol and barbiturates for narcotics, and much more abstinence. Within sex, the deceased show less abstinence and more addiction than the living subjects, and again this difference is greater for the women than for the men.

This measure, therefore, adds no new information at this point. Its value will become evident later, as a convenient dependent variable against which individual characteristics of the subjects may be compared.

Other Measures

The measures described in the preceding sections seem to provide the most meaningful ways to describe the posthospital adjustment of subjects with respect to drug use. They are not, however, measures which have been used in previous followup studies of addicts. This section will

335-199—69——4

Table 3.4. Patterns of posthospital drug use, by sex and survival status (percentages)

	Male				Female			
Posthospital Pattern	Living	Dead	T	N	Living	Dead	T	N
Addicted Narcotics	23	35	30	63	12	45	24	13
Addicted Substitutes	24	19	21	44	3	--	2	1
Some Abstinence	31	21	25	53	24	20	22	12
Much Abstinence	11	7	9	19	32	10	24	13
Complete Abstinence	9	6	8	16	29	10	22	12
Unknown	2	8	6	12	--	--	--	--
No Posthospital time	--	4	2	5	--	15	6	3
Total	100	100	[1]100		100	100	100	
N	88	124		212	34	20		54

[1] Percentages do not add to 100 due to rounding.

use the measure most commonly employed in previous studies, so that the findings of this study can be compared with those of others.

Previous studies have used a dichotomy, relapsed or abstinent, to characterize subjects. "Relapsed" is usually defined to indicate that there was a period of addiction (or of daily use of narcotics) during the followup period, without regard to what proportion of the total period was spent addicted. "Abstinent" is defined to mean complete abstinence from narcotics through the entire followup period.

The upper half of table 3.5 classifies subjects by this criterion, and by a similar criterion based on alcoholism and barbiturate addiction as well as on narcotic addiction. By the measure most commonly employed in other studies, whether or not there was a period of addiction to narcotics, 73 percent of the men and 63 percent of the women can be counted as "relapsed." If relapse is defined to include alcoholism and barbiturate addiction too, these percentages increase to 85 and 65 respectively.

The lower half of the table presents other facts which are equally true, and equally significant. Sixty-two percent of these subjects had some period of abstinence from narcotics between their first admission to the hospital and the time of interview or death. Forty-one percent had some period of complete abstinence from all drugs. These periods were sometimes quite long. For the 71 men with one or more periods of complete abstinence, the mean length of abstinence was 6.2 years. For

Table 3.5. Classification of subjects by relapse-abstinence dichotomies and by sex (percentages)

	Male	Female	T	No. of Cases
A. Addiction:				
1. To Narcotics:				
Some period of addiction	73	63	71	184
No known period of addiction	27	37	29	74
2. To Narcotics, Barbiturates or Alcohol:				
Some period of addiction	85	65	81	209
No known period of addiction	15	35	19	49
B. Abstinence:				
1. From Narcotics:				
Some period of abstinence	59	73	62	159
No known period of abstinence	41	27	38	99
2. From Narcotics, Barbiturates and Alcohol:				
Some period of abstinence	34	69	41	106
No known period of abstinence	66	31	59	152
Total				[1] 258

[1] Five men and three women are not included in the table because they had no posthospital time outside of institutions.

the 35 women with such a period, the mean length of abstinence was 6.7 years.

Discussion of Measures

Two points about these various measures of posthospital drug use require emphasis. First is the fact that addiction in this sample was usually a sporadic, repetitive pattern of periods of drug use and abstinence. There are cases in which persons were continually addicted for 20 or 30 years or longer, and there are cases in which addicts ceased using narcotics and remained abstinent for equally long periods of time. But these are in the minority. The most frequently observed pattern is one of alternating periods of use and abstinence, but this ranges from long periods of use and brief periods of abstinence to the opposite. Further, it is clearly a question of practical and theoretical importance whether, in these periods of abstinence from narcotics, the addict also abstained from other drugs or became addicted to some substitute for narcotics.

The second point to be made is that an evaluation of the significance of this study requires that the reader keep in mind the relationship between the measures of addiction and abstinence used here, and the first measure, the relapse-abstinence dichotomy of table 3.5. The findings of this chapter have been partially reported before, and such facts as that only 17 percent of living subjects were currently addicted, and only 33 percent of man-years were spent addicted to narcotics, were regarded by some as indicating that the findings of this study are much different from those of previous studies. This interpretation is not correct. The only legitimate basis for comparison is a measure used in common by this and other studies.

By such a comparison, this sample falls within the range of findings reported in other studies. The 29 percent classified as abstinent in table 3.5 is higher than the 7 percent reported by Hunt and Odoroff,[3] the 15 percent reported for California addicts,[4] and the 5 percent reported by Trussell.[5] It is lower than the 45 percent reported by Diskind.[6] It does not differ by more than a few percentage points from the figures reported by Duvall [7] or Pescor [8] or Knight,[9] if in the latter two cases the large proportion of unknowns is distributed among the other classifications.

The relapse rate in this sample is therefore within the range of rates reported by other studies, by the measure used in those studies. Since that correspondence exists, others might be found if the new measures used here could be applied to earlier studies. Specifically, a high relapse rate by the dichotomous measure might coexist with a finding of more time off narcotics than on. There is, indeed, some evidence that such further correspondences would be found. Hunt and Odoroff, for example, reported only 7 percent of New York patients abstinent; in the majority of cases this was a classification as of a time shortly after discharge from the hospital.[10] Duvall followed part of this sample longer, and reported the percentage abstinent increased to 17 at 2 years and 25 at 5 years.[11] Vaillant followed some of the men in the sample still longer, and reported 46 percent abstinent at death or at 12 years after discharge.[12] This is even higher than the 31 percent of living men classified as currently abstinent after 11 years, on the average, in this study. The pattern of findings is such as to suggest that the wide variations in relapse rates reported by different studies may be largely explainable by variations in the length of time between hospital discharge and the time at which addiction status was assessed.

Summary

By the measure usually employed in followup studies of addicts, the percentage who have relapsed to drug use for some period of time, most of these subjects have relapsed. The facts about their drug use, however, are much more complex than is suggested by such a measure.

On the negative side, abstinence from narcotics cannot be assumed to indicate a good posthospital adjustment, or to indicate successful hospital treatment, because subjects are found who have simply substituted barbiturate addiction, or alcoholism, for narcotic addiction. On the positive side most subjects have had some period of abstinence from narcotics, and only about one-third of the man-years from first admission to death or the end of the followup period were spent addicted to narcotics. About one-quarter of the years of male subjects, and one-half of the years of female subjects, were not spent addicted to any drug, nor in institutions. For 10 percent of the subjects, addiction ended with their first admission to the Lexington hospital.

The category "relapsed" in previous studies has been interpreted by many readers as if it meant that subjects so classified had spent all of their time out of institutions addicted to narcotics. This is a misinterpretation of these studies, and it could be as true of other samples as of this one that only about one-third of subjects are addicted to narcotics during all of their posthospital noninstitutional time. At the other extreme, only 10 percent can be classified as completely abstinent from all drugs during all of their posthospital, noninstitutional time. In six out of ten subjects, these clear-cut patterns are not found. Rather, subjects are seen to shift from one status to another, with periods of narcotic addiction broken by shifts to other drugs, and frequently by periods of complete abstinence, sometimes quite long.

By the measures used here, it is evident that there are significant differences between the sexes, with women showing about the same amount of posthospital narcotic addiction as the men, but much less time in institutions, less shifting to barbiturates and alcohol, and more complete abstinence. To a slight extent among the men, and to an appreciable extent among the women, those subjects who were alive and interviewed show less posthospital drug use, and more abstinence, than was found for the deceased.

Footnotes, Chapter 3

[1] The 118 interviewed by October 1963, plus the one women who was interviewed later. Her status is coded as of October 1963.

[2] The exclusion of institutional time from these patterns may be questioned, since some subjects spent years in institutions. At first it had been planned to count time in institutions as equivalent to time addicted to narcotics, but case records show that this would not be justified. Some subjects had been abstinent from narcotics, and a few from all drugs, for years before they received a sentence to prison; there was no basis to assume they would have been addicted if they had not been in prison. It was next thought that the time in prison might be counted as a continuation of whatever drug pattern had been shown immediately before incarceration. But this, in some cases, would have meant assigning a long period of time to a pattern which

had been shown for only a brief time; any such procedure would amount to little more than coding a guess as to what a subject would have been doing if he had not been in prison. The same considerations apply to periods of hospitalization. The safest procedure seemed to be the one adopted here, to look only at the time when a subject could have been using drugs, and when it was known what drug, if any, he was then using.

[3] HUNT, G. H., and ODOROFF, M. E. Follow-up study of narcotic drug addicts after hospitalization. *Public Health Reports,* 77:46, January 1962.

[4] Senate Interim Narcotic Committee. A critical analysis of eight years operation at Spadra. *Report on Drug Addiction in California*. Sacramento: State Printing Office, 1936, p. 57.

[5] TRUSSELL, R. E.; ALKSNE, H.; ELINSON, J.; and PATRICK, S. *A Follow-up Study of Treated Adolescent Narcotic Users.* School of Public Health and Administrative Medicine, New York: Columbia Univ. May 1959. (mimeo.) p. 57.

[6] DISKIND, MEYER H., and KLONSKY, GEORGE. *Recent Developments in the Treatment of Paroled Offenders Addicted to Narcotic Drugs.* New York State Division of Parole, 1964. p. 103.

[7] DUVALL, HENRIETTA J.; LOCKE, BEN Z., and BRILL, LEON. Follow-up study of narcotic drug addicts five years after hospitalization. *Public Health Reports,* 78:186, March 1963.

[8] PESCOR, MICHAEL J. Follow-up study of treated narcotic drug addicts. *Public Health Reports,* Supplement No. 170, p. 16, 1943.

[9] KNIGHT, ROBERT G. and PROUT, C. T. *American Journal of Psychiatry,* Volume 108, p. 306.

[10] Hunt *et al., op. cit.* p. 46.

[11] Duvall *et al., op. cit.* pp. 186–187.

[12] VAILLANT, GEORGE E. A twelve year follow-up of New York City addicts: I. The relation of treatment to outcome. *American Journal of Psychiatry,* 122:7, January 1966.

CHAPTER 4

Validity of the Drug Status Classifications

The meaning and value of the findings reported in the previous chapter depend on the definitions used, the evidence available for classifying cases, and the procedures used in arriving at the classifications from the evidence. The researcher who classifies a subject as abstinent is not a white-coated scientist in a laboratory, taking readings from a calibrated dial. His classification is more nearly analogous to the diagnosis of a physician, or the vote of a juryman, on the basis of incomplete and possibly conflicting evidence.

The classifications are based on reports of informants and the content of different kinds of records. Informants vary in their knowledge about subjects, in the accuracy of their memories for past periods, and in their willingness to disclose the truth as they know it. Records are not always complete or accurate. When numerous sources of information are used, they may conflict, and the conflicts must be reconciled to arrive at the classification.

In this study, the writer coded each variable in each case. Each was also coded independently by one or two others of the staff. When the codes were in agreement, they were accepted; when they differed, they were reviewed by the coders, and the writer decided on the "correct" classification. The procedure was designed to detect errors, oversights and inconsistencies by the writer, and the classifications represent his judgments. This chapter will report, for each measure used in the previous chapter, data on which the reader can form an opinion on the correctness of the judgments.

Current Addiction Status

1. *Institutionalized.* Thirteen men and one woman were in institutions when they were located. Nine of the men were seen during a subsequent admission to the Lexington hospital, for the treatment of addiction. Three were seen in prisons, and one in a State hospital. One of these had been addicted prior to his sentence. The other three had been abstinent from narcotics for long periods prior to institutionalization, but had been severe alcoholics. It would be reasonable to assume that if these 13 men had been located out of institutions, 10 would have been addicted to narcotics, and 3 would have been classified as alcoholics.

The one woman was found in a hospital; her physician said her illness was terminal and she was not expected to live a week. She had been out of Lexington about 15 years, and was using narcotics most of that time. She had, however, been abstinent for 27 months before her hospitalization. Narcotics were then prescribed occasionally for about 4 months, with regular, addicting doses for several weeks before the interview.

2. *Addicted to narcotics.* Fifteen men and six women are classified as currently addicted to narcotics. This term had been defined as the use of narcotics one or more times per day, over a period of at least two weeks. Two points may be made with respect to this classification.

First, one-third or more of the subjects may not have been using sufficient quantities to produce physical dependence. Physical dependence can be demonstrated after use of as little as one-fourth grain of morphine four times daily for 2 weeks.[1] Table 4.1 shows that seven subjects were using this amount or less per day. The amount may have been this little in several cases of the four for whom the amount is unknown, and their use may have been less than once a day. The classification rule was that when there was evidence of regular use, and no clear evidence that the use was less than addicting, the subject was classified as addicted.

Second, two-thirds of these addicted subjects were receiving all of their narcotics by prescription from physicians. Some of this use, and conceivably most of it, was medically justified. The label "addict" today is used mainly for those who use narcotics illicitly, and some might prefer not to use it for those who had a medical need for narcotics. The decision here to call all of them addicted is based on two considerations. In some cases, while the narcotics were medically prescribed, the justification for their use, or for the quantity used, was questionable, but there was no satisfactory basis for establishing a cutting point between the extreme cases. Further, one of the interests in this study was in the prevalence of addiction, and changes in prevalence. Older estimates of prevalence included as addicted cases such as those so classified here, and comparisons can be made only if similar definitions are used.

Ten of the addicted men, and four of the women, received all of their narcotics by prescription. Three men and one woman said they were using exempt narcotics they bought from pharmacies. One man told a highly believable story of abstinence, fully confirmed by three close relatives, but his urine tested positive (for codeine). It is possible that the positive test was due to a cough medicine, or other temporary medication which he did not know to be a narcotic but the possibility of regular use, untruthfully denied, cannot be ruled out, and it is more conservative to classify him as addicted. One man was evasive, denied regular use, but admitted one shot of narcotics, and refused to give a urine specimen for fear that it might be used as evidence against him. He could have

Table 4.1. Amount of morphine (or equivalent doses of other narcotics[1]) used daily by subjects classified as currently addicted

Amount	Male	Female	Total
One grain or less	3	4	7
Two grains	3	--	3
Three grains	2	--	2
Five grains	1	--	1
Eight grains	2	--	2
Ten grains	1	--	1
Twelve grains	--	1	1
Unknown	3	1	4
Total	15	6	21

[1] Equivalents to morphine based on Table 1, p. 282, of Chapter D, "Analgesic and Antipyretic Drugs," by William R. Martin, M.D., in *Physiological Pharmacology* Vol. I, 1963, Academic Press, New York, N.Y.

been telling the truth, but again the more conservative classification is as addicted. One woman, unlocated until long after the field work was completed, was classified as addicted on the basis of available evidence, and confirmed this as correct on her later admission to Lexington.

In short, this report classifies as addicted all persons who could be so regarded by any reasonable definition, though some of them would not be so defined by some reasonable definitions.

3. *Addicted to barbiturates, or alcoholic.* Four subjects, all men, were classified as addicted to barbiturates. Sixteen men and one woman were classified as alcoholics. The classification required that narcotics use be ruled out, and regular use of barbiturates or regular and excessive use of alcohol established.

In two of the barbiturate cases, the use of sizeable amounts of barbiturates (up to 14 grains of seconal per day) was established by positive urine tests, statements of the subject, and the use of these drugs and abstinence from narcotics were confirmed by the physicians who prescribed the barbiturates. The third man denied any drug use; his urine test was negative for both barbiturates and opiates, but the interviewer could not be sure the specimen was furnished by the subject. He had been treated shortly before and again 4 months after the interview in a State hospital. There he required withdrawal from barbiturates, but not from narcotics. The fourth man tested positive for barbiturates; his sister stated and hospital records confirmed that he was receiving amytal for seizures in quantities which would be short of addicting. He himself denied drug use, but was confused and probably was a case of chronic brain syndrome. Police and hospital records indicated he had been alcoholic up to 2 years before the interview, and his lifelong behavior pattern suggested he would be likely to supplement his prescribed medication with other drugs. His classification as addicted to barbiturates is not unreasonable, but may overstate the extent of his use.

No definition of alcoholism was established for classification purposes, but the definitions of informants were accepted. Seventeen subjects were regarded as alcoholics in their communities and were so described by informants, and they are here classified as alcoholics. In 13 of the 17 cases, the subject also admitted regular or frequent episodes of drunkenness up to the date of the interview, or to at most a few months before it, and most of these had police records showing frequent arrests for drunkenness and/or repeated hospitalizations for alcoholism. In three more cases, the subject denied or minimized use of alcohol, but was regarded as an alcoholic by so many informants, and these were in so good a position to know, that there is little question of the correctness of the classification. The one woman classified as alcoholic denied drinking to excess but was called an alcoholic by her sister and her employer. She had no arrests or hospitalizations for drinking. In this case the classification may exaggerate the extent of her drinking.

The fact that these alcoholics were not using narcotics is established by their statements, by urine tests that were negative for opiates, and by statements of physicians and relatives to whom their past use of narcotics was known, and who clearly differentiated their behavior on narcotics from their behavior on alcohol.

4. *Occasional users.* In these cases there was positive evidence, from urine tests, and from statements by subjects, physicians, and relatives, that the subjects were not, and had not recently been, addicted to narcotics or barbiturates. But there was evidence of some fairly recent use of drugs, or of alcoholic excesses, which justified this classification to indicate a state between addiction and abstinence.

Eight of these 13 cases were men who were breaking a pattern of alcoholism. They claimed that their alcoholism had ended a few years before, but they still went on occasional drunks, much less frequently than before. They were not currently regarded as alcoholics by any informants, and their claims were confirmed by others, or confirmed to the extent that a regular pattern of drunk arrests had ended when the subject claimed to have ended his period of alcoholism.

One denied all drug use, and tested negative for opiates and barbiturates, but hospital records established brief periods of barbiturate use some months before and after the date he was interviewed.

In the remaining four cases, and in four more not included in this classification, the subjects admitted occasional opiates or barbiturates, all explaining that these were prescribed for transient needs. By virtue of their previous familiarity with drugs, these subjects were sensitized, and reported as drug use treatment which might not have been recognized or reported as drug use by nonaddicts.

In the four cases not included in this classification, the physician who had prescribed or administered the drug confirmed that he had done so, and that the use was far short of addicting. This use was clearly within the limits of normal medical practice, was ignored for the purpose of classification, and these four are classed as completely abstinent. But this degree of confirmation was not available in four cases, and they are here included as occasional users.

5. *Abstinent.* The most important category in table 3.1 in the previous chapter is that of complete abstinence from narcotics, barbiturates and alcohol. This is intended to include only those cases in which there is positive evidence that the subject was not using these drugs when seen, had not used narcotics or barbiturates for at least a few weeks (except for the four confirmed cases of recent medical use discussed above), and was not currently regarded as an alcoholic. In short, it denotes not only abstinence on the date of the interview, but that there is a stable pattern of abstinent behavior for a period of time up to that date. The kinds of evidence regarded as sufficient to justify this classification are discussed in a later section, on the urine test, and case examples are given at the end of this chapter.

6. *Current addiction status of unlocated subjects.* Of the three living subjects who were never interviewed, no current information was obtained on one, so his status is given as unknown. One had been living in Chicago for years, and had repeatedly been arrested for drunkenness, with weekly arrests around the two occasions when unsuccessful efforts to locate him were made. On these arrests, he was normally jailed at least overnight, and sometimes for a week or more, so that withdrawal symptoms could have appeared. In Chicago, many addicts are identified as such by the appearance of withdrawal symptoms after arrests on charges which had nothing to do with narcotics, and the police and medical staffs are experienced in identifying symptoms as those of withdrawal. That this subject had been an alcoholic for years, and was an alcoholic during the period in which efforts were made to locate him, seems certain; that he was not also using narcotics, at least to the point of addiction, is a reasonable inference from the circumstances described above. This inference was partially confirmed by interviews with his ex-wife and a sister with whom he kept in touch, in which they described a shift from narcotics use to regular excessive drinking about 10 to 12 years before. He was therefore classified as an alcoholic.

Another man showed an identical pattern of alcoholism in Indianapolis, up to April 1963, when he ceased reporting to his probation officer and became a fugitive. He also was classified as an alcoholic. A fourth subject, a woman, could not be located during the data collection stage of the study. She had had several admissions to Lexington, and later applied again for admission, as late as 1962. She had been arrested in May 1963, and was found to be addicted to narcotics. Project staff located two prescriptions, each for fairly large amounts of dolophine, both dated September 21, 1963, one under her maiden name and one under her current married name, in two pharmacies in a small town in Kentucky. The pharmacists stated that there had been about four or five such prescriptions filled over a period of not more than a few weeks. Federal and State narcotic agents had information that she and her husband were travelling over three or four States, regularly obtaining prescriptions for narcotics. She was classified as addicted to narcotics. When she was again admitted to Lexington in 1965, she confirmed the classification as correct.

7. *Urine tests.* With the exception of these four, and the 14 who were institutionalized, subjects were asked to furnish a urine specimen. Of 104 subjects asked, 101 furnished the specimen. All of these were tested for opiates and, when the quantity was sufficient (in slightly less than half the cases) for barbiturates also. The results of these tests are shown in table 4.2.

In this table, the test result is classified by the possibility that a specimen of some other person was substituted for that of the subject. In 12 cases, no possibility of substitution existed, since the specimen was produced in the presence of the interviewer. In 57 cases, a slight possibility existed. These were cases in which the subject produced the specimen out of the interviewer's sight, but no other person was present who could have produced it. For example, the interview took place in a hotel room, the subject going into the bathroom and returning in a few minutes with the specimen. While substitution in such cases was not impossible, it would mean assuming that the subject was carrying someone else's specimen, in a container which maintained it at body heat, for reasons which are difficult to imagine, since in very few of these cases did the subject have any prior knowledge of the study.

In 20 cases, there was a fair chance of substitution, as when the interview was conducted in the subject's home, he left the room to produce the specimen, and there were other persons around, out of the interviewer's sight, who might have produced it for him. Here substitution cannot be ruled out. In many cases, however, the subject had given signs that he did not want his family to know what the interview was about, and seemed to be trying to conceal the specimen container from others. It seems improbable that he would, in such circumstances, ask another person to produce a urine specimen for him, and in no case did the interviewer have any reason to believe that this occurred.

In the remaining 12 cases, the subject was unable to produce the specimen at the time of the interview, and the container was left with him and picked up a few hours later. Here substitution could have occurred, though again there was no case in which there was any specific reason to suspect it.

Table 4.2. Urine test results for opiates and barbiturates, by circumstances of obtaining specimen

Possibility of Substituting Specimen	Positive for Opiates and/or Barbiturates		Opiates Neg., Barbs. Neg., or Not Done	
	N	Percent	N	Percent
No chance	1	8	11	92
Slight chance	15	26	42	74
Fair chance	4	20	16	80
Good chance	2	17	10	83
Total	22	22	79	78

If substitution occurred, presumably it would have been because a subject expected his own specimen to test positive, and substituted another person's which he expected to test negative. One might then expect a decrease in the percentage of positive results as the possibility of substitution increased. While table 4.2 shows a slight decrease in the percentage of positive tests in the last three rows, it is negligible, and all of the percentages, where there was a chance of substitution, are higher than when there was no chance. The table affords no support at all for the hypothesis that the result of the test depended on the circumstances under which the specimen was obtained.

A negative test result therefore established that the subject had not used narcotics for some hours and, with somewhat lower probability, within a day or two prior to the test. A more precise statement is not possible, since the frequency of false negative results will vary with the kind of narcotic used, the length of time since last dose, the amount used, the route of administration, and similar factors, and these relationships have not been adequately studied. But addicts normally take their drug at least twice daily, and more often three or four times a day. False negatives just a few hours after a dose would be rare, so a negative finding strongly suggested the subject was not currently addicted, though further evidence was needed to rule out occasional use, or even addiction up to a week or so earlier.[2] A positive result established current use, though further evidence was needed to conclude that the subject was addicted. The probability of false positive results is so low that the possibility may be ignored.

8. *Credibility of informants.* The additional evidence needed for classification came partly from interviews with subjects, and a word is in order on the credit to be given to statements by these addicts or ex-addicts. On the whole, interviewers were convinced that only a few of them deliberately lied or concealed information. Of the 17 classified as alcoholics, 13 readily admitted excessive drinking, and for the others it was not so much a denial of excessive drinking as the use of phrases like "I drink a little," to indicate excesses. Of the four classified as addicted to barbiturates, three admitted the use of barbiturates, and two of these admitted that the quantities were large enough to produce physical dependence. Of the 21 classified as addicted to narcotics, 18 admitted current use, and in two more cases it is likely that subjects were not aware that their medications were narcotics.

The question of believing the subject was more important when he denied current use, and more efforts were made to obtain confirmation in these cases. Of the 52 subjects classed as abstinent, an average of two informants other than the subject made statements about current use, including one or more physicians in 28 cases. In four of these 52 cases, narcotics use was indicated, but the informant was a physician who also confirmed that the use was temporary, for a transient illness, and in frequency and quantity far short of addicting. These are the cases in which subjects were not classified as occasional users because it was clear that the usual pattern was one of complete abstinence.

Little reason was found to doubt the statements of relatives when they said the subject was abstinent. There was one case (case 199, later in this chapter), in which the subject's wife denied narcotic use when she may have been aware his medication was a narcotic, and there was only one other case (discussed under the classification "Addicted to narcotics," above) in which there was evidence for drug use in the face of denial of use by relatives.

In summary, the classification of living subjects on current addiction status is considered to be valid. Classifications as abstinent are supported by negative urine results, as well as by statements of the subjects and relatives, and in more than half of the cases by statements from physicians. If there are any errors in this classification, they amount to no more than a few subjects who could be called occasional users of drugs, but there seems to be no real possibility that any who were classified abstinent were actually addicted. Errors are more probable in the classifications as addicted to narcotics, or as alcoholics, where in some cases the use may have been short of addiction. The findings on living subjects reported in the previous chapter may, in short, somewhat overstate current addiction, but not current abstinence.

Measures of Earlier Addiction Statuses

The other measures used in the previous chapter may be treated together, since all are based on the assignment of past man-years to the different addiction statuses. Their validity is necessarily more questionable than is that of current addiction status; there was no objective measure comparable to the urine test, and it was more difficult to obtain evidence for a long span of time than for the current moment. These measures apply to the dead as well as the living subjects, so for many of them a major souce of information was missing.

The problems of classification were logically the same as for current addiction status, and the definitions and procedures used were identical in principle. The problems were more complex, however, because of the longer time span covered and the fact that subjects might have spent some time in all possible addiction statuses. Only case examples which describe the data on an individual subject and the classification based on the data can handle this complexity, and these will be given in the next section. A few general points, however, may be made.

It was pointed out in the previous chapter that fewer than half of the subjects showed an unbroken pattern of drug use or abstinence from first admission to the end of the followup period. For more than half there were changes from one addiction status to another. To assign man-years to these statuses, the changes had to be dated. It may be asked, of changes which occurred perhaps 10 or 20 years before, how precisely can they be dated?

There were a few cases in which subjects and relatives could give the exact date and even the hour of giving up drug use, with dramatic details. But these were a small minority. More typical was the subject, discharged from the Lexington hospital in 1941, who said he used narcotics until 1945, then became alcoholic until 1949, and after that was completely abstinent, except for extremely rare shots administered by his physician, until the interview in 1962. By tying these changes to other events in the subject's life, to events in the lives of his brother and physician, who were able to confirm his account, and to records of repeated treatment for physical illness in Veterans Administration hospitals, it was possible to date the changes fairly accurately. The subject had been out of the Lexington hospital 263 months, of which 8 were spent in V.A. hospitals. For table 3.2 he was counted as addicted to narcotics for 58 months, to alcohol for 48, as completely abstinent for 146, with 3 months unknown. That these figures indicate the relative length of the different patterns with some accuracy is highly probable; but it is clearly improbable that the patterns of drug use lasted exactly 58, 48, and 146 months.

In most studies, and for most research purposes, errors introduced by such spurious accuracy are not troublesome, because it may be assumed that errors in one direction will be cancelled by errors in the other. But this assumption would be dangerous in histories of addiction and abstinence. Many subjects who had become abstinent were proud of that fact, as were their families; interviewers were repeatedly told that a given subject was the one addict who had achieved a cure. When people are proud of a fact, they may tend to exaggerate it a little. In short, in a case like the above, the years of abstinence are somewhat more likely to be inflated than are the years of drug use.

To counterbalance this assumed tendency in informants the data collection and classification procedures tried to fix the date by which the change had almost certainly occurred, rather than an earlier date when the change was probable, but less sure. In practice this meant that if the transition point occurred within a period of a few months, but could not be fixed within those months, abstinence was dated as starting at the end of the period, and the dubious months were assigned to the previous pattern or were classified "unknown." If there is an error in the classification of the case cited, it is likely to be that the subject was abstinent for slightly more than the 146 months credited to him.

Specific evidence was required for crediting subjects with periods of abstinence. This had an appreciable effect on those cases in which shifts from one pattern to another were frequent, and time periods in any one pattern were short. Some subjects had been institutionalized many times; as many as 50 periods could be documented and exactly dated from records of the Lexington hospital, Veterans Administration hospitals, State hospitals, and prisons. Such subjects were usually addicted to narcotics, or were alcoholic, between periods in institutions. But drugs were withdrawn in the institution, and the subject was abstinent on release. Most subjects said they then remained abstinent a few days to a few months before relapsing to addiction or alcoholism.

There was often no reason to doubt these brief periods of abstinence, and indeed other informants frequently agreed that this was the general pattern of behavior. But this confirmation was rarely for a specific period of time, and subjects themselves could not remember which hospitalization had been followed by a few days, and which by a few months, of abstinence. Since abstinence, by the coding rule, could not be credited without specific confirmation, all such brief periods were counted as belonging to the prevailing pattern of addiction to narcotics, or of alcoholism. But numerous brief periods could add up to a few years, and so to this extent the man-years of abstinence in table 3.2 are underestimated, and years of addiction, to narcotics or substitutes, overestimated. It might be added that subjects of this type only occasionally claimed periods of abstinence of more than 3 months, and these were usually confirmed by other informants, being memorable as distinct breaks in the usual pattern of behavior.

Any errors in the assignment of man-years to the addiction statuses will also affect the measure of status on anniversaries of first admission, as used in figure 3.1. In addition, this measure would be subject to the chance variation inevitable in using one day per year to represent change over decades. It is reasonable to assume, however, that such errors would cancel out.

It is certain that there are some errors in table 3.2 and the graph of the previous chapter. In the opinion of the writer, these are minor, and no appreciable error would be made in the analyses of following chapters, if they were based on the distribution of man-years in table 3.2. But a more conservative basis is available, and will be used.

The errors in man-years arise from the attempt to achieve a degree of precision which is not fully warranted by the data available for analysis. A better measure is provided in table 3.4, in the patterns of posthospital drug use. These patterns constitute a better measure, paradoxically, because they are less precise, and therefore less subject to error. In the cited case of the man with 58, 48, and 146 months in different drug statuses, these figures may be incorrect, and possibly more incorrect than the writer believes. But in terms of patterns he falls without question into the "Much abstinence" classification. He clearly does not belong in either of the addiction patterns, or in the completely abstinent category. The only possible error would move him no more than one category, into the "Some abstinence" classification. This would mean that at least 20 months are wrongly assigned to abstinence and should be counted in one of the addiction statuses, and error of this magnitude is unlikely in view of the amount of evidence which confirmed the subject's claim of abstinence.

Similarly, the subjects with repeated short periods of abstinence which were not credited to them were beyond any doubt addicted or alcoholic for almost all of their posthospital time. It might be more accurate to label the patterns as addiction "practically all of the time" rather than "all of the time," but the latter will serve, for brevity, and the classification may be accepted as accurate.

The man-years, as used in table 3.2 and figure 3.1, do then contain some error, but little enough to justify using them for an estimate of the relative amount of time the sample spent in each status, and of the change over time. The man-years constitute what appears to be a ratio

335-199—69——5

scale, to which the most powerful statistical measures could be applied. But the appearance is deceptive, probably to a negligible extent but perhaps to a serious degree. So analysis in later chapters will use the patterns of posthospital drug use instead. These patterns constitute a nominal, or for some purposes an ordinal scale, and will require use of the less powerful nonparametric statistical tests. But this is a reasonable price to pay for the assurance that errors in the man-year measure disappear or become minimal in the patterns of posthospital drug use.

Case Examples

The remainder of this chapter consists of 10 examples for which the classification on posthospital pattern, and (for the living) the classification on current addiction status, are given, with a summary of the evidence on which the classifications are based. Cases were selected representing both living and dead subjects, more examples of abstinence than of the other patterns, and varying degrees of confirmation of abstinence. Once the groups to be represented were defined, cases were selected randomly within the groups.

Where the posthospital pattern is one of abstinence, a judgment as to the strength of confirming evidence is noted. This judgment of the coders, based on the number of informants, their knowledge of subjects, their professional training, the degree of agreement or disagreement among sources of information, and any factors seen as affecting credibility, was recorded on a four-point scale, as follows:

1. No confirmation. Only one informant was available, in addition to the negative confirmation of locating no arrest record, hospital record, Bureau of Narcotics record, and so on. Only 4 percent of years of complete abstinence were credited at this level.
2. Some confirmation. At least two informants, usually more, but no positive medical confirmation of abstinence; 32 percent of years of abstinence were credited at this level.
3. Strong confirmation. Three or more informants, who knew the subject well, including at least one physician; 44 percent of years of abstinence had this level of confirmation.
4. Very strong confirmation. As before, plus additional interviews with physicians or, in a few cases, where the relationship between subject and physician was unusually close, to the point that it is almost inconceivable drug or alcohol use could have been concealed from him; 20 percent of years of abstinence had this level of confirmation.

CASE 258. Male, living

Current status: Institutionalized

Posthospital pattern: Addicted to narcotics

This man was born in 1902, became addicted in 1943, and was first admitted to Lexington in 1946. His second admission was within 9 months of his first discharge, and his third admission 10 months after his second discharge. He then remained in the hospital as a prisoner until March 1963, and was interviewed there.

On his later admissions he made contradictory claims of abstinence after the previous discharges, but in neither case claimed over 5 months. When interviewed for the study, he claimed that his use of narcotics was sporadic, not regular, after his first discharge, but could not give the lengths or dates of any period of abstinence, even approximately. Criminal record showed arrests in 1946, 1947 and 1949 on drug charges, and in 1947, 1949 and 1955 on charges of uttering worthless checks, his usual means of obtaining money for drugs. He served two 2-year sentences on the latter arrests, and his abstinence during these incarcerations may explain his claim of sporadic use. While short periods of abstinence may well have occurred after his various institutionalizations, none was dated precisely and none was confirmed by his daughter and his ex-wife, the only other informants.

CASE 266. Male, dead

Posthospital pattern: Addicted to narcotics

This man was born in 1890, became addicted in 1905 and was first admitted to Lexington in 1936.

He had a total of six admissions to Lexington over the next 7 years, and on each admission said his relapse had occurred a few days or a few weeks after the previous discharge. The subject lived 5 years after his sixth discharge from Lexington, during which time he was treated once in a State hospital for narcotic addiction, and was once diagnosed an opiate addict in a local hospital. His widow and two friends stated he had never been abstinent, though alcohol replaced narcotics for brief periods in the years before his death. These informants quoted him as saying, "You can cure the body of addiction, but you can't cure the mind."

At age 58 he was arrested on the charge of possession of morphine, was jailed and hospitalized, and died. His death certificate shows the cause of death as "acute morphinism withdrawal."

CASE 088. Male, living

Current status: Alcoholic

Posthospital pattern: Addicted, substitutes

The subject was born in 1908 and became addicted at age 39, after years of alcoholism. He used narcotics a few months, was withdrawn and returned to alcohol, which led to his relapse to narcotics some 8 or 9 months later. After 8 more months of addiction, he entered Lexington in late 1949, remaining only 10 days, and had no readmissions.

He was interviewed in 1961, and was the subject who came closest to refusing an interview. He denied any use of narcotics or barbiturates since his discharge from Lexington, admitted occasional excessive use of alcohol, but minimized this, and refused to go into details on these points or to answer other questions. On the other hand, he agreed to furnish a urine specimen, and himself suggested that he produce this in the presence of the interviewer so that the latter could be sure he was not using drugs.

Two physicians in his community described him as a chronic alcoholic, and as having been one for years. His local police record showed four arrests between 1957 and 1959, of which one was for driving while intoxicated, and one for violation of the local option law. State hospital records showed treatment in 1947, 1957, twice in 1959, and again in 1960, always for alcoholism. These records also noted his use of narcotics in 1947 (before his admission to Lexington) but specifically denied the use of drugs other than alcohol on two of the later admissions, and did not mention drugs on the other two.

CASE 252. Male, dead
Posthospital pattern: Addicted, substitutes

The subject was born in 1890 and became addicted at age 21, with his first Lexington admission in 1938.

He was admitted to Lexington five times, his last discharge being in 1951. On the subsequent admissions he claimed to have used only small amounts of narcotics but addicting quantities of barbiturates, and this is confirmed to the extent that on his last three admissions he required little or no treatment for withdrawal from narcotics, but did require treatment for barbiturate withdrawal.

He also had five hospitalizations in a State hospital. Four of these were between 1923 and 1937, for morphine addiction. The last was in 1958, after his last discharge from Lexington, and the diagnosis was chronic brain syndrome associated with drug intoxication, barbiturates and morphine. The only clear references to current drug use, however, were to barbiturates.

This subject's brother was an unusually good informant, a highly successful business man who had supported the subject most of his adult life, lived in the same city, and saw him regularly. The brother was definite in his statement that the subject had never been abstinent for any period since his addiction began, except for the last year of his life, when he was cared for in a rest home. The drug had been obtained steadily through physicians, and he believed it was morphine, but it is not known whether the informant could have identified a shift to barbiturates if this took place.

Of the 249 months out of institutions after first admission to Lexington, 219 were assigned to narcotic addiction and 30 to barbiturate addiction. It may well be that the number for narcotics is too high, and for barbiturates too low, but it seems certain that there was no significant period of abstinence, and that barbiturates replaced narcotics at least occasionally or for some period of time.

CASE 032. Male, living
Current status: Abstinent
Posthospital pattern: Completely abstinent (some confirmation)

This man was born in 1903, became addicted in 1946 and used morphine regularly for 2½ years before his one admission to Lexington, in 1949.

He was interviewed in 1963, and claimed complete abstinence from narcotics and barbiturates since his discharge. He admitted moderate drinking with very infrequent excesses. His urine specimen was produced under circumstances where there was no more than a slight possibility of substitution; it was negative for opiates and insufficient in quantity to test for barbiturates.

His wife was present during the interview, ironing clothes out of his sight but in sight of the interviewer, and confirmed his story by occasional remarks which added a detail to what he was saying, or by reminding him of incidents which had occurred, or correcting dates. The interviewer felt that the interview rang true, and believed the account he received.

The subject had no physician who could be interviewed. All of the record checks were negative; he was not known to the Bureau of Narcotics, the Kentucky Department of Corrections, and so on. He had, however, been living out of the State for over half of the time since he had left Lexington, so this absence of information does not carry the weight it does for most subjects.

CASE 105. Male, dead
Posthospital pattern: Completely abstinent (some confirmation)

The subject was born in 1881 and became addicted in 1915, after at least 3 years of alcoholism. His only admission to Lexington was in 1935, and he died in 1947.

The Lexington record contains a letter from the subject, dated 1940, in which he stated he had been "cured" since his discharge. In 1962 and 1963 his widow, his sister, a niece and a sister-in-law, all interviewed separately, agreed that he had been abstinent from his discharge in 1935 to his death. In his latter years (but it was not clear how many years this meant) he was too ill to leave home, and could not have acquired drugs without his wife's knowledge.

Another subject from a nearby community stated that this man continued to use narcotics until he was too feeble to leave home, and thought that a little of this use was after his discharge from Lexington. This informant was unable to date his knowledge, and so he may have been referring to the pre-Lexington period. This was one of the few cases in which informants gave such directly contradictory information, and the choice in this case was to accept that given by the relatives, since they were in a better position to know about drug use, and had shown no signs of minimizing those aspects of his earlier addiction which could be checked against his own statements in the Lexington record.

It may be noted that if the decision had been to accept as accurate the statement of the other subject, the classification would shift from "Complete abstinence" to "Much abstinence." These categories are usually combined for statistical tests in later chapters.

CASE 199. Male, living

Current Status: Abstinent

Posthospital pattern: Completely abstinent (strong confirmation)

The subject was born in 1897, began to use narcotics occasionally in 1933, and his use probably did not amount to addiction for more than a few months before his single admission to Lexington in 1948.

A physician being interviewed about another subject in 1962 mentioned this subject's drug history, and doubted that he ever had been an addict because he had not used the drug regularly enough. He believed that the subject might be using some meperidine currently, prescribed by another physician.

The subject was seen in 1962, bedfast and paralyzed since a stroke in 1955. He was able to talk only with much difficulty, and the interview was mainly with his wife, in his presence. She denied any narcotic use since his discharge from Lexington, except possibly during hospitalization once after surgery and once after his stroke.

The physician named by the first informant was then interviewed, and stated he had prescribed 30 cc. of meperidine for the subject about a week before. The last previous prescription, however, had been at least 6 months before that. The wife was then seen again, and agreed about the prescription, emphasizing that it was not morphine. She may have felt that nothing but morphine is a narcotic, or that meperidine is not as serious as morphine, but the interviewer felt she might have avoided mentioning the meperidine at first because she feared it would be stopped. She dated the last prescription as a year earlier.

The subject furnished a urine specimen under circumstances which allowed no possibility of substitution, and it tested negative for opiates. He had been known to the Bureau of Narcotics in 1935, but not reported after that. All of the other routine checks were negative, except for a circuit court record of a breach of the peace charge in 1930, on which the court instructed the jury to bring in a verdict of acquittal. The subject had lived just outside the same small community all of his life, so that all of the records which might contain his name were checked.

Two points might be made. First, this is one of the four cases in which occasional use of narcotics was known, and ignored because it was clearly within the limits of normal medical practice. Second, it is evident that the subject's addiction before his treatment at Lexington was minimal, in comparison with the other histories summarized in this section. This was one of the cases considered for exclusion from the sample; if it appeared that a subject had never been addicted he was to be excluded because his later abstinence would not represent any real change. In this case the decision (made prior to the field investigation) had been that the case should remain in the sample, because he had shown withdrawal symptoms when hospitalized, and was not completely withdrawn from narcotics until the 8th day of his hospitalization at Lexington.

CASE 084. Male, dead
Posthospital pattern: Completely abstinent (strong confirmation)

The subject was born in 1884. He was a physician, whose drug use began in 1945 and amounted to addiction for at least 1 year before his single admission to Lexington in 1947. He died in 1956.

A questionnaire completed by his wife in 1948 checked the statement that he had not relapsed, with a remark in parentheses "except, maybe, a little" and a further explanatory remark that he had been practicing medicine regularly, and told her that occasionally he took Vitamin K when necessary. The wife was dead before the study began, and could not be asked to clarify this report. Two physicians in the subject's community were seen. One had lived across the street from the subject, and had never suspected drug use after his return from Lexington (but had not suspected it before, either). The other had been the subject's physician, had arranged for his hospitalization in Lexington, and stated that there was definitely no relapse after his discharge.

CASE 087. Male, living
Current status: Abstinent
Posthospital pattern: Completely abstinent (very strong confirmation)

The subject, a professional in the health field, was born in 1906. After some years of alcoholism he became addicted to barbiturates and then narcotics at least 2 years, and possibly 4 years, before his single admission to Lexington in 1959.

In May 1961, a health department official, who had known the subject in his professional capacity and also because he was close to the subject's family, stated that he had not used drugs, or even much alcohol, since leaving Lexington, and had been employed in his profession in a hospital since discharge. The subject was seen in 1963, in the hospital where he had been head of his department since 1959. He claimed complete abstinence from narcotics and barbiturates, and only occasional moderate drinking since leaving Lexington. His urine specimen, produced with no possibility of substitution, was negative for opiates and untested for barbiturates because of insufficient quantity.

He referred the interviewer to his physician, who specialized in the treatment of alcoholics, had known the subject for years, and had worked very closely with him in recent years. This physician confirmed that the subject had abstained from his previous use of narcotics, barbiturates and alcohol, but stated he had become a compulsive eater, reaching almost 260 pounds (height 5′7″). The subject's pattern of behavior when he was using drugs had been so outrageous that he had been well known to pharmacists, physicians, police, and the Federal Bureau of Narcotics, but there was no hint of such difficulty in police or Bureau of Narcotic records after his period of treatment in Lexington.

CASE 113. Male, dead
Posthospital pattern: Much abstinence (Very strong confirmation)

The subject was born in 1899, became addicted to morphine in 1949, and after 3 years of addiction was admitted to Lexington in 1952. This was his only admission. He died in 1960.

His widow stated he was completely free of narcotics until the last months of his life when some medication was given. He drank only moderately. Two physicians were seen. The first had treated the subject from 1952 to January 1959, seeing him at least once each year except in 1955, and hospitalizing him on several occasions. He knew of the subject's past addiction, and avoided giving him narcotics, despite the subject's requests for narcotics when first treated in 1952. In late 1958 a specialist, who did not know of the past addiction, recommended regular use of meperidine. The first physician then gave him a few prescriptions but could not agree with this treatment, and suggested he see another physician.

The second physician was also interviewed, and described treating the subject from early 1959 to his death, prescribing meperidine and administering dilaudid, for a few months on an irregular basis, and then regularly to death. He had known the subject for at least 15 years, and agreed he had been abstinent from his Lexington discharge to 1959, when it was medically necessary to resume narcotics. If anything, it seems conservative to classify him as showing only "Much abstinence," rather than as completely abstinent.

Summary

With respect to the classification of living subjects on Current Addiction Status when interviewed, there is no serious danger of enough errors to invalidate the findings reported in the previous chapter. The most probable errors are in classifying a few subjects as addicted when they were only occasional users, and some readers might prefer not to label as addicts those subjects who received their narcotics from physicians, or who were using less than one grain of morphine per day.

With respect to the classification of subjects on their history of drug use from first admission to the followup interview or death, some errors undoubtedly exist in the number of years assigned to the different addiction statuses. There is reason to believe that these errors are minor, and do not invalidate the use of man-years to estimate the relative amount of time the sample spent in each addiction status, or to estimate the change in status over the followup period.

These errors disappear, or are minimized, in the classification of table 3.4, the patterns of posthospital drug use. Ten examples of the evidence available for assigning subjects to these patterns are given.

Footnotes, Chapter 4

[1] WIKLER, ABRAHAM. Opiate Addiction: Psychological and Neurophysiological Aspects in Relation to Clinical Problems. Published as a monograph in *American Lectures in Neurology* series, C. D. Aringe, ed. Springfield, Ill., 1953. Narcotics are usually measured in milligrams. Subjects, however, usually reported their dosage in terms of grains. This report will use the measure employed by subjects.

[2] If the subject had been addicted up to a few days before the urine specimen was obtained, the test would probably be negative, but the subject would still be showing signs of withdrawal. This happened in one case in this study.

CHAPTER 5

Preaddiction Histories

Information on subjects before they became addicted can be used to examine two of the theories which have been advanced to explain addiction.

Most studies of addicts find that some psychiatric diagnosis can be made, and that the scores of addicts on psychological tests differ markedly from those of normal populations. For these and other reasons, preexisting personality disorders can be seen as the cause or precondition of the later addiction. But the addicts were studied long after addiction began; the disorders found could be a result of the addiction, or greatly increased from what might have been negligible or imperceptible personality characteristics before addiction.[1] The issue would best be settled by testing or psychiatric examination of people before they become addicts. In lieu of this, the history of the sample can be examined for signs of instability and personality disorder prior to addiction.

Another theory attributes much deviant behavior, including addiction, to blocked opportunities. Americans are taught to value and seek success and status, but the paths to success are blocked for some, such as the poor, most minority groups, and the uneducated. Among the possible responses to this frustration is addiction. An extension of the original theory holds that for some persons not only are legitimate avenues to success blocked, but illegitimate routes also are unavailable, and persons who experience "double failures" are particularly prone to addiction.[2] The background of the subjects in this sample can be examined to see how well it fits this formulation.

This and the following chapters will report on, and use as variables, dozens of historical events in the lives of subjects. When questions of the reliability and validity of the data are of special importance, they will be discussed in some detail. To avoid the necessity for a discussion of each variable, a brief general note will be in order here.

Fundamentally, all of the historical data are based on the statements of subjects and other informants. Even when records were found, these usually represented earlier statements. Such statements may be incorrect through deliberate falsification, faulty memory, or for other reasons. On the other hand, the same error is not likely to be repeated in the numerous sources of information which were used. If these agreed on a fact, it could be regarded as confirmed; if they disagreed, they usually also furnished a basis for deciding which version was closest to the truth.

Some of the data were collected as late as 1963; most of the records consulted were 20 or 30 years old, and some went back as far as 1908. Men might be wrong by a few years in remembering when they were first married, but the date given on an application for a Veteran's pension, some 40 years earlier, would be exact. A subject might be vague now about when his addiction began, but the record of his first treatment for it, some 30 or more years ago, would describe the onset in detail. The span of time covered by different sources of data minimized errors due to poor memory and, since few motives for deliberate falsification apply equally in all situations, reduced this source of error too. Men may be vehement in maintaining their innocence before trial, and a few continue to maintain it after they are sentenced, but most then describe the offense to prison interviewers with no hesitation.

This is not to say that this study is unaffected by the limitations of historical data based on statements by informants, but that the limitations are much less serious than in studies based on statements by only one informant at one point in time. The procedures and principles described in the previous chapter for handling the followup data were also used in coding the data of this and following chapters. The reader therefore can transfer to the following the same level of confidence he felt in the earlier data, and perhaps more, since there would be less reason to falsify most historical data than to conceal drug use.

Family Background

The birthplace of subjects was Kentucky in 229 cases; 36 more were born in the South Atlantic, North Central and South Central States which surround Kentucky. Only one was foreign-born, and his parents brought him from Europe to Kentucky as a young child.

Kentucky was also the birthplace of 205 of their fathers, and 211 mothers; 49 and 42, respectively, were born in other States, mostly those contiguous to Kentucky. Seven fathers and five mothers were foreign-born, and birthplace is unknown for five fathers and eight mothers. In 78 cases the subject and both parents were born in the Kentucky county from which he was later admitted to the hospital, and in another 48 cases the subject and one parent were born there. Data were not collected on the birthplace of grandparents, but incidental comments showed that many had also been lifetime residents of the State, or even the county, where subjects lived. The family names of subjects were common in their counties, and many were the names listed by Caudill as indicating the peasant and yeoman ancestry, in England, Scotland, or Ireland, of the settlers in eastern Kentucky between 1750 and 1775.[3]

Religion was unknown for 139 parents of subjects. Of the remaining 393, 338 belonged to Protestant churches, with Baptists and Methodists most frequent; 29 were Catholic, 3 Hebrew, and church membership was specifically denied for 23. The whole range from clearcut rejection of church membership, or merely nominal attachment, to almost fanatical observance of the practices of fundamentalist churches, was found, but data in this area were not firm enough to deserve analysis.

Subjects in the study, then, were not minority group members, nor first- or second-generation Americans, but the product of native and long-established families. Few groups could be more accurately described as white, Anglo-Saxon Protestants.

Table 5.1. Educational level of parents of subjects

	Father		Mother	
	N	Percent [1]	N	Percent [1]
Professional Training	11	6	--	--
College Graduate	3	2	8	4
Some College	4	2	3	2
High School Graduate	12	6	18	10
10th or 11th Grade	6	3	11	6
7th, 8th or 9th Grade	44	23	46	26
Sixth Grade or Less	115	59	92	52
Unknown	71	--	88	--
Total	266	[2] 100	266	100

[1] Percentages are computed on the known cases only.
[2] Figures do not add to 100 because of rounding.

Table 5.1 reports on the highest grade completed by parents, and table 5.2 on the highest occupational level achieved by fathers of the subjects. It may be observed that 8 percent of the fathers and 4 percent of the mothers were college graduates or had more than college education. The percentage for the fathers is higher than for white males, 25 years old and over, in Kentucky in 1960, and the percentage for mothers is identical with that for white females in Kentucky in 1960. Sixteen percent of both fathers and mothers were high school graduates or had more education, and this is identical with the percentage of white Kentuckians 25 or older who had high school or more in 1940.[4] The year of birth for these subjects ranged from 1866 to 1933, with median year about 1905. Their parents' education would best be compared with the educational levels from the turn of the century to about 1930. These can be assumed to be lower than the eductional level of 1940 or 1960. It is therefore evident that the educational level in the families of these subjects was no lower, and probably somewhat higher than the average of their day.

Table 5.2. Highest occupational status of fathers of subjects

	N	Percent [1]
Major Executive and Professional	15	6
Managerial, Proprietors	14	6
Small Business, Administration	54	23
Sales and Clerical	18	8
Skilled Labor	47	20
Semi-skilled	12	5
Unskilled	16	7
Farming	56	23
No Occupation	3	1
Illegal Occupations	4	2
Unknown	27	--
Total	266	[2] 100

[1] Percentage computed on known occupations only.
[2] Figures do not add to 100 because of rounding.

Similarly, 6 percent of the fathers achieved professional or major executive positions, about the percentage of Kentucky males at this level in 1960.[5] Excluding farmers and the unknowns, 45 percent of fathers were above the sales and clerical level.

It is impossible to assign status levels to the 56 fathers who were farmers; one is known to have been a tenant farmer, several owned large and profitable farms, and most probably owned small farms which merely supported the family at an average level. If it is assumed that the status of farmers among the fathers of subjects was about the same as that of other Kentucky farmers of their day, and this seems a fair assumption from what information is available, the data on education of parents and occupation of fathers strongly suggest that the social status of the families of subjects was somewhat higher than, if it differed at all from, the status of the white population of their time.

In Kentucky, as elsewhere, the percentage employed as farmers has been decreasing steadily for decades, but it was only in 1950 that the percentage fell as low as 23 percent, which is precisely the percentage of farmers in the known occupations of fathers of subjects. The families of subjects, therefore, were less rural than the general population of Kentucky of their generation. This is even more true if it is recalled that the sample was selected in such a way as to overrepresent the rural population.

Sibling Position. Subjects had from none to 18 brothers and sisters. Both the number of children and the subject's position were known in 245 cases. First-born and last-born children were almost identical with the expected numbers. If children are divided into the older and younger groups (or older, middle and younger), the numbers observed in the divisions are very close to the expected numbers. The sample supplies no indication that sibling position was related to the fact of later becoming an addict.

In the study which best indicates the possible importance of sibling position in determining later behavior, Schachter suggests that ordinal position in the sibship may be associated with later dependence.[6] Some studies he cites suggest that first-born or only children are more dependent than later born, which might arise from the fact that a mother is more ill at ease, more worried, with her first child. She responds to more signals from the infant, responds more quickly, and stays longer, than she will for later children. In short, she is a more effective anxiety-reducer for her first child than for later ones.

The implication is that the importance of sibling position, if it is important, may lie in the fact that it indicates a "special" position within the family, which led to child-rearing practices which differed from those used with the siblings. This fits with the common-sense observations that only children may be "spoiled," that the first child or the first son may be the favorite of the parents, that the youngest may be "babied" too long, and so on. The number of "special" positions which could be defined is indefinite. Some were found in this sample.

Twenty-five subjects were only children. Where there were two or more children, 43 were the oldest, and 49 the youngest in the family. Thirteen were the only boy and four the only girl. Fifty were the oldest of their sex, 58 the youngest. One subject was the second of two children, born after the death of his older brother, and was raised as an only child, so his position was "special" in several ways. One was born more than 10 years after the birth of the preceding sibling, so may have been much wanted or much unwanted. Of all the subjects, 141, over half, had "special" positions in at least one of these ways, and many in more than one way. The difficulty with such a classification, however, is that there is no way to decide if these "special" positions are more or less numerous than would be expected. But these facts may be connected with another fact, which will be seen below, that there is evidence of marked dependence among male subjects.

Pathogenic Factors in the Parental Families. Table 5.3 reports on the incidence of narcotic addiction, alcoholism, mental illness and prison records among the parents and siblings of subjects. For siblings, the table gives the number of cases in which one or more siblings had such a history, not the total number of siblings .Thus there were 22 subjects who had alcoholic siblings, but the number of alcoholic siblings was 47.

Table 5.3. History of selected deviant behaviors in parents and siblings of subjects

	Fathers	Mothers	Siblings	Total
Narcotic Addiction	7	5	12	24
Alcoholism	57	4	22	83
Mental Illness	7	8	12	27
Prison	7	1	14	22
Total	78	18	60	156

There is some duplication in table 5.3 in that both parents were addicted, or a father and brother were alcoholic, and so on. There were, however, 75 cases in which at least one parent had a history of at least one of the behaviors reported on. This is almost 30 percent of the sample. It seems a fairly high percentage, but there are no data to permit an estimate of the comparable percentage in the population of Kentucky in the days of the parents of subjects, so no inference can safely be drawn that these parental characteristics are associated with the later addiction of subjects.

Table 5.4. Broken homes in childhood, by age of subject at break and cause of break, and by sex of subjects

Age of Subject at Break	Male				Female			
	Total	Death of F	Death of M	Other	Total	Death of F	Death of M	Other
Below age 6	24	10	11	3	13	7	4	2
Age 6–10	16	7	2	7	3	--	2	1
Age 11–15	13	3	4	6	6	1	4	1
Total	53	20	17	16	22	8	10	4

Broken homes have been reported to be associated with many types of delinquent or deviant behavior, and table 5.4 reports on the frequency of broken homes in this sample. Again, there are no data on the general population against which these figures can be compared, but an interesting difference within the sample may be noted. Forty-one percent of the homes of female subjects, as against 25 percent for male subjects, were broken. The difference is even more marked among homes broken before the subject was 6 years old, with 24 percent for women as against 11 percent for men.

Many of the subjects left the parental home early, by today's standards, though possibly not by those of their own generation. Fully one-fourth of the women left the parental home before age 16, but this indicates only that marriage at age 14 or 15 was acceptable in many families. A surprising finding was that when informants were asked at what age the subject left home, the answer for 32 men was "He never really left home." This meant that the subject remained with both parents, or with the mother, until the present or until their death. When the parents died, they lived with siblings.

Some of these 32 men never married, or had only brief marriages, and were away from the parental home only for a short time. In several cases, the wife moved in with the subject's parents too. These men fall into two types. A few were ill from childhood, or at least were so regarded by themselves and their mothers, and some were injured or became ill in early adulthood, including a few who were "shellshocked" in service. These were regarded as too ill to work regularly or be self-supporting. The other group consists of those who became addicted or more often alcoholic in their adolescence, and seemingly for this reason were unable to support themselves. Only a few of the 32 did not fall into these groups. A couple remained on the family farm, and were probably self-supporting, and one or two more worked fairly regularly, but in these cases an emotional dependency, if not a financial one, seems probable.

Education

Table 5.5 compares the years of school completed by subjects with the years completed by white Kentuckians, 25 years old or over, in 1960. The distributions are almost identical, with two minor exceptions. The percentage of men with 4 or more years of college was double that of white Kentucky males in 1960. Second, most Kentuckians tend to end their education at one of the natural breaks in the educational process, the 8th, 12th, and 16th years. The percentage of Kentuckians who left school at the end of the 12th year slightly exceeded the percentage who left at the end of the 9th, 10th, and 11th grades combined. In the sample, on the other hand, the first percentage is much less than the second. This suggests it was common for age, rather than grade completed, to determine when subjects left school.

The large majority of the sample subjects had completed their education long before 1960. Median years of school completed have increased by about 0.2 years in each of the last three censuses in Kentucky, yet the median of 8.5 years for white Kentucky males in 1960 is short of the 8.8

335-199—69——6

Table 5.5. Years of school completed, by sex, for the sample compared with white persons 25 years old and over in Kentucky in 1960 (percentages)

Years of School Completed	Percent Distribution					
	Male		Female		Total	
	Sample	Kentucky [1]	Sample	Kentucky [1]	Sample	Kentucky [1]
None	1	3	--	2	1	2
1 to 4	14	13	2	9	12	11
5 and 6	10	12	13	10	10	11
7	9	8	9	8	9	8
8	21	24	33	26	23	25
9 to 11	19	13	22	16	20	15
12	7	14	9	19	7	17
13 to 15	8	6	7	7	8	6
16	2	} = 6	4	} = 4	2	} = 5
Over 16	10		--		8	
Total	100 [2]	100 [2]	100 [2]	100	100	100
Number of subjects	207 [3]		54		261 [3]	

[1] From U.S. Census of Population: 1960, PC (1)-19C, Table 47.
[2] Figures do not add to 100 due to rounding errors.
[3] Years of School Completed unknown for five male subjects.

years for male subjects, and the 8.8 years for white Kentucky women in 1960 is identical with the median for women subjects.

The educational level achieved by the subjects, therefore, is as high as, or even higher than, the level expected for them. They were not deprived educationally, in comparison with their peers.

Military History

Sixty-two of the men in the sample served with the armed forces of the United States, 144 did not, and for six it is not known if they served. No women subjects had military service.

Thirty percent of the men were veterans; 33 percent of civilian males, 14 years old and over, were veterans in Kentucky in 1960.[7] The two groups are not, strictly speaking, comparable. The age structures of the sample and the Kentucky population were different, as reflected by the fact that the ratio of World War I to World War II veterans in Kentucky was roughly 1 to 4, and in the sample 1 to 1. It is known that a few subjects were rejected for service because of a drug history or felony history, but on the other hand many subjects passed through the age at which service is most likely in periods when the country was at peace, the military establishment small, and the likelihood of service much lower than it has been in recent decades. On the whole, there is no reason to believe that the sample subjects differ from their contemporaries in the proportion who were in military service.

They do differ, however, in the quality of that service. The type of discharge is known for 55 of the 62 men who were in service. Only 33 (60 percent) received the normal "honorable" discharge. Nine received medical discharges, for psychiatric rather than physical disabilities. Thirteen received dishonorable or undesirable discharges, or discharges for ineptness.

Strictly comparable data, for a group matched on age or year of discharge (to control for presumably different discharge rates in wartime service) are not available. Data are available, however, on the 7 million separations of enlisted male personnel from the armed services of the United States in 1942–45. Of these, 18.4 percent were for medical reasons, 3.3 percent inapt and unsuitable, and 1.7 percent other than honorable.[8] These total to 23.4 percent, as against the 40 percent of such discharges in the sample. About 35 percent of the 1942–45 medical discharges were for psychiatric reasons, while most or perhaps all of the medical discharges in the sample were for psychiatric reasons.

Even 60 percent of normal discharges overstates the adequacy of the service of men in the sample. One physician, for example, was given an honorable discharge despite the facts that a dishonorable discharge had been recommended, and that his service was terminated by a court-martial which imposed a long sentence. Two subjects were addicted throughout their military service, and one had nine courts-martial, with much of his service time spent in AWOL status or in the stockade.

Employment

Table 5.6 reports the highest employment status reached by subjects prior to their addiction. This also represents the highest employment status they ever reached, except for a few at the lower end of the scale. A few of those who were unskilled laborers prior to addiction later achieved skilled or clerical jobs at least for short times.

Ten percent of the male subjects achieved major executive or professional status. Twenty-nine percent (again excluding farmers and unknowns) achieved a level higher than sales and clerical work. Both figures compare favorably with the 1960 census, though the latter figure falls short of their fathers' achievement.[9]

Table 5.6. Highest level of employment prior to addiction, by sex

	Male	Female
Major Executive or Professional	22	--
Managerial	4	4
Small Business, Admin	27	3
Sales and Clerical	45	5
Skilled Labor	28	--
Semi-skilled	28	6
Unskilled	26	1
Farming	18	5
Unknown or None	13	3
Housewife or Student	1	27
Total	212	54

The 1960 census classified 19 percent of male Kentuckians as farm owners, managers, or workers; but farming was the major occupation for only 8 percent (18) of the subjects. Others had also done some farm work in their youth, but it is clear that male subjects, like their fathers, were less likely than their contemporaries to be farmers.

The subject of employment will be discussed again in chapter 8, in terms of the change in employment pattern associated with addiction. To study that change, the pattern of employment was classified for three periods of time; prior to addiction, during addiction and, for those to whom it applied, the period after addiction ended. The classification uses only three levels. At the one extreme, employment was classified as steady if the subject worked steadily and was self-supporting at a legitimate occupation. At the other, some were classified as having little or no legitimate employment during the period. The middle category includes anything between the extremes.

The measure is obviously crude. The periods of time classified ranged greatly in length; some related to the first decades of the century and others to the 1950s or 1960s, so that they occurred under widely differing economic conditions; and the details secured on employment history did not always justify the finer discriminations that would be desirable. This crudity limits the utility of the measure, but does not detract from the significance of the gross differences disclosed by it. It was not useful for the female subjects, since for housewives there is nothing as visible as unemployment for men. For men, the striking finding was that prior to addiction only 97, less than half, could be regarded as showing a steady pattern of employment. Thirty-four (16 percent) had little or no legitimate employment before addiction, and 69 more (35 percent) fell into the intermediate category, of less than steady employment. Data were insufficient to classify 12. No comparable data on the general population are available, but it seems a safe guess that the male subjects showed a less stable employment pattern, even before their addiction began, than would be expected in a random sample of a comparable population.

Summary

The subjects were born into the dominant cultural group in Kentucky, into white, Protestant, long-established families. The education of their parents, and the occupations of their fathers, were level with or higher than the average for the State. As far as social status and access to opportunities are indicated by these variables, subjects were not underprivileged in comparison with their contemporaries. In education, too, they equalled or surpassed their contemporaries.

Records of addiction, alcoholism, mental illness, or imprisonment were found in at least one parent for almost 30 percent of the subjects, and broken homes were frequent, especially for the women in the sample. But no comparable data on the general population are available, so it may not be inferred that these facts are significant. Sibling position was not found to have any relationship with their later addiction.

Indications of inadequacy in social adjustment, prior to addiction, were found for a sizeable minority of the men. Fifteen percent of the men never achieved independence from their parental families. Of those who were in military service at least 40 percent were discharged dishonorably, for psychiatric disabilities, or as undesirable or inept. Fewer than half of the men showed a pattern of steady employment prior to addiction. Similar indications were not found for the women, but this may be because similar indicators were not available.

Footnotes, Chapter 5

[1] The evidence of personality disorders may be found in numerous publications. A useful summary is available in MEYER, ALAN S. *Social and Psychological Factors in Opiate Addiction.* New York: Bureau of Applied Social Research, Columbia University, 1952, pp. 71–80, 92–109. The argument that findings on institutionalized addicts are weak evidence of their preaddiction personalities has been made well by ALFRED R. LINDESMITH. See his *Opiate Addiction.* Bloomington, Indiana: Principia Press, 1947, pp. 141–164; or his paper, "Basic problems in the social psychology of addiction and a theory," in O'DONNELL, JOHN A., and BALL, JOHN C., eds. *Narcotic Addiction.* New York: Harper and Row, 1966, pp. 91–109. But see also HILL, HARRIS E., *et al.* "Personality characteristics of narcotic addicts as indicated by the MMPI." *Journal of General Psychology,* 62:127–139, 1960. Hill found MMPI profiles in teenage addicts very similar to those of teenage delinquents and adult addicts, supporting the interpretation that the per-

sonality characteristics measured do not materially change following addiction.

[2] For the basic theory see MERTON, ROBERT K. *Social Theory and Social Structure*. Revised ed. New York: The Free Press, 1957, pp. 131–194. The extension is in CLOWARD, RICHARD A., and OHLIN, LLOYD *E. Delinquency and Opportunity*. New York: The Free Press, 1960. Lindesmith and Gagnon have criticized the theory, as it applies to addiction in: CLINARD, MARSHALL B., ed., *Anomie and Deviant Behavior*. New York: The Free Press, 1964, pp. 158–188.

[3] CAUDILL, HARRY M. *Night Comes to the Cumberlands*. Boston: Atlantic-Little, Brown, 1962.

[4] U.S. Bureau of the Census. *U.S. Census of Population: 1960 General Social and Economic Characteristics, Kentucky*. Final Report, PC(1)–19C, Table 47. The classification used for education, and with minor modifications the classification used for occupation, are those used by Hollingshead in his two-factor index of social class, and may be used together as an indication of the class position of families. See HOLLINGSHEAD, A. B. and REDLICH, F. C. *Social Class and Mental Illness*. New York: John Wiley and Sons, 1958.

[5] The estimate for Kentucky in 1960 is based on the 1960 Census, Final Report, PC(1)–19D, Table 123. Among professional, technical and kindred workers, the last seven occupations are not counted as "major" professions, and it is assumed that one-fourth of managers, officials and proprietors were "major" executives. The data on fathers are not strictly comparable with census data; the former represent the highest level ever achieved, while the census counts levels at a point in time. Young men who will later achieve higher status fall in lower census levels. On the other hand, the percentage of professional and executive workers in the population was much lower in the decades when subjects' fathers were employed. On the whole, the comparison is probably sufficiently valid to justify the conclusion that fathers of subjects were not below the average for their time in higher-level positions.

[6] SCHACHTER, STANLEY. *The Psychology of Affiliation*. Stanford: Stanford University Press, 1959.

[7] U.S. Bureau of the Census, *op. cit.*, PC(1)–19C, Table 48.

[8] GINZBERG, ELI, *et al. The Ineffective Soldier: Volume I, The Lost Divisions*. New York: Columbia University Press, 1959. pp. 60–61.

[9] See Footnote 5.

CHAPTER 6

Onset of Addiction

Addiction may be defined in several ways; in terms of tolerance and physical dependence, or of the development of craving and drug-seeking behavior, or of being regarded by others or self as an addict. Common to the first two, and usual in the last, is the fact of daily use of narcotics. Daily use can therefore serve as a practical definition. Whether or not a person is addicted, by this definition, is determined fairly easily, while it might be difficult to determine by the others, especially for past points in time.

Even by this definition, addiction may follow the first use of narcotics by some period of time, possibly by years. To date the first use and ascertain the reasons for it is not necessarily to date or understand the eventual addiction. In most cases in this sample, however, no clear distinction could be made. Drug use began, continued, and rapidly became daily use. Neither in subjects' minds nor in objective data was there a basis to select some date, after the first use, as the start of addiction. Addiction is therefore here regarded as beginning with first use, except in the minority of cases where a distinction was made between first use and the onset of daily use.

One subject was addicted as early as 1897, and the most recent year of onset was 1959. Table 6.1 classifies subjects by the decade in which addiction began, except that three decades are grouped together as "before 1920." The distribution is seen to differ for the sexes; seven out of ten women, against four of ten men, began their addiction in 1940 or later.

The age at onset of addiction ranged from 9 to 66 years for the men, and from 15 to 74 for the women. The table shows that the age distribution is roughly the same for the sexes. The median age at addiction was 30 for the women, and slightly higher for the men, but the women slightly exceed the men in the percentage of those who became addicted at age 40 or later.

The table also shows that subjects who became addicted in recent decades were appreciably older—by more than ten years—than those whose addiction began in earlier decades. This suggests a similar, though lesser, increase in age at onset with recency of addiction for Kentucky addicts in general. That the increase was smaller, among all Kentucky addicts, arises from the fact that subjects addicted in the early decades are necessarily less representative of their contemporaries than are more recent addicts. The hospital did not accept men before 1935, nor women

Table 6.1. Age at onset of addiction by decade of onset and by sex (percentages)

Age at Onset of Addiction	Before 1920	1920–29	1930–39	1940–49	1950–59	Number of Subjects
	Decade of onset of addiction—Male					
Under 20	41	13	9	5	--	23
20–29	41	46	42	25	14	73
30–39	18	28	23	28	48	58
40–49	--	10	17	28	24	38
50 or over	--	3	9	15	14	20
Total	100	100	100	[1] 100	100	
Median Age	22.5	26.0	29.0	37.0	36.0	
Number of Subjects	22	39	65	65	21	212
	Decade of onset of addiction—Female					
Under 20	50	17	60	7	--	8
20–29	50	50	--	30	45	18
30–39	--	17	20	22	9	9
40–49	--	17	--	30	18	11
50 or over	--	--	20	11	27	7
Total	100	[1] 100	100	100	[1] 100	
Median Age	20.5	28.5	18.0	33.0	32.0	
Number of Subjects	4	6	5	27	11	[2] 53

[1] Percentages do not add to 100 due to rounding.
[2] One woman omitted because onset could not be dated.

before 1941; of persons who became addicted before 1920, those who were 20 or 30 at onset had a better change of living to become patients. Those addicts who were addicted before 1920, and were 40 or older at onset, are absent in the table and in the sample.

But the increase is not merely an apparent one. Age at onset would not appreciably affect the chance of becoming a patient for men whose addiction began in the 1930s, and they too are seen to be younger at onset than more recent addicts. Further, the increase shown by the table is attributable not only to small numbers in the lower left cells, but also in the upper right cells. Very few subjects became addicted before age 20, and not many before age 30 in recent decades, while addiction at those ages was fairly common in earlier decades.

In only 29 cases was there a distinction between the reason given for first use and the reason for becoming addicted. In 19 of these 29, the change consisted in first receiving narcotics in the treatment of illness or injury, and then continuing its use for, and explaining addiction as due to, the treatment of alcoholism. Table 6.2 uses the latter reason; it shows the reasons given for becoming addicted rather than for first use.

Table 6.2. Reason for first addiction, by sex

Reason	Male		Female		Total	
	No.	Percent [1]	No.	Percent [1]	No.	Percent [1]
Treatment of illness or injury	86	42	43	83	129	50
Treatment of alcoholism	75	37	2	4	77	30
Pleasure	38	18	6	12	44	17
Other	6	3	1	2	7	3
Unknown	7	--	2	--	9	--
Total	212	100	54	100 [2]	266	100

[1] "Unknown" not included in computation.
[2] Figures do not add to 100 due to rounding.

Addiction was most often attributed to the treatment of illness or injury, but twice as often for the women as for the men. Over one-third of the men began their addiction through treatment of alcoholism; they were given a narcotic to help in the sobering-up periods after prolonged drinking, preferred the narcotic to alcohol, and shifted to its use. Almost one-fifth of the men attributed their addiction to the euphoric effects of narcotics; they were seeking pleasure—"kicks." The percentage of women in the two latter classifications is small; only two took the alcoholic road to addiction, and six the pleasure-seeking road.

Only seven subjects do not fall into one of these three groups. The woman's husband, an addict and a subject in this study, gave her narcotics for the "confusion and pain" associated with a post-partum psychosis. The men were: a physician who attributed his addiction to worry and overwork; another physician who referred to overwork and marital problems; one man who attributed it to marital problems; another with a long history of alcoholism, who began to use codeine for a chronic cough, but also attributed its use to marital problems and problems with his father. One man began smoking opium overseas while in service, because without it the heat kept him from sleeping. Another, a bootlegger who had trouble staying awake on long drives, noticed that an addict was always able to rouse himself quickly, and he began using morphine to stay awake.

Whether the reasons given in table 6.2 are the only reasons or the "real" reasons for addiction is an unanswerable question, and in a sense an unimportant one. What emerges from the classification is a variable which clearly relates to the subject's perception of himself as an addict, as of the time when addiction began. Most of the women, and less than half of the men, then perceived themselves as patients taking medicine. One-third of the men considered themselves alcoholics who had found a better intoxicant, and one-fifth more recognized their drug use as pleasure-seeking.

The first source of narcotics is unknown for 10 percent of the subjects. Among those for whom it is known, 66 percent of the men and 83 percent of the women first received narcotics from a physician. One-fourth of the men and the remaining women received the first narcotic from a friend or relative. This most often meant that an addict was introducing the subject to a pleasurable experience, but in a few cases represented treatment of illness; one person suggested to another a medicine he had found helpful. All other sources combined amount to less than 10 percent of the sample. One man bought codeine in a drug store, 9 physicians used narcotics from their own supply, and three men stole their first drug. In only two cases was the first narcotic supplied by a peddler of drugs.

Morphine was by far the most common first narcotic, with other narcotics which are normally prescribed in medical practice making up most of the remainder. Heroin and opium, usually acquired illegally, were the first drug in only 14 cases. Even of these, two subjects began their use while heroin was still legally available. But this does not mean that only these few began with drugs illicitly acquired. It indicates that in Kentucky the illicit narcotic traffic was largely traffic in morphine, rather than in heroin.

When physicians prescribe or dispense narcotics, the drug is normally taken orally or by hypodermic. In the latter case, the needle is inserted into a muscle, or into subcutaneous tissues, but is rarely, if ever, inserted into a vein. The intravenous route, which is preferred by many addicts, is normally taught to them by other addicts. Similarly, taking narcotics by sniffing or smoking is not normal in the medical use of drugs, but occurs in the context of an addict subculture.

The first route used by subjects is unknown for more than half of them, but among the rest, the usual routes of medical administration are much more common, as the first route, than the addict-taught routes. Among the 24 women for whom the first route is known, only four used the intravenous route. Among the 102 men, 84 used the normal medical routes. Thirteen took their first narcotic intravenously, four began by smoking opium, and one by sniffing heroin. Only about 17 percent of the subjects, therefore, began with addict-taught routes, and the sexes were almost equal in this respect.

But by the time of their first admission to Lexington, the usual route of administration had changed greatly. The less effective routes, sniffing, smoking, and oral, had almost disappeared. About 95 percent of subjects were using the needle, and for over half of the men and not quite a quarter of the women this meant the intravenous route.

Once a subject learned to use the intravenous route, he tended to continue using it as long as he used drugs. Of the 111 men who ever used the IV route, 84 continued with it, and 27 eventually shifted, 13 to other needle routes and 14 to the oral route. Of the 12 women, two eventually shifted from the intravenous route. It will be seen later that these shifts were usually due to difficulty in obtaining narcotics, so that, for example, an addict who had used morphine was no longer able to obtain anything but paregoric or cough syrups. When this happened, most subjects used these drugs orally, though a few processed them so that they could inject the narcotic intravenously. In only a few cases did subjects shift from the intravenous route because veins became too scarred to be useable.

Sources of Narcotics

Learning to use the intravenous route of administration was paralleled by learning new sources of narcotics and new ways of obtaining them. These can be classified in 10 categories, which will be referred to as sources for brevity, though some would more accurately be called methods. They may be described as follows:

1. *One physician.* This was counted as a source when there was a period in which all narcotics were administered or prescribed by one physician. Two-thirds of the men and 87 percent of the women obtained some of their narcotics in this manner.
2. *Peddler.* This refers to buying narcotics from another person who had no legal right to possess or dispense narcotics. Many of the peddlers were themselves addicts, and some were also subjects in this study. Forty-two percent of the men and 17 percent of the women are known to have bought narcotics from peddlers.
3. *Multiple physicians.* This was coded when subjects simultaneously obtained narcotics or prescriptions from more than one physician. It includes three subtypes:
   a. For nomadic addicts, visiting those physicians who in the addict subculture had the reputation of being "script doctors," i.e., who were ready to write a narcotic prescription for anyone with the price.
   b. Visiting physicians more or less at random, usually within a circumscribed area around the addict's residence, to obtain narcotics on the basis of a real or faked illness.
   c. Visiting physicians to request narcotics, on the claim that the subject was on the way to a hospital for treatment, and needed narcotics to prevent withdrawal symptoms before he got there. If this approach failed, explicit or veiled threats might be made to embar-

rass the physician by "throwing a wing-ding" in sight or hearing of his waiting patients.

The second and third of these methods are what subjects meant when they spoke of "making" doctors. One in three men, and one in four women, obtained narcotics in these ways.

4. *Exempt narcotics.* This refers to the buying of paregoric, or cough syrups containing codeine or dihydrocodeinone from drugstores. In earlier years, when large quantities of paregoric could be obtained, it was common to process it and obtain the opiate in fairly pure form, then taking it by the intravenous route. Only one subject, a woman, was found to be doing this currently; other subjects were taking the paregoric orally. One-fourth of the men and one-eighth of the women used this source at some time.
5. *Relative or friend.* The reference is to cases in which the relative or friend was an addict himself, had obtained the narcotics from any of the other sources described, and gave them to the subject. This appeared most often as the first source of narcotics, and in only three cases is it the only known source.
6. *Forged prescriptions.* The usual elements were to steal a pad of blank prescriptions, fill them out for narcotics, forge the physician's signature, and then "cash" them at a drugstore. All elements might be handled by one addict, but often there was a division of labor, with one person doing the stealing and forging, another the cashing. When two or more addicts of different sex cooperated in obtaining drugs by this method, it seems to have been usual for a woman to have the prescription filled because the pharmacist would be less likely to question a prescription presented by a woman, and less likely to call the police if he did question it. Also included here are those cases in which the addict obtained a prescription from a physician and altered the amount of narcotics upwards before cashing the prescription. One in six men, and one in 12 women, obtained drugs in these ways.
7. *Physician or pharmacist as peddler.* This includes those cases in which subjects bought narcotics from pharmacists or physicians, with no pretense of a professional relationship or a medical need for the narcotics. During the 1920s and the 1930s there were a number of such physicians who supplied addicts for years. Twenty men and one woman, almost 10 percent of the sample, obtained narcotics from unethical professionals, and this is probably an underestimate, since some of the cases reported for sources 1 and 3 may belong here.
8. *Stolen.* Most cases so coded were subjects who occasionally or regularly broke into drugstores. In a few cases, it involved stealing from other addicts. For nurses it meant stealing from the hospital supply of narcotics, and in one case a woman's only source of narcotics seems to have been stealing from the supply of her husband, a physician. Seventeen men and four women obtained narcotics by stealing them.
9. *Supply in own possession.* This includes those subjects, mostly physicians, but a few pharmacists and drugstore employees, whose legally acquired narcotics were illegally diverted to their personal use. Seventeen men, of no more than 20 who had the legal right to order and stock narcotics, are known to have used them.

10. *Prescription supplied to relative or friend.* In these cases, narcotics were prescribed for one person, and the subject took part or all of these for his own use. This might occur with the knowledge and consent of the person for whom the narcotics were prescribed, as for example when one addict persuaded the physician to prescribe more narcotics than he was actually using, and sold or gave the excess to other addicts. More usually, in this sample, the narcotics were taken without the knowledge of the patient for whom they had been prescribed.

While the data presented show how many subjects ever obtained narcotics from each source, they do not reveal how important these sources were over the narcotic history of a subject. They show that 141 men and 47 women obtained narcotics from one physician at some time, but about two-thirds of these men and over 40 percent of these women also obtained narcotics from other sources. How many obtained drugs only from one physician? To what extent did subjects get drugs from legal sources, and how much from illegal?

Table 6.3 is constructed to answer such questions. It combines the data on sources each subject used, and the length of time drugs were obtained from each source, to characterize the major source of narcotics, over the entire drug history, for each subject. The classifications are arranged to reflect the decreasing legitimacy of the source.

Table 6.3. Major source of narcotics over entire narcotics history, by sex

Major Source	Male		Female	
	Number	Percent [1]	Number	Percent [1]
One physician only	45	24	28	53
Multiple physicians; exempt	22	12	6	11
Own supply	12	6	--	--
Medical plus some illegal	30	16	8	15
Mostly or all illegal	82	43	11	21
Unclassifiable	21	--	1	--
Total	212	100 [2]	54	100

[1] "Unknowns" omitted.
[2] Figures do not add to 100 due to rounding.

The first group consists of those subjects, 24 percent of the men and 53 percent of the women, who got all narcotics from one physician at a time. This sometimes means the subject got drugs from several different physicians, as when one physician died or retired and he became the patient of another. But these subjects never received narcotics outside of what was, or may have been, a normal physician-patient relationship. It will be seen later that the medical need for the drug was questionable in some cases, but no illegal activity was involved for subjects who obtained their narcotics only from physicians.

The second category in the table combines subjects who sought narcotics from several physicians simultaneously and those who used exempt narcotics. The subjects in this classification, therefore, have in common the fact that they showed drug-seeking behavior. These ways of obtaining narcotics are not *per se* illegal, though they involve a technical violation of the law if false names and addresses are given in order to obtain narcotics. Almost equal percentages of men and women, 12 and 11 percent, fell in this group.

The third category refers to 12 addict physicians most of whose drugs were taken from the supplies which they were legally permitted to order. Their diversion to the personal use of the physician, of course, was illegal. The group is a small one, but is best not combined with any of the others because the physicians differ from other subjects in so many ways that combining them with others would obscure some relationships to be discussed later.

The fourth category includes subjects who obtained some narcotics by illegal acts—stealing them, buying from peddlers, or forging prescriptions, but who obtained most narcotics as did the first and second groups. Again equal percentages of men and women, 16 and 15 percent, are found in this category.

Finally, the fifth group consists of those who acquired most or all of their narcotics from peddlers or by stealing and forging prescriptions. This category contains the largest number of men, 43 percent of all classifiable cases. Only 21 percent of the women fall in it.

With regard to possible errors in this classification, there are probably none in the last category. Good evidence, including usually the statements of the subjects themselves, is available to establish that illegal sources were a major source for all of these subjects. It is unlikely that there are errors in the first category or the third, since subjects were not placed in these without clear and plausible claims by the subjects that they belonged there, and confirmation from other sources. If there are errors in the first category, they probably consist in the occasional obtaining of drugs from other physicians than the one who was regularly prescribing.

The second category may include a few errors of classification. These subjects had shown drug-seeking behavior, and it would be easy to believe that they would have sought drugs from other sources such as peddlers, if they could. If this happened, they should be in the fourth rather than the second group, but probably still are different in that the degree of use of illegal sources, if it occurred, would have been less for them than for most of the subjects in the fourth category.

The fourth, those whose sources were mostly medical, with some illegal, may also contain some errors of classification. If so, the probable error would be that most of their drugs came from illegal sources, and they should be in the fifth group. Even if such errors occurred, the subjects would still differ from those in the fifth category, in that medical sources were an important source of narcotics for them, while medical sources were of minor importance for the fifth group.

It may be noted that 21 men and one woman, almost 10 percent of the sample, are not classified on this variable. The loss of information for these subjects, where the history of drug sources was not clearcut, is a price paid for assurance that errors are minimized in the classification. It may be taken as identifying the sources of narcotics, over the entire drug history of subjects, within a tolerable degree of error, and as placing subjects along a legal-illegal continuum of sources in essentially accurate order.

Only subjects in the first category completely avoided illegal acts in obtaining narcotics—a quarter of the men and half of the women. But it is a fact which will be seen to have great significance that even the narcotics acquired by illegal acts came to the addict in the great majority of cases through legitimate channels, rather than from an illicit market. This is suggested in table 6.3, where less than half of the men and only one-fifth of the women are shown as having acquired all or most of their narcotics from illegal sources. It becomes clearer in an analysis of the 10 sources which were identified earlier.

For seven of the ten sources, the narcotic had travelled through legitimate channels up to the last transfer to the addict himself. In many cases the last transfer too was legal, though it may have involved deceit, as when an addict obtained prescriptions by feigning illness, or unethical practice when a physician supplied medication for an illness he knew did not exist. Violations of law occurred when health professionals used narcotics from their supply, or peddled them to addicts, or when prescriptions were forged, but in all these cases the channels of supply, up to the addict himself, were legitimate.

Even for the other three sources, most were also diverted from legitimate channels no more than one or two steps before they reached the addict. When drugs were obtained from friends or relatives, the latter had obtained them from the other sources listed. When drugs were stolen, it was usually from drugstores, occasionally from physicians' offices or bags, or hospital supplies, and occasionally from other addicts. The one source which suggests an illicit channel was peddlers. This did include some offshoots of the illicit heroin traffic, and to an even greater extent what seems to have been a completely analagous traffic in morphine. But much of it, in Kentucky, consisted in retailing the narcotics which had been bought in wholesale quantities from a few unethical physicians.

Only 20 men and one woman were classified as using narcotics they had bought from physicians and pharmacists who were no more than licensed peddlers, but most of these then sold part of their purchases to other addicts, and the peddlers counted as a source for the others. So even the narcotics bought from peddlers were largely diverted from legitimate channels at only one remove from the addict. This is a pattern much different from what is found today in the metropolitan centers of addiction. There the major drug, heroin, is not only illicitly bought by the addict; the original opium was clandestinely produced, the heroin was illicitly manufactured, illegally smuggled into the country, and moved to the ultimate consumer through an elaborate and illegal distribution network. It is evident that more effective controls on the legitimate channels for distributing narcotics would have no effect on the prevalence of heroin addiction, but might have a great effect on the pattern of addiction that prevailed in Kentucky. It will be seen later that as controls became more effective, addiction became less prevalent in Kentucky.

Involvement in the Drug Subculture

It was clear in the consideration of routes of administration of narcotics that subjects learned such techniques as the intravenous route from other addicts. Some drugs were bought from peddlers who themselves were addicts. The literature on addiction emphasizes the existence and importance of a drug subculture, and in these facts there is evidence that it existed in Kentucky.

The concept of a drug subculture implies that addicts are in contact with each other. In this contact, learning takes place. The learning can be of facts and techniques. For example, the neophyte can learn from more experienced addicts that his withdrawal symptoms are the result of not having had his usual dose of narcotics, and will be relieved by a dose; that the intravenous route enhances the drug effect; how to obtain narcotics, or money for narcotics; new sources of narcotics; how to prepare narcotics for administration, and other knowledge of this kind.

He will usually learn new attitudes too. He may learn to define himself as an addict, learn new justifications for his drug use, and new and negative attitudes toward the laws which try to prevent drug abuse. In his contact with other addicts he learns their argot, with the implicit value orientations built into it. As with other forms of deviant behavior, he is likely to feel more and more at home with other addicts, spend more time and invest more interest in those new contacts, and gradually withdraw from ties to family, friends, and old associations. This in turn means that his old values are no longer reinforced by the old ties, so that it becomes still easier to adopt the values of the addict subculture. Finally, he is perceived by himself and other addicts, by his family and other older associates, and often by police and health agencies as a member of a deviant subgroup, whose values and orientations are shared with them but are opposed to those of the wider culture.

This concept is clearly relevant for the large majority of addicts today, the minority-group addicts from large metropolitan areas, who buy heroin from peddlers, who live in areas where there are many other addicts, who know many of them as addicts, and whose addiction is frequently interrupted by hospitalizations or prison sentences in institutions where they are labelled by staff and inmates as addicts. There is also evidence that involvement in the addict subculture plays an important part in their relapse to addiction after voluntary or enforced periods of abstinence. The concept, however, may not be relevant at all for some addicts, for example physicians and nurses. It may not have meaning for those addicts who come from rural areas or small towns where there are few or no other addicts. At the least, it is clear that in a sample like the one studied here, subjects may differ in the extent to which they are involved in the drug subculture, and that other facts, such as their tendency to relapse after a period of abstinence, may be related to such differences. An examination of this possibility requires a measure of the degree to which individual subjects were involved in the drug subculture.

Since involvement includes learning, it changes over time, and if subjects are to be compared on involvement, the measure should be made as of an event in time which can be dated for all of them. The event chosen here is their first admission to Lexington. It offers the practical advantage that more data were recorded for subjects as of that point in time than for any other. It is immediately prior to the posthospital behavior, with respect to abstinence and relapse, for which predictors would be desirable.

The data available at first admission were examined to see which could be taken to imply contact with addicts, learning from addicts, or self-concept as an addict, and seven were identified. These were treated as dichotomies; the subject was coded as positive on the variable if it was known to be true of him, and negative if it was not known to be true of him. The seven variables, roughly in order of the degree to which they imply involvement, are:

1. Sold narcotics.
2. Obtained narcotics from nonmedical sources.
3. History of heroin use.
4. Usual route is intravenous.

335-199—69——7

5. Had one or more "cures." This refers to hospitalizations for the treatment of addiction, or to periods of imprisonment which interrupted addiction. In either case, the subject came into contact with other addicts, and (with a few possible exceptions in the case of prison sentences) was defined as an addict by others.
6. Was known to the Bureau of Narcotics.
7. Had used more than one narcotic.

The last two of these variables were considered to be less certain indicators of involvement in the drug subculture than the first five. Subjects normally became known to the Bureau of Narcotics when they were arrested for some offense connected with their drug use. In a few cases, however, they were reported to the Bureau as "medical addicts" or were identified as addicts by investigations of pharmacy prescription records. These ways of becoming known to the Bureau would not imply that they had been in contact with other addicts.

On the seventh variable, it is characteristic of addicts that they learn of new drugs and obtain them from other addicts, so that most addicts will have used a number of different narcotics. In medical practice, on the other hand, a physician normally prescribes the same narcotic regularly, so that persons whose source of narcotics is strictly medical will often have used only one narcotic. But it is clear that sometimes physicians may consider it advisable to shift to a different narcotic, so the fact that a subject has used two narcotics is not sufficient in itself to establish that he has been in contact with other addicts.

For the immediate purpose, a three-point scale was defined as the measure of involvement in the drug subculture. The three categories are:

1. *No involvement*. This category includes those subjects who were negative on all seven variables, or were positive on only one variable, if this was being known to the Bureau or having used more than one narcotic.
2. *Some involvement*. This includes subjects who were positive on one to three variables, with the exception that when positive on only one, it must be one of the first five variables.
3. *Much involvement*. This includes subjects who were positive on four or more of the seven variables.[1]

It may now be asked to what extent the variables relating to the onset of addiction predict involvement in the drug subculture. Table 6.4 shows that for men the probability of involvement was greater, the earlier the decade in which addiction began. The percentage of men with much involvement drops steadily with each decade, from 86 percent of those addicted before 1920, to only 5 percent of those who became addicted in the 1950s. The most marked change, however, came about the end of the 1930s. Before that time over half of the men became much involved;

Table 6.4. Involvement in drug subculture by decade in which addiction began, and by sex

Involvement in Drug Subculture	Male—Decade of First Addiction					
	Before 1920	1920–29	1930–39	1940–49	1950–59	Total
	Percent	*Percent*	*Percent*	*Percent*	*Percent*	
Much	86	67	51	18	5	91
Some	9	31	31	57	48	81
None	5	3	18	25	48	40
Total	100	[1] 100	100	100	[1] 100	
Number of Subjects	22	39	65	65	21	212
	Female—Decade of First Addiction					
Much	25	17	40	15	9	9
Some	75	33	60	33	18	19
None	--	50	--	52	73	25
Total	100	100	100	100	100	
Number of Subjects	4	6	5	27	11	[2] 53

[1] Figures do not add to 100 due to rounding.
[2] Date of onset unknown for one woman.

after it, less than one in five in the 1940s, and only one in twenty in the 1950s.

It is not clear if the pattern for the women is essentially the same or not. The decrease in involvement in the last three decades parallels that for the men, but the involvement before 1930 was much less for the women. The number of cases in the earlier decades, however, is so small that no inference of a real difference would be justified.

The age at which addiction began is also seen, in Table 6.5, to be associated with later involvement in the drug subculture. The younger the men were at onset, the more likely they were to become involved, and to show much involvement rather than only some. This relationship holds for the women as well as for the men, though it is also true that within any age group the women show less involvement than the men.

Table 6.6 groups the reasons for addiction into three groups. The seven "other" reasons are classified with "medical treatment," and the table contrasts them with those who began in the treatment of alcoholism

Table 6.5. Involvement in drug subculture by age at onset of addiction and by sex

Involvement	Age at onset of addiction—Male					
	Under 20	20–29	30–39	40–49	50 or over	Total
	Percent	*Percent*	*Percent*	*Percent*	*Percent*	
Much	91	63	31	13	5	91
Some	9	29	41	61	55	81
None	--	8	28	26	40	40
Total	100	100	100	100	100	
Number of subjects	23	73	58	38	20	212
	Age at onset of addiction—Female					
Much	50	22	--	9	--	9
Some	50	44	44	18	14	19
None	--	33	55	73	86	25
Total	100	[1] 100	[1] 100	100	100	
Number of subjects	8	18	9	11	7	[2] 53

[1] Figures do not add to 100 due to rounding.
[2] Age at onset unknown for one woman.

or in the search for pleasure. The three groups constitute, in crude form, a continuum. The "medical treatment" category includes, but is not restricted to, subjects whose addiction began in the context of legitimate and needed medical treatment. It also includes cases where either the legitimacy or the need for narcotics may be questionable, but at the minimum there was some pretext of a legitimate reason for administration of narcotics, for conditions not brought about by the subject's actions. In most of the cases of treatment for alcoholism the drug was administered by physicians (50 of the 75 men who so began got their first shot from a physician), but here most informants, including the subjects, regarded the condition which required narcotics as existing due to the subject's fault. In addition, these subjects by virtue of the fact that they had been alcoholic had exhibited a readiness to abuse one drug. Finally, those who gave pleasure seeking as a reason pretended no legitimate need for the narcotic. In very rough terms, therefore, the legitimacy of the addiction decreases from left to right across Table 6.6.

This continuum is associated with the degree of involvement for the men. Only 27 percent of men who began addiction in medical treat-

Table 6.6. Involvement in drug subculture by reason for addiction and by sex

Involvement	Medical Treatment	Alcoholism	Pleasure	Total
	Reason for addiction—Male			
	Percent	*Percent*	*Percent*	
Much	27	45	79	89
Some	43	43	18	79
None	29	12	3	37
Total	[1] 100	100	100	
Number of Subjects	92	75	38	205
	Reason for addiction—Female			
Much	4	100	83	9
Some	41	0	17	19
None	55	0	0	24
Total	100	100	100	
Number of Subjects	44	2	6	[2] 52

[1] Figures do not add to 100 due to rounding.
[2] Seven men and two women unknown on reason.

ment became much involved in the drug subculture, while almost half of the alcoholics and three-quarters of the pleasure seekers did. It is also noteworthy, however, that most of the men showed at least some involvement, regardless of the reason for the start of addiction.

The pattern for the women could be called similar, but they fall at the two extremes of involvement. Of the women who began narcotics use in the course of medical treatment, only a few became much involved in the drug subculture, and over half of them had no involvement. The other women, whether they began for alcoholism or pleasure seeking, all showed later involvement, and seven of the eight showed much involvement.

Tables 6.4 through 6.6, therefore, show that there was more involvement in the drug subculture the earlier the decade when addiction began, the younger the age at which it began, and the less legitimate the reason for first addiction. Since the latter three variables relate to the point in time when addiction began, and involvement to the period after that time, the variables can be interpreted as determinants of the later involvement. When any two of the three are controlled, the third is still associated with involvement; each has some independent effect. While interactional effects are also suggested, the small numbers involved make these difficult to evaluate, and they will be ignored here.

Some of the ways in which these variables contribute to involvement in the drug subculture can be seen in their effect on more specific variables. With respect to the reason given for becoming addicted, for example, 33 percent of the men who began in medical treatment eventually learned to use the intravenous route of administration. The corresponding percentage for those who began using drugs in the treatment of alcoholism was 65 percent, and for pleasure seeking 89 percent. The average number of known types of sources of narcotics was 2.1 for the medical treatment males, 2.6 for the alcoholics and 3.0 for the pleasure seekers. It appears that drug-seeking behavior and seeking the most pleasurable method of using the drug were more frequent as the original reason for using narcotics was less legitimate.

Table 6.7. Major source of narcotics over entire history of addiction by reason for first becoming addicted, male subjects

Major Source of Narcotics	Reason for first addiction			
	Treatment of Illness	Treatment of Alcoholism	Pleasure	No. of Subjects
	Percent	*Percent*	*Percent*	
One physician	41	15	--	45
Multiple physicians	18	8	3	22
Own supply	7	8	--	11
Medical; some illegal	21	14	6	29
Mostly or all illegal	13	56	92	81
Total	100	[1] 100	[1] 100	
Number of subjects	86	66	36	[2] 188

[1] Figures do not add to 100 due to rounding.
[2] Twenty-four men unknown on one or both variables.

The same conclusion is suggested by table 6.7. Of those men who first used narcotics in the treatment of illness or injury, 41 percent obtained narcotics only in the context of medical treatment, and another 25 percent avoided the illicit market. Only about one-third of the men who began using narcotics for this reason used illicit drugs, and only 13 percent of them got most or all of their drugs from illegal sources.

Those who began in the treatment of alcoholism were much more likely to depend on illegal sources later, and that was true of almost all who first used narcotics for pleasure.

Similarly, the men who became addicted before age 40 were much more likely than those addicted at an older age to learn the intravenous routes, to use more later sources or narcotics, and to have illegal sources as the major source of narcotics. The same pattern of findings is more common for men addicted before 1940 than later.

Table 6.8. Involvement in drug subculture by major source of narcotics over entire narcotics history and by sex

Involvement in Drug Subculture	One Physician	Many Physicians, Exempt	Own Supply	Medical, Some Illegal	Most or All Illegal	Total
	Major Source of Narcotics—Male					
	Percent	*Percent*	*Percent*	*Percent*	*Percent*	
Much	2	9	33	50	79	87
Some	49	50	50	50	20	70
None	49	41	17	--	1	34
Total	100	100	100	100	100	
Number of Subjects	45	22	12	30	82	[1] 191
	Major Source of Narcotics—Female					
Much	--	--	--	38	54	9
Some	29	50	--	62	18	18
None	71	50	--	--	27	26
Total	100	100	--	100	[2] 100	--
Number of Subjects	28	6	--	8	11	[1] 53

[1] Twenty-one men and one woman unknown on major source.
[2] Figures do not add to 100 due to rounding.

Table 6.8 relates the major source of narcotics to the degree of involvement in the drug subculture. The fact that a strong association exists between the two measures is illustrated rather than established by this table, since the measures depend in part on the same data. It will be argued below from case material that the sources of narcotics which were available played an important part in determining the degree to which subjects became involved, and the table will serve the purpose of indicating which cases most deserve attention. The table also will help to clarify two concepts which are important in considering the addiction history of these subjects.

Self-Concept As Addict

One of the major hypotheses of the study was that there would be a difference in relapse behavior between addicts who perceived themselves as taking a medicine for an illness and those who perceived themselves as using narcotics for "kicks." The difference is one in self-concept, and presumably would best be measured by psychological measures, which are not available in this study. If a plausible assumption is made, however, the major source of narcotics can be used as an indicator of self-concept.

It was true of most subjects, and probably of all, that they preferred to obtain drugs from one physician. The reasons are obvious; the narcotic then was more pure and powerful, was cheaper and safer. The source was stable, removing the worry and inconvenience of getting drugs for the next shot. Finally, this source removed danger of trouble with the law for illegal possession and much of the need for other punishable drug-seeking behavior.

The assumption with regard to self-concept as a patient taking medicine is that this requires, or is greatly facilitated by, validation by a physician. If there was originally some medical need, or a reasonable medical pretext, for the first use of narcotics, and all subsequent narcotics were obtained from one physician at a time, the subject might well perceive himself as needing medication, which happened to be a narcotic, for some physical illness.

If, on the other hand, he had to buy narcotics on the illicit market, or forge prescriptions, if he could not persuade a physician to prescribe for him regularly, it was difficult for a subject to avoid the conclusion that he had no medical need for the drug and was seeking it for reasons which were not medically valid. This is not to deny the possibility that individuals may feel that they are ill, and that physicians are too incompetent to diagnose the illness or prescribe the indicated narcotic. But this possibility demands more self-deception than would be expected in most people and more than was observed in this sample. On the whole, it seems reasonable to assume that if the sample includes subjects whose self-concept was that of a patient using medicine, most of them are included in the group who obtained all of their narcotics from one physician. It is unlikely that more than an exceptional subject who obtained narcotics from any of the other sources shared this concept. To test the hypothesis about self-concept, therefore, the comparison will be that of the "one physician" source against all other sources.

Medical Addicts

Another concept that might be clarified by source of drugs is that of the "medical addict." The term is used in the literature with several meanings. One is that the narcotic was originally needed and continued to be needed for some medical condition other than addiction itself. A second is that the original addiction began in the course of medical treatment, regardless of reasons for continuing use of the drug.

Medical addiction in the second sense is clearly common in this sample. Table 6.2 showed that 42 percent of the men and 83 percent of the women had received their first narcotic as treatment of illness or injury. In the first sense, that addiction continued to meet a continuing medical need, the "medical addicts" in this sample presumably fall in the group of 45 men and 28 women who received all narcotics from one physician at a time. If they had to seek narcotics from other sources, this must mean that they could not find a physician who saw a continuing need for narcotics. About one man in five, and one woman in two, therefore, would be the highest estimate of medical addiction in the sense of continuing need.

But how real was the medical need for narcotics? This can be answered, if the medical staff of the Lexington hospital are accepted as the judge of medical need. If they continued to order narcotics for the subject during a lengthy hospitalization, and discharged him still on narcotics, he can be assumed to have needed narcotics. If he was successfully withdrawn from narcotics, or if he was undergoing a normal withdrawal but left the hospital against medical advice before it could be completed, the hospital staff judged that he did not need narcotics, and this judgment will here be assumed to be correct.

Ninety percent of all subjects were withdrawn from narcotics and got along satisfactorily in the hospital without narcotics for some period of time, on their first or a subsequent admission. In the remaining cases the subjects had only one admission to the hospital and were still receiving narcotics when they were discharged, so the possibility exists that withdrawal would not have been successful and the hospital staff would have decided to maintain the subject on narcotics indefinitely. For most of these, however, the hospital record clearly shows that withdrawal was progressing normally, and that the subject left against medical advice a day or two before withdrawal would have been completed.

There are only seven cases in which withdrawal was not completed, or well on the way to completion. In three of these there clearly was a continuing need for narcotics. One woman (No. 232) and two men

(Nos. 89 and 147) were treated for 14 months, 6 weeks and 8 weeks respectively, and received narcotics throughout these periods. The woman died in the Lexington hospital, and both of the men died, within 7 months after discharge, in other institutions to which they had been transferred, and where they continued to receive narcotics until death. The hospital diagnoses and the causes of death were respectively, carcinoma, pulmonary tuberculosis and cirrhosis of the liver.

The other four cases are of subjects who left the hospital on the first or second day after admission, before medical workups were completed, and before withdrawal was well under way. From the hospital records, it is not possible to establish that these subjects did not need narcotics. Two of the four, however, quit using narcotics shortly after their hospitalizations, and had subsequent periods of abstinence of 8 and 11 years. The other two continued to use narcotics until death, but from the following case material it is probable that there was no medical need for narcotics.

> One of the two was a 70 year old woman (Case 253) who left the hospital the day after her admission. She had a history of some use of codeine as a young woman, and then four years before her admission became addicted to twenty grains of codeine per day, originally for a severe cough. At the time of admission to the hospital, however, she had no complaints except for her dependence on drugs. The physician who referred her for treatment saw the problem as her loss of control over narcotics, and neither he nor the admitting physician at Lexington diagnosed any physical illness except addiction itself. After she left the hospital her physician continued to prescribe for her until her death three years later.
>
> The other (Case 254) had been using morphine three years for arthritis and bronchiectasis, had tried several times to quit, and gave as his reason for failure "Just seems that I can't do without it, as I get nervous and sick at stomach and worry about every little thing that happens and I get excited easily." The physician who had been prescribing for him wrote "He is suffering from bronchial exidus (sic) which I think is incurable." The admitting physician at Lexington diagnosed bronchiectasis, probable heart disease, and malnutrition in addition to drug addiction, and noted that the arthritis was then dormant. He felt that the subject "should receive therapy directed towards the relief of his malnutrition and after this has been instituted, probably should receive routine therapy towards withdrawal from narcotic drugs." The subject left the hospital two days after admission and according to his widow and daughter used morphine until his suicide 3 months later. They also stated these drugs were prescribed by the physician who had originally started the subject on narcotics, and who kept raising the price until he was charging $50 per vial of morphine; it was as a protest against this that the subject shot himself in front of the physician's office.

While many subjects had taken their first narcotic in the treatment of illness or injury, therefore, it seems clear that only three subjects in the entire sample had a continuing medical need for narcotics at the time of their first admission to Lexington. These three had no posthospital time except in other institutions, and are not included in the figures on posthospital relapse and abstinence.

The fact that 73 subjects obtained narcotics only from one physician at a time, and many of these after their treatment at Lexington as well as before, does not mean, then, that this number needed narcotics. It does mean that they could have regarded themselves as needing the drugs, even in spite of successful withdrawal in the hospital, because most of them left after so brief a time that they would still have been feeling ill. The fact that Lexington physicians regarded their drug use as unnecessary must have made them question their self-concept, but it may have been easy to decide that these physicians were wrong, especially if their own physician was willing to resume prescribing narcotics immediately after they left the hospital.[2]

Relationship Between Source and Involvement

Returning to table 6.8, the cases in the upper left and lower right corners of the table deserve examination, since they involve apparent contradictions. Why should a subject who received all narcotics from one physician at a time show "much" involvement in the drug subculture, and how can there be subjects who obtained all or most of their narcotics illegally, but had "no" involvement? Similarly, why should physicians, using mainly drugs from their own supply, be involved in the drug subculture? Examination of the cases that fall in such cells in the table may point to inadequacies in the measures, or suggest explanations for the apparent discrepancies.

The one case in which there is a combination of much involvement in the drug subculture and one physician as the major source of narcotics is one in which the coding of the latter variable may be incorrect.

> This (Case 45) subject's father had tuberculosis, and became addicted to narcotics about the turn of the century. His mother became addicted so she could keep going, to take care of her husband. When the subject was 9 years old, the family physician began giving him narcotics for asthma. He continued using them until his death.
>
> The start was before the passage of the Harrison Act, but after it the physician continued to prescribe narcotics until the mother's death. Some seems to have been prescribed for the subject, but most for his mother, and he used all of his own and much of hers. Then the mother died, the physician refused to continue prescribing for the subject, and he was finally arrested and sent to Lexington as the result of his pressures on the physician to continue prescribing, and eventually for impersonating a narcotics agent to get prescriptions. For a few years his source of narcotics was unstable, and it may be that he bought some illegally, and even more probable that he tried "making" physicians, but no evidence of these sources was found, and he regularly denied them on his seven admissions to Lexington, over a 7-year period. Then

he developed tuberculosis, and found a physician who prescribed for him to the time of death.

Four physicians are shown with much involvement, despite having used drugs mainly from their own supply. The involvement consisted in the facts that three sold drugs to addicts, all had numerous cures and were known to the Bureau of Narcotics, and three regularly used the intravenous route.

One man and three women are shown with no involvement in the drug subculture, but as having obtained all or most of their narcotics by illegal means. The explanation for the man and one woman is that they obtained their narcotics by forging prescriptions. Another woman was the wife of a physician, and stole her narcotics from his supplies. The last was a nurse, who got some narcotics on prescription but stole most from the hospital where she worked.

Statistical associations of variables suggest, and anecdotal material from case records shows, that the source from which narcotics were obtained was an important determinant of several aspects of the drug history. Of the men who got all or most of their drugs from illegal sources, 84 percent learned to use the intravenous route. Of those who got only some from illegal sources, 59 percent used the intravenous route. The percentage drops to 45 for those who "made" doctors and 36 for the physician addicts themselves, but only 9 percent of those who got all of their drugs from one physician at a time learned the intravenous route.

As an example of how the source of narcotics affected drug history, two cases which are alike in many ways can be contrasted. Both men are successful gamblers, both began using narcotics as young men in the course of somewhat dubious medical treatment, and both were found to be currently addicted, with the narcotics prescribed by a physician.

The first (Case 285) became addicted about age 19, codeine being prescribed by a physician for pain due to gonorrheal arthritis. At the time the subject worked in a pharmacy, filled his own prescriptions, and soon shifted to morphine. For years after he gave up this job to devote his time to gambling, he found it no problem to get various physicians to write prescriptions for morphine in the amount he wanted. When it became difficult to find such physicians he began to deal in narcotics, and from the statements of other subjects he was for many years the major illicit supplier of narcotics in his part of the State. In recent years he has been receiving eight grains of morphine per day by prescription. This man scored positive on all seven of the variables included in the measure of involvement early in his 45-year career of drug use. He managed, however, to avoid trouble with the law except for one 2-year sentence and one period of probation, both on drug charges. Indeed, he is today a wealthy man, retired on the profits of his drug sales and the brothel he and his wife operated.

> The second man (Case 80) is also a gambler, not so successful in terms of present wealth. His addiction began about age 25, for headaches, and has continued for about 30 years, at a level of nine grains of morphine per day for most of that time. All drugs were prescribed by the same physician, except for a few occasions when he was traveling and got prescriptions from other physicians. His gambling kept this subject at least on the fringes of the underworld, and he was arrested and charged numerous times, never on drug charges but usually for crimes of violence, and served one 2-year sentence for malicious shooting and wounding. This man scored positive on only two variables of the involvement index. He did have several "cures," and he was known to the Bureau of Narcotics. Unlike most subjects, however, he was not known to them as the result of some offense, but was identified as an addict by investigations of drug-store prescriptions and of a private institution that specialized in the treatment of addicts. He never used heroin, or any drug but morphine, never used the intravenous route, never obtained drugs from a nonmedical source, and never sold narcotics.
>
> This subject, then, is classified as having only "some" involvement. The classification does not exaggerate the extent of involvement, because the case material shows that he was closely associated with another subject, another gambler and an intravenous user, and was at least acquainted with other addicts. His whole life pattern suggests it was no middle-class value orientation that prevented him from becoming more involved with addicts, and learning, for example, to use the intravenous route. But he never had to "hustle" to find a source of drugs, and never had to engage in any drug-seeking behavior which could not easily be rationalized as asking for medicine for his headaches. There are other differences between the two cases described, but it seems plausible that the difference in legality and stability of the source of narcotics, perhaps acting through an intervening variable, self-concept, played an important part in the difference in involvement in the drug subculture.

It will be noted that both of these men began drug use in the context of medical treatment, and that in the second case the physician continued to prescribe while in the first the subject was unable to continue getting narcotics from his early sources. Since a physician is known to have been the first source of narcotics in 166 cases and continued to be the only source for but 73 cases, it is clear that many other subjects faced the problem of a change from the first source. Their actions when this became necessary are instructive.

> One man (Case 179) was given oral dilaudid by a physician after an injury. He had never before experienced the rest, relaxation and general feeling of well-being which followed drug use. When his original supply ran out, he went to another physician for more, and soon found himself going to several physicians at once to get the quantity he desired. He also began going to sanataria for cures, seemingly in part because he wanted to get rid of the habit and in part because in such sanitaria narcotics were dispensed rather freely to those who had the money to pay. Next, he made contact with sellers of morphine, and bought much of his narcotics on the illicit market. Some time during this process he learned to take the drug by intramuscular shots, but never in the vein.

> Finally, when he was in his late sixties, a physician began prescribing narcotics regularly enough to maintain him on about five grains of morphine per day.

This was the pattern for the large majority of subjects in this sample. When the original source no longer supplied narcotics, the subject looked for a similar source, and if need be eventually went to illegal sources. This can be contrasted with the less frequent pattern.

> One woman (Case 229) became addicted at about age 33. This followed surgery and a series of illnesses, and it is not clear for precisely what reason morphine was given, but the physician continued to prescribe it for 15 years. She used five to six grains per day, subcutaneously.
>
> Then she moved from one city in Kentucky to another, and was referred to another physician, who knew of her addiction and attributed it to personality problems. He agreed to accept responsibility only if she would enter the Lexington hospital for treatment. She did so, but left after a week. She relapsed to drug use, but this time it was only one grain of morphine per day, orally, plus some barbiturate. Where she got these is not clear. She returned to Lexington about a year later, during a period when patients who had left against medical advice on the previous admission were not readmitted unless they submitted to the "Bluegrass" procedure. This involved pleading guilty to being an addict in a local court and being sentenced to 1 year, with sentence suspended on condition that the addict enter the Lexington hospital and remain until released by the hospital staff. The threat of the year in jail kept most such patients in the hospital for the 4 to 5 months recommended by hospital staff, and this subject remained hospitalized.
>
> When released, therefore, she was completely free of narcotics for the first time in about 16 years. She was also known to the narcotics agents for the first time, since her court appearance was reported to them. For the next 10 years she continued to ask her physician, and another specialist to whom she went occasionally, for narcotics, but they were able to meet these needs with verbal reassurance and tranquilizers. They refused to prescribe narcotics, and the fact that the subject was now known to the Narcotics Bureau made this easier, perhaps in two ways. The physicians may have feared they would have trouble with the narcotics agents if they prescribed, or more probably they encouraged her to believe this was one reason for their refusal, thus shifting the onus of refusal from their own shoulders. This knowledge may also have kept the woman from seeking other sources of narcotics. It would seem more reasonable, however, to explain her acceptance of the refusal of physicians to prescribe as indicating a value system in which physicians were the only conceivable source of narcotics.

In this case, then, the pattern is one in which the original source was no longer available, and the addict gave up the addiction after a period of trying to find a second source, with partial success. All indications are that the personality problems of this woman were as serious as those of other addicts, and that she did not accept abstinence easily or gracefully.

During her two periods at Lexington, she inevitably would have heard of the various ways in which narcotics can be obtained, but there is no indication that she tried any of these. One reason for this is brought out more clearly in other cases; the middle-class, small-town Kentucky white woman is likely to perceive the other women addicts in the hospital as alien creatures. Many are minority-group members, most are lower-class, most have been guilty of criminal offenses and sexual promiscuity. The reaction frequently (for male patients too) is a combination of awe, fear, fascination and sometimes of envy, mostly below the threshold of awareness. But it rarely includes the feeling that their way of life is a possibility. Indeed, the experience can reinforce desires to quit drug use—"If that was what an addict was, I certainly didn't want to be one." In such cases, the addict's perception of himself as a patient using medicine seems to have enabled him to accept the fact that a physician would not prescribe, and prevented him from seeking other sources. When, on the other hand, the subject had recognized the fact that he was using narcotics largely or wholly for the pleasurable effects, he was likely to seek new sources.

In this sample, the seeking of new sources was much more frequent than accepting that drugs were no longer available. But it may well be that the latter reaction is the more common one. It must happen frequently in the course of medical practice in Kentucky that after an illness or an operation the patient has developed some physical dependence on narcotics. It is probable that most of these patients give up the drug easily, without being aware that there had been any question of addiction, and perhaps even if they had become aware they were addicted. But such persons would have no chance to be represented in this sample, except for the very rare cases of those sent to Lexington for withdrawal. Of all persons who become physically dependent on narcotics, it is a minority who exhibit continued drug-seeking behavior, and who find it extremely difficult to give up the use of drugs. Those admitted to Lexington or similar institutions are drawn almost entirely from this minority.

Posthospital Variables

It remains to be asked to what extent the variables considered in this chapter may be predictive of the posthospital variables discussed in earlier chapters.

There are minor and unimportant relationships between several drug history variables and mortality, which suggest no additional reasons why the death rate was so much higher than expected. But the data of this chapter do make one possible explanation of the high death rate seem improbable.

This is the possibility that the high death rate is attributable to serious illnesses antedating addiction. Even if it were assumed that all addiction which began in the course of medical treatment indicated a serious illness at that time, the evidence suggests that in most cases the illness was a transient one, or was successfully treated. The data on sources of narcotics show that only about 30 percent of the sample continued to get all narcotics from a physician. The small number of diagnoses of serious illnesses at Lexington, and the fact that the hospital staff successfully withdrew drugs from almost all subjects, including those with a regular source from a physician, establish that the original illness was not of major importance at the time of hospitalization.

Table 6.9 shows that involvement in the drug subculture is associated with the posthospital pattern of drug use and abstinence. The less involvement, the less addiction to narcotics there is, and more abstinence.

Table 6.9. Posthospital drug pattern by involvement in drug subculture and by sex (percentages)

Posthospital Drug Pattern	Involvement in drug subculture—Male			
	Much	Some	None	No. of Subjects
Addicted, Narcotics	36	33	22	63
Addicted, Substitutes	20	30	14	44
Some Abstinence	33	23	22	53
Much or Complete Abstinence	11	14	42	35
Total	100	100	100	
Number of Subjects	89	70	36	195[1]
	Involvement in drug subculture—Female			
Addicted, Narcotics	44	28	17	13
Addicted, Substitutes	--	6	--	1
Some Abstinence	44	22	17	12
Much or Complete Abstinence	11	44	67	25
Total	100[2]	100	100[2]	
Number of Subjects	9	18	24	51[1]

[1] Seventeen men and three women not included; unknown on drug pattern or no post-hospital time.
[2] Figures do not add to 100 due to rounding.

This difference is statistically significant. For the men, chi-square is 20.3, 6 d.f., $P<.01$. Over half of this chi-square value comes from the lower right cell of the sub-table, from the fact that only 6 or 7 of the men with no involvement would be expected to show a pattern of much or complete abstinence, if pattern and involvement were independent, but 15 of them do show such patterns.

If the sub-table for the women is collapsed into a 2×2 table, the relationship is also significant for them; chi-square$=4.4$, $P<.05$.

That this relationship exists is anything but a startling finding. If the literature on addiction agrees on any point, it would be that relapse is associated with involvement in the drug subculture, whether because contact with old addict friends triggers a conditioned response, or because they seek to readdict the "cured" addict, or through other aspects of involvement. The finding may serve more to validate the measure used here as one of involvement than to add to knowledge. Still, this is the first report, as far as the writer knows, of a statistical association between empirical and independent measures of involvement and relapse. The finding of a significant association is therefore of some importance.

It should also be pointed out, however, and the fact will later be seen to have implications for social policies aimed at the control of addiction, that this statistical association would be of little practical value in predicting posthospital drug pattern from the degree of involvement known to exist at the time of hospitalization. If one predicted that no men would show a pattern of much or complete abstinence, regardless of degree of involvement in the drug subculture, he would make fewer errors in prediction than if he predicted that those with no involvement would show such patterns. For the men, in short, knowing the degree of involvement would not help in prediction.

It would help, however, for the women. If one predicted that all women would show patterns of abstinence, or that none of them would, he would be right about half of the time. If he predicted that none would show such patterns, if they had some or much involvement in the drug subculture, but that all would show such patterns if they were not involved, the prediction would be correct for two-thirds of the cases.

There is no similar clear-cut association between the major source of narcotics and posthospital drug pattern. This may relate to the reason why, when it was hypothesized that self-concept as an addict would be associated with posthospital relapse and abstinence, the direction of the association could not be predicted. Self-concept was conceived as affecting the probability of relapse through its effect on drug-seeking behavior. Subjects who saw themselves as addicts desiring kicks would be expected to seek drugs, but they might not succeed if drugs were difficult to obtain. Those who saw themselves as patients taking medicine

335-199—69——8

were likely to be abstinent if their physician refused to prescribe, and to relapse if he would prescribe. The pattern observed would depend not only on differences in self-concept, but also on the circumstances subjects faced after hospitalization, and there was no way to predict these.

But a modification of the original hypothesis, suggested by the drug patterns which could be distinguished, is testable. For those who perceived themselves as ill, and using medicine, it may be predicted that the pattern depends on their physicians; they will either be abstinent or addicted to narcotics. For the other subjects, to the extent that narcotics are unavailable it may be predicted that they would seek substitute drugs, alcohol or barbiturates, or would use narcotics on the infrequent occasions they could obtain them. In short, they would be found relatively less often in the patterns of addiction to narcotics or of abstinence, and more often addicted to substitutes, or occasional users.

Using the fact that all narcotics were obtained from one physician as an indicator of self-concept as a patient using medicine, and all other sources as an indicator of self-concept as an addict seeking kicks, table 6.10 supports the hypothesis. The differences are as predicted, and statistically significant, independently for the sexes.

Table 6.10. Extreme posthospital drug patterns compared with intermediate patterns, by major source of narcotics and by sex

	Major source of narcotics—Male		
	One Physician	All Other	Total
Addicted to Narcotics or Much Abstinence	25	65	90
Addicted to Substitutes or Some Abstinence	11	78	89
Total	36	143	179
	Chi-square=5.7, 1 d.f., P<.02.		
	Major source of narcotics—Female		
Addicted to Narcotics or Much Abstinence	23	14	37
Addicted to Substitutes or Some Abstinence	3	10	13
Total	26	24	50
	Chi-square=4.4, 1 d.f., P<.05.		

Not too much should be made of this finding. The hypothesis was not originally stated in this form, nor was this test of it explicitly planned. To some extent it is a *post facto* explanation of findings, found in a search for combinations of patterns which would be logically justifiable and might produce significant differences. Still, it is a finding, and the logic of the hypothesis was inherent in the considerations which led to avoiding a prediction of more relapse for one type of subject than the other.

The other variables discussed in this chapter—age at addiction, year of addiction and reason for addiction—are not predictive of posthospital drug pattern.

Summary

This chapter has described the onset of addiction in the sample and shown how changes occurred, in such variables as the source of narcotics and the route of administration, as addiction continued. These changes were shown to be related to the degree of involvement in the drug subculture, for which a measure was devised. The findings of the chapter were then used as a partial test of a major hypothesis of the study, that self-concept of subjects would be related to relapse behavior, and to measure the extent of "medical addiction" in the sample.

One of the main impressions left by the description of the history of addiction in this sample is how much these subjects differ from the "typical" addict of the 1960s. These differences are important, but should not be allowed to obscure some basic similarities. There is a sizeable subgroup of the male subjects, 38 cases, who were introduced to narcotics at an early age, by relatives or friends who were themselves addicts, and who took their first shot—sometimes intravenous—for "kicks," or out of "curiosity." In all these respects they resemble present-day addicts; one subtype in the sample looks very much like present addicts, though it accounts for only a minority of the sample, and probably a large majority of today's addicts.

An even larger group began their addiction by using narcotics to sober up after alcoholic excesses. This is a relatively rare road to narcotic addiction today, but from the older literature on addiction it was as frequent, or more frequent than in this sample. In this respect, the sample represents the addicts of a couple of generations ago more than it does present addicts. One may wonder, however, if beginning addiction in this manner is functionally different from beginning directly with narcotics, or with marihuana and then narcotics. Both roads to addiction suggest a readiness to use intoxicants for the effect of the drug, presumably pleasurable in most cases, though perhaps desirable for other reasons in some. It may be that relative availability of the drugs determines which will be used first, and that it is essentially hedonistic individuals who use either road to addiction.

Most subjects in this study began their addiction in the treatment of illness, and most received their first narcotics from a physician. But this is more informative about the culturally acceptable ways of handling an illness and about the standards of medical practice in Kentucky one or two generations ago than it is about the subjects themselves. More than half the subjects were medical addicts, if this refers to beginning use in the context of medical treatment. Very few were medical addicts, if the term refers to a continuing need for narcotics for some physical condition other than addiction.

Whatever the reason for onset of addiction, continued addiction tended to produce involvement in the drug subculture. This involvement was greater for those addicted in earlier decades, for those who were younger at the start of addiction, and for those whose reason for first use was less legitimate. Some avoided all involvement. But in general, most whose addiction continued for years showed at least some involvement in the drug subculture, as evidenced by such facts as learning to use the intravenous route and obtaining narcotics from illegal sources.

Case material strongly suggests that the stability of the early sources of drugs largely determined the degree of involvement in the drug subculture. Those who first got narcotics from a physician, and continued to get it from him, or from a successor after his death or retirement, were not likely to become involved with other addicts, or to learn such things as the intravenous route from them. If narcotics were first obtained from a physician, who later refused to continue prescribing, or for whom a successor could not be found, it may be that many addicts gave up their addiction. These, however, would not be found in a sample drawn as was this one. The subjects in this sample tended to seek out new sources, and were most likely to find them with the help of other addicts, who also taught them new techniques, like the intravenous route, and probably new values and viewpoints.

Many of the variables discussed in this chapter varied with the decade in which the subject became addicted, suggesting that the pattern of addiction has been changing in Kentucky over the time period covered by this study, some 60 years. It will be found that this is supported by data on other variables in later chapters, and the changes will be described after these are introduced.

The variables introduced in this chapter do not help to explain the mortality in the sample. Two of them—involvement in the drug subculture and the major source of narcotics—were found to be associated with posthospital patterns of drug use, to a statistically significant degree.

The association was not strong enough, however, to provide a useful practical prediction of which subjects would relapse, and which would show patterns of abstinence.

Footnotes, Chapter 6

[1] Those who are interested in research methodology will note that the measure of involvement assigns equal weights to the first five variables, and lesser weights to the last two. This indicates assumptions which have not been explained or shown to be justified. The writer considered this looseness permissible in the initial attempt to develop a measure. When the measure's validity and utility were suggested by its associations with other variables, it would be time to examine the measure more rigorously.

The associations, it will be seen, do suggest validity. The question then arises whether or not better weights can be assigned. Further, is it justified to assume the measure refers to one dimension, involvement, especially in view of the fact that at least three different concepts—contact with addicts, learning, and self-concept—were used in selecting items? Guttman's scalogram technique is designed for such questions, and was applied. This led to the finding that one item, history of heroin use, merely duplicated information given by the history of having obtained narcotics from non-medical sources. The remaining six items come very close to a Guttman scale, in the order: selling narcotics; intravenous use; non-medical sources; cures; more than one narcotic; and known to the Bureau. Five of the marginals are between 40 and 60; index of reproducibility is .87; more than twice as many subjects fall in the pure-scale types as would be expected by chance.

The measure falls short of Guttman's criteria of scalability in two respects. Only six items were used, and these were dichotomized. Certain non-scale types appear in sizeable numbers. These, however, are easily explained. If the scale measures psychological involvement, the subject who is willing to sell drugs should be willing to buy illicit drugs, or if he is ready to use the intravenous route he should be ready to try several different narcotics. In this sample, some sold drugs or used the intravenous routes, and presumably would have been ready to act in the less seriously involved ways, but did not need to—they had a physician who supplied morphine regularly. Some "errors," too, probably reflect failure to obtain information on behavior that did occur.

In view of the fact that the sample contains medical addicts, hedonistic addicts, and physicians and nurses, the time range over which addiction began is more than 60 years, and subjects differ in the other ways noted and to be seen later, an index of reproducibility of .87 seems amazingly high. The measure is therefore a promising one, and will be tested and, if possible, expanded in other studies.

If the six items are accepted as a Guttman scale, subjects could be classified by the closest scale type, or by the number of positive responses. Either classification correlates highly with the original arbitrary measure used in this study, and cross-tabulations against other variables lead to the same inferences.

[2] In fairness to physicians, it should be pointed out that private practitioners would find it much more difficult than hospital staff to avoid the use of narcotics. The latter had available consultants in all the specialties,

trained and experienced ancillary personnel, hospital and laboratory resources, and all of these in a setting designed primarily to find a cure for addiction. Without these sources of support for his tentative judgment that narcotics were not indicated, and in the face of demands from his patient and the patient's family, it is understandable that the private physician sometimes found no alternative to prescribing narcotics.

CHAPTER 7

Criminal Records Of Subjects

It is generally agreed that narcotic addiction and crime are associated, but there is disagreement on the nature, extent and significance of the association, and on its implications for public policy.

Several ecological studies establish that some relationship exists between addiction and crime. The general findings are clear and consistent: high rates of addiction or drug use are associated with high rates of crime and delinquency. In New York City in the 1950s, and Chicago about 1930 and again in the early 1950s, addiction was found to be concentrated in areas of the city in which other social problems, including adult crimes and juvenile delinquency, were also frequent.[1]

Other studies establish that histories of addiction and crime are frequently found in the same individuals. Most of these study a group of addicts in a prison, or in a hospital for the treatment of addiction, and demonstrate that some sizeable percentage of these addicts have criminal records.[2] A few study a group of prisoners, and demonstrate that some appreciable percentage of them have a history of addiction.[3]

These studies establish that crime and addiction are associated. Disagreement begins when an attempt is made to explain the association, and particularly when a causal connection between them is postulated.

There is certainly a connection leading from crime to addiction. To become an addict one must have access to drugs, and outside of the health professions, drugs are available mainly through contacts with criminals. Some prior contact with criminality is therefore a necessary condition of addiction for most addicts.[4]

Most authorities agree that there is also a causal connection in the opposite direction. At least three ways in which crime results from addiction have been suggested. First, drug addiction *per se* "causes a relentless destruction of character and releases criminal tendencies."[5] Others hold that it is the laws and attitudes of society which are responsible for the increase in crimes associated with addiction, first by defining as crime the behavior which is part of addiction (e.g., possession of heroin), and second by making drugs expensive, so that addicts are forced by their need for money to commit crimes they would not have committed in a different social situation.[6]

But the crimes committed by addicts might have been committed even if the offenders had not become addicted. Anslinger and Tompkins argue that many addicts were criminals before they became addicts, and imply that they would have continued to commit crimes whether or not they became addicts.[7] The studies which bear most directly on this point are those which date the beginning of addiction for individuals, and examine their criminal records before and after addiction.

Among such studies, Dai reports that of 1047 addicts arrested in Chicago about 1930, 81 percent had no criminal record before addiction.[8] By virtue of the way his sample was selected, all had such a record after addiction. Their postaddiction offenses were mainly violations of narcotic laws; offenses against property were frequent and crimes of violence infrequent. Pescor analyzed the records of 1036 addicts hospitalized in Lexington in 1936–37, and reported that 75 percent had no history of delinquency prior to addiction, but 86 percent had a record of delinquency after addiction.[9] It is to be noted, however, that 82 percent of his subjects were prisoners or probationers, so that the high percentage of postaddiction delinquency could again be due to the way the sample was selected.

Finestone studied 84 noninstitutionalized young addicts in Chicago in the early 1950s. He does not report the percentage with official records of delinquency before and after addiction, but implies that most had committed delinquent acts before their addiction, and all had committed such acts after it. He sees both their criminality and use of narcotics as results of the same causes.

> . . . it is irrelevant to ask whether the delinquency preceded the addiction or vice versa. Many of those who became addicted and were forced to engage in crime to support the high cost of their addiction would probably have gone on to engage in crime as adolescents regardless of whether or not they had become addicted.[10]

Chein studied 100 drug users under 20 years of age in New York in the early 1950s. They were chosen so that about half had delinquency records before drug use began and half had no such record, and it is not possible to estimate what percentage of drug users in New York had prior records. It is clear that all or almost all of them committed criminal acts after addiction, primarily crimes of profit, though the percentage with official records of arrests and sentences is not reported.[11]

In a recent 12-year followup of 100 New York City addicts treated at Lexington in 1952–53, it is reported that although many began drug use before age 18, "at least 57 percent of our group were antisocial (chronically truant, dishonorably discharged, in juvenile court or in reform school) prior to the use of drugs. . . . Although prior to Lexington only 46 percent of the patients had been arrested, after leaving 92 percent of the patients served time in jail." [12]

From the questions asked in these studies, and the ways in which their findings have been used, the statement that addiction causes crime can be rephrased as the hypothesis that those individuals who become addicts then begin to commit crimes, or more crimes than they would have committed if they had not become addicts. A test of the hypothesis logically requires that crimes after addiction be counted, and compared with the number of crimes that would have been expected if these persons had not become addicts. There are two difficulties with such a test.

The data available for testing the hypothesis include the number of arrests and sentences of subjects after addiction began, but it is evident that these figures do not represent a full count of all criminal acts. In the analysis which follows it will be necessary to estimate the discrepancy between offenses which were officially recorded and offenses which were actually committed.

The recorded offenses must be compared against the number of expected offenses. Criminology today does not provide as firm a basis for estimating expected offenses as do vital statistics for estimating expected deaths in a population, but criminal statistics on age of offenders do offer a basis for estimates accurate enough to test the hypothesis. The logic of these can be discussed when the estimates are made.

In looking for evidence of an increase in observed over expected crimes, attention must be given to the type of offense. The popular stereotype has been that addiction makes rapists and killers of addicts, but this is negated by most available data. Compared with other offenders, the criminal records of addicts show a preponderance of drug and property arrests and a low proportion of violent crimes.[13] Ecological correlations show that high drug rates are associated with profitmaking, rather than violent crimes.[14] Finestone and Chein both report that after addiction their subjects committed more property offenses and fewer crimes of violence.[15] One pharmacological effect of the opiates has been said to be that they "change drunken, fighting psychopaths into sober, cowardly, nonaggressive idlers." [16] It may be, therefore, that crimes against the person will be reduced, and crimes for profits increased after the onset of addiction.

The remainder of the chapter presents data on the criminal records of the Kentucky subjects, and compares findings with those of the studies described, in relation to three questions:

1. What proportion of addicts were criminals prior to their addiction?
2. Was addiction followed by more crimes than the addicts would have been expected to commit?
3. If there is an apparent increase in crimes after addiction, with what aspects of addiction is it associated?

Findings

Table 7.1 shows that before they became addicted, 133 (63 percent) of the men had no arrests. Fifty-nine (28 percent) have a known number of arrests and in 20 cases the number is shown as unknown. In four of these 20 cases, there was at least one arrest. Only 15 percent of the men served a sentence before they became addicted. Four of the women had arrests prior to their addiction, and none served a sentence.

Table 7.1. Number of subjects with specified number of arrests and sentences, prior to and after addiction, by sex

	Number of Subjects			
	Male		Female	
	Before Addiction	After Addiction	Before Addiction	After Addiction
Number of Arrests:				
0	133	80	50	40
1 or 2	26	24	0	5
3 to 5	14	32	1	3
6 or more	19	56	--	4
Unknown	20	20	3	2
Total Cases	212	212	54	54
Number of Sentences:				
0	180	122	54	50
1 or 2	23	41	--	4
3 to 5	8	29	--	--
6 or more	--	17	--	--
Unknown	1	3	--	--
Total Cases	212	212	54	54

After they became addicted, the men show an increase in arrests and sentences. Only 80 (38 percent) had no arrests after addiction, and those arrested tend to have a large rather than a small number of arrests. More than half of the men, however, were not sentenced after addiction. Eighty-seven (41 percent) were sentenced, and about half of these had three or more sentences.

More women were also arrested and sentenced after addiction, but the pattern is much less marked than for the men. Forty (74 percent) of the women had no arrests, only four (7 percent) were sentenced, and these had only one or two sentences.

The table therefore indicates that prior to addiction this sample was not composed of known criminals. Addiction was followed by an increase in arrests and sentences for both sexes, but the increase was less marked for the women. It is to be noted, however, that even after addiction most of the women and over half of the men had no sentences.

Table 7.2 examines the criminal record of the male subjects before addiction in more detail. For this table, the arrests, sentences and time served before addiction are combined into an index of criminal behavior by the following definitions:

1. None; no arrests or sentences before addiction—133 men.
2. Some; one or more arrests but no sentences, or sentences totalling under 10 months—39 men.
3. More; one or more arrests, and one or more sentences totalling 10 months or more—24 men.

There were 20 men on whom the number of arrests before addiction is unknown. Four of these are known to have had sentences before addiction, and these are included in the table. The other 16 are omitted.

Table 7.2. Crime before addiction related to year of addiction and age of addiction, male subjects (percentages)

	N	Crime Before Addiction			
		None	Some	More	Total
1. Year of Addiction:					
Before 1920	20	95	5	--	100
1920–29	35	77	20	3	100
1930–39	62	65	16	19	100
1940–49	60	62	30	8	100
1950–59	19	53	16	32	[2] 100
Total Cases	[1] 196	133	39	24	196
2. Age at Addiction:					
Under 20	22	86	9	5	100
20–29	65	54	25	22	[2] 100
30–39	54	67	22	11	100
40–49	35	74	23	3	100
50 or over	20	85	5	10	100
Total Cases	[1] 196	133	39	24	196

[1] Sixteen men not included because of insufficient data for classification on Crime Before Addiction.
[2] Figures do not add to 100% due to rounding errors.

Table 7.2 shows a clear relationship between crime before addiction and the year of addiction; the more recent the year of addiction, the more likely are the men to have a criminal record before their addiction. Further, except for a minor reversal in the 1940–49 decade, the more likely is this to be a more serious prior criminal record. The table indicates that over the past five decades addicts in Kentucky have increasingly been recruited from the ranks of criminals. Only one of the 20 men addicted before 1920 had had prior arrests, as compared with 9 of the 19 who became addicted in the 1950s.

The table also shows that crimes before addiction are inversely related to the age at which addiction began, with the exception of the group who became addicted before age 20. This is also the only age group for which there are specific reasons—statements by the subjects that they had stolen, or that their major income was from gambling—to believe that illegal acts were committed which did not lead to arrest, in the period prior to addiction. Taking this into consideraton, the table indicates that in general, the younger a man was at the beginning of his addiction, the more likely was he to have committed criminal acts before addiction.

The two relationships shown in table 7.2 are independent and additive. If either age or year of first addiction is controlled, the relationship of the other with crime before addiction holds. The increased probability that a man who became addicted after 1930 will have a prior criminal record is greatest for those who began in their 20s, next greatest for those in their 30s.

Table 7.3 uses the number of sentences imposed after addiction began as an index of postaddiction crime. A table using arrests rather than sentences, not included here, shows exactly the same associations described below.

Table 7.3 shows that the men are more likely to have some sentences after addiction, and are more likely to have a large number of sentences:

1. The earlier the year of addiction;
2. The younger their age at addiction; and
3. The greater their criminal record prior to addiction.

Each of the three relationships holds when the other two variables are controlled. From the pattern of gamma and chi-square values in the partial tables (not included here), it is clear that age at onset of addiction is the most powerful predictor of postaddiction sentences. Prior criminal record also determines the number of sentences, though its effect adds only a little for the younger men. The relationship of year of addiction with postaddiction sentences achieves statistical significance only when one or both of the other variables are also operating. But its effect is in the same direction under all conditions of controlling the other

Table 7.3. Sentences after addiction related to year of addiction, age at addiction and criminal record before addiction, male subjects (percentages)

	Number of Sentences After Addiction					
	N	0	1 or 2	3 to 5	6 or More	Total
1. Year of Addiction:						
Before 1920	22	36	27	27	9	[3] 100
1920–29	38	47	13	24	16	100
1930–39	64	53	27	9	11	100
1940–49	65	75	11	11	3	100
1950–59	20	65	30	5	--	100
Total Cases	[1] 209	122	41	29	17	209
2. Age at Addiction:						
Under 20	23	9	30	26	35	100
20–29	72	42	24	22	12	100
30–39	56	75	14	11	--	100
40–49	38	76	21	3	--	100
50 or older	20	95	5	--	--	100
Total Cases	[1] 209	122	41	29	17	209
3. Criminal Record Before Addiction:						
None	133	68	13	11	8	100
Some	38	45	34	10	10	[3] 100
More	23	17	39	35	9	100
Total Cases	[2] 194	112	39	26	17	194

[1] Three men not included; unknown on number of sentences.
[2] Sixteen men not included because of insufficient data for classification on Crime Before Addiction.
[3] Figures do not add to 100% due to rounding errors.

variables, so it may be regarded as having an independent but weak effect.

The relationship of age with postaddiction sentences may appear to be somewhat stronger than it actually is, since the younger men had longer life expectancies to accumulate a number of sentences. But this consideration would not explain away the fact that the proportion with zero sentences increases with age; all age groups had time to acquire at least one sentence.

Offenses

Table 7.4 examines the increase in crime after addiction in terms of the specific offenses committed. Arrests as well as sentences were coded as

Table 7.4. Percent of subjects who committed specified offenses before and after they became addicted (percentage)

	Male		Female	
	Before Addiction	After Addiction	Before Addiction	After Addiction
Offenses Against Persons:				
Murder and Homicide	3	2	--	--
Assault	2	2	2	6
Weapons	1	1	--	--
One or more of above	6	5	2	6
Robbery	2	5	--	--
Other Offenses:				
Burglary	6	10	--	--
Other Theft	7	22	--	4
Liquor Laws (moonshining)	7	7	--	--
Sex Offenses	(*)	--	4	6
Other	25	38	4	11
One or more of above	30	47	4	15
Drug Offenses:				
Sale of Narcotics	--	11	--	--
Prescription Forgery or Fraud	--	14	--	6
Other Narcotic Offenses	--	18	--	11
Other Drug Offenses	--	2	--	--
One or more of above	--	33	--	15
One or more offenses of any type	33	60	6	24

*Less than 1 percent.

offenses, so the percentages in table 7.4 do not coincide exactly with those in previous tables. Only three offenses before addiction, and three after, were coded per subject, so the full range of offenses is not included. The more serious and more frequent offenses were coded, and few subjects had committed more than three kinds of offense, so the practical effect of this restriction seems negligible.

The offenses are grouped; the first includes offenses against the person, except that robbery, which is both an offense against the person and a money-producing crime, is listed separately. The next group includes mainly property offenses, or money-producing crimes, except for a few cases of vagrancy and drunkenness. The last is exclusively drug offenses.

The proportion of men with recorded offenses increased from 33 percent before addiction to 60 percent after addiction. The increases which occurred after addiction are for robbery and other income-producing crimes, burglary and other theft, and in drug offenses. Comparing the major groups of offenses, drug offenses are recorded for one-third of the men after addiction, against none before it. The miscellaneous group, mainly of income-producing crimes, increased from 30 to 47 percent for the men. Crimes against the person did not increase. It may be inferred that the increase in robbery was related to the fact that it produced money, rather than to its status as a crime against the person.

The pattern for the women is generally the same, though less marked. It is perhaps worthy of special note that there is no significant decrease in any group of offenses after addiction, and no decrease in the frequency of any specific offense except homicide. Six men committed homicides before their addiction, and only four after addiction began.

Table 7.5. Sentences after addiction by sources of narcotics during history of addiction, male subjects (percentages)

Sources of Narcotics	N	Number of Sentences After Addiction				
		0	1 or 2	3 to 5	6 or More	Total
Doctors only, one at a time	45	91	9	--	--	100
Several doctors, and/or exempt narcotics	22	77	--	18	5	100
Mainly own supply	12	75	8	8	8	[1] 100
Mainly medical, some illegal	29	62	28	10	--	100
Mostly or all illegal	82	28	29	26	17	100
	[2] 190	57	19	15	8	100

[1] Figures do not add to 100% due to rounding errors.
[2] Twenty-two men cannot be classified on Sources of Narcotics.

While there is evidence of an increase in offenses after addiction, these are not recorded for all subjects. It may be asked why more subjects are not shown with offenses after addiction, and table 7.5 presents a variable from the previous chapter which provides a partial answer to this question. This is the source from which subjects obtained their narcotics. Subjects are grouped under five headings:

1. The first group, 45 subjects, obtained all their narcotics from one physician at a time. The drugs were obtained legally, and the cost was not high. There would be little reason for such subjects to commit crimes unless drug use *per se* caused crimes, and 91 percent of them had no sentences.
2. The second group, 22 subjects, obtained narcotics by going to several physicians simultaneously to obtain prescriptions, or by buying exempt narcotics. Technical violations of the law, mainly by giving false

names and addresses, occurred in this group, but when these were detected the addict was usuall ypressured into seeking treatment, not prosecuted. The expense of the drugs was little or no greater than for the first group, but the travel involved could approach a full-time occupation, and make it difficult to hold a job. Some crimes, therefore, might be expected, and more are found than for the first group, but 77 percent of these men avoided any sentences.

3. The third group consists of 12 physicians who used drugs from the supplies they acquired legitimately and cheaply. This involved a technical violation of the law, but again one which was more likely to lead to treatment than prosecution. The status of these subjects as physicians implies a number of factors which would make other offenses improbable and prosecution unlikely. It is therefore not surprising that 75 percent of this group had no sentences.
4. The fourth group includes 29 subjects who obtained most of their narcotics from medical sources as in the first and second groups, but who also used at least some illicit narcotics. For them the proportion with no sentences drops to 62 percent.
5. The last group of 82 subjects includes those who bought all or most of their drugs on the illicit market. Here the percentage with no sentences drops sharply, to 28 percent, and the proportion with three or more sentences is much higher than in the other groups.

The pattern for the women is identical. Only four women had sentences. Of these, one came from the 8 women in the fourth group, and three from the 11 women in the fifth.

The percentage with sentences was higher after addiction, for each of the five groups, than the corresponding percentage with sentences prior to addiction. With respect to types of offenses committed, the following differences can be noted. The men in the fifth group slightly exceeded the other four in the proportion who committed offenses against the person before addiction. The other four groups committed fewer such offenses after addiction. The fifth committed as many as before addiction, and they account for all of the increase in robbery. All five groups committed more income-producing offenses after addiction than before, but the increase was most marked for the fourth and fifth groups. Drug offenses were found for some members of each group after addiction. These were committed by only one or two persons in the first three groups, but by about one-fifth of the fourth group and one-third of the fifth—the illegal users.

Discussion

The findings can be related to the studies summarized earlier on a number of points.

1. *What proportion of addicts were criminals prior to their addiction?*

   Only one-third of the men in this sample and less than ten percent of the women had any arrests before they became addicted. The proportion with a prior record, however, increased steadily with the recency of addiction. Ninety-five percent of the men addicted before 1920 had no prior record, and this percentage dropped to 53 for men who became addicted in the 1950s. The finding that the proportion with prior criminal records has changed over time is consistent with the low percentage of prior records reported by Dai and Pescor, whose samples were collected in about 1930 and 1936 respectively. It is equally consistent with the high percentage of prior delinquency indicated by Finestone, Chein and Vaillant, whose samples were collected about 20 years later. These five studies, plus the one reported here, thus interlock to indicate that the degree to which addicts are recruited from delinquents has been increasing. The Finestone, Chein and Vaillant samples are of metropolitan addicts, who today greatly outnumber the type exemplified by the Kentucky subjects, and therefore justify the inference that for the past 15 years or more most new addicts have had prior criminal records.

2. *Was addiction followed by more crimes than the addicts would have been expected to commit?*

It is clear that in this sample there was an increase in the number of arrests and sentences after addiction, and in the proportion of subjects with arrests and sentences. With respect to criminal acts which were not recorded, there are specific reasons to believe these occurred, before addiction, only for about half of the men who became addicted before age 20—for about 5 percent of the sample.

After addiction, it is probable that almost all subjects except those who received all of their drugs from one physician at a time were guilty of drug offenses (e.g. illegal possession of narcotics), so the percentage who committed drug offenses was closer to 75 for the men and 48 for the women than the figures of 33 and 15 percent shown for drug offenses in table 7.4. There are also specific reasons—in statements by subjects and other informants—to believe that the number of money-making offenses committed after addiction was appreciably greater than is shown in official records. These unrecorded offenses were attributed to those men for whom some offenses are recorded, rather than to those with no official record.

If, in short, information were available on all criminal acts committed but not recorded, it is probable almost to the point of certainty that they would add something to preaddiction crimes, but more to postaddiction crimes. The increase in postaddiction over preaddiction criminal acts would be even greater than the increase in arrests and sentences. But do these postaddiction arrests and sentences exceed what would have been expected in this sample?

Table 7.3 shows that the median age at addiction in the sample is slightly over 30; the exact figure is 31.3 years for the men, 30 for the women. Most of the sample, it has been shown, had had no arrests before addiction. Restricting the question to men, because most of the sample and most criminals are men, it can be rephrased to ask: What is the probability that men will reach the age of 31 with no history of arrests, and then acquire such a history? More specifically, what is this probability for those offenses in which increases were noted?

335-199—69——9

Glaser uses the Uniform Crime Reports to show that in 1962 the median age of persons arrested was 17.9 for burglaries, 17.5 for larceny, and 21.9 for robbery.[17] Since these medians are based on all arrests, and some of these would have been second or subsequent arrests, the median age at first arrest on these charges must be even lower than the figures cited. Such figures suggest, and it is the consensus of criminologists, that as men grow older the expectation that they will be arrested on such charges grows smaller rather than larger.[18]

That the observed number of postaddiction arrests exceeds the expected number, therefore, is supported by two facts. First, the observed increase is in drug offenses and in money-producing crimes, and is greatest for those who used expensive illicit drugs. This makes it plausible that the increase is connected with the addiction. Second, the statistical expectation would have been a decrease from the number of arrests noted before age 30, approximately when addiction began, to the number after that age, rather than the increase which was in fact found.

The findings of this study thus repeat the findings of five previous studies, all of which report more crime after addiction than before. It differs from these studies in two ways which tend to give stronger support to the interpretation that the increase was greater than would have been expected.

The studies by Dai and Pescor selected samples from among persons who had been arrested recently; if there were addicts with no postaddiction criminal records, they had no chance of being selected by Dai, and little of being selected by Pescor. In this study, on the other hand, only 47 of 212 men and 3 of 54 women were prisoners or probationers on their first hospital admission, the basis of sample selection. An absence of postaddiction offenses had a chance of being observed, and in fact was observed for a large proportion of the sample.

In the studies by Finestone, Chein, and Vaillant the majority of subjects had, before their drug use, committed offenses or acts which the investigators interpreted as predictive of later crimes. They were also in the age range for which most arrests are recorded. The postaddiction crimes they committed, therefore, must to some extent be regarded as a continuation of criminal patterns antedating addiction, and statistically expectable. In this study, on the other hand, only a minority of subjects had committed offenses before addiction, and in only part of this minority was there any indication of a stable criminal pattern which would be expected to continue. Further, their addiction began and then, for most, their first arrests were noted after the age for which most first arrests are recorded. The increase in crime after addiction was not statistically expectable for them.

In passing, it might be noted that this study does not support the findings of previous studies that crimes against the person decrease after addiction. The decrease from 6 percent of men who committed such crimes before addiction to 5 percent after addiction is insignificant, and if robbery is counted with crimes against the person, as is usual, there was an insignificant increase in these crimes after addiction began.

The findings would be consistent with the hypothesis that increasing age and/or the direct effect of drug use reduce the probability of crimes against the person, while an indirect effect of drug use, through the way of life needed by users of illicit drugs to maintain the habit, is to increase the probability. The net effect, in this sample, is that the two opposed expectations cancel out, and for the sample as a whole there is no appreciable change in the number of crimes against the person. These do constitute a smaller proportion of all crimes after addiction than before, but this is because others have greatly increased, not because crimes against the person have decreased.

The conclusion that addiction is followed by more crimes than would have been expected supports, though it alone is not enough to establish, the inference that addiction causes crime. It is equally important, however, to note that crime is not a necessary consequence of addiction. More than half of the men in the sample had no sentences after addiction, and over one-third had no arrests. With respect to acts which could have led to arrests and sentences, there are good reasons to believe that no such acts were committed by about one-fifth of the men and about one-half of the women. For about another one-fifth of each sex, there are good reasons to believe that the only illegal acts committed were drug offenses, like illegal possession of drugs. (These statements represent the writer's evaluation of the case material on subjects, including his evaluation of the credibility of subjects and other informants.) This is an additional indication that there are distinct types of addicts, and that knowledge of addiction can be advanced by studying the differences among them.[19]

3. *What specific aspects of addiction cause the increase in crime?*

The data presented in table 7.5 confirm the generally accepted conclusion that drug use *per se* does not cause crimes. The subjects who received drugs from a physician were using as much narcotics as others, and in recent years probably more, since their drugs were not diluted like illicit heroin or exempt narcotics. Yet only a few of them have a record of arrests, and there is much less indication for them than for others of undetected offenses.

The table shows that in this sample addicts with a stable legal source of narcotics were unlikely to acquire a criminal record, while those who bought most of their drugs on the illicit market were likely to acquire one. This is consistent with the fact that most metropolitan minority-group addicts, who normally use illicit heroin, acquire criminal records. It is equally consistent with the fact that "medical addicts," addicts in the 19th century, and addicts in countries where drugs are legally available are reported not to engage in crime.

The table implies that if stable and legal sources of narcotics had been available to more subjects in this sample, they would have committed fewer crimes. It does not justify an inference that if stable legal sources were opened to all users of illicit drugs these users would become noncriminals, because this sample is not representative of all users.[20]

Criminal Careers

The statistics on arrests and sentences do not bring out as clearly as does case material, primarily in statements made by subjects themselves, that the criminal behavior in some cases amounted to a criminal career.

Almost all of the subjects in this study lived through the period of prohibition in the United States, and since the repeal of prohibition many counties in Kentucky have remained "dry." There has existed, therefore, a market for illicit liquor in an area where the skills of small-scale distillation of liquor are traditional, and where a sizeable minority of the population regard the private production and sale of liquor as not really wrong, though illegal.

Bootlegging, therefore, has been a potentially profitable occupation. Twenty-five of the male subjects, and one female, are known to have engaged in bootlegging at some time, and it was probably a major lifetime occupation for some of these. All except two are known to have engaged in it during their addiction, the exceptions being one man and one woman whose activity can be proved only before and after addiction, respectively. Of the others, at least 17 committed illicit liquor offenses before addiction also, and at least two continued in a postaddiction period. Bootlegging, however, was usually associated with some legitimate employment, and there are no cases in which one can be completely certain that it was the subject's major occupation.

Twenty-seven men made their living as professional gamblers for at least some part of their working lives. Most of these were card players, with a few operators of gambling devices in carnivals, and one pool expert. For at least 10 of these, gambling must be regarded as the subject's major occupation.

About one-half of the men in the sample, in all probability, were guilty of stealing in one form or another, at some time in their lives, but most often during their addiction. At least 13 men, from their official criminal records and from their own statements, were professional thieves before their addiction began. All continued as thieves during their addiction and after addiction ended, in the six cases where it did end. Most of their stealing took the form of burglary or store-house breaking, with one specialist claiming over 250 successful drugstore break-ins. A few committed armed robberies, some passed cold checks, one was a highly skilled and successful pickpocket, and one engaged in widespread insurance frauds.

In addition to the 10 professional gamblers and 13 thieves, six men were carnival or circus workers, two beggars and one a race track tout. These occupations, at least in this sample, involved gambling, confidence games, petty thievery, and short-changing. A total of at least 32 men, therefore, 15 percent of the sample, may be regarded as professional criminals, and it is clear for most of them and probable for the others that these criminal careers began before their addiction.

Among the women, eight are known to have engaged in prostitution. This can be shown to have started before addiction in only two cases, but it may well have begun before addiction for several of the others too. The information available is too scanty to justify conclusions as to whether or not some of the prostitution can be seen as due to the addiction.

Since there are a fair number of professional criminals in the sample, it may be asked if it is their numerous crimes which account for the findings reported above, particularly the increase in crime after the beginning of addiction. Analysis shows that these 32 exceeded others in the frequency and number of arrests and sentences before addiction, and that the increase after addiction was greater for them than for others. But the crimes of the professional criminals do not account for all of the increase. Indeed, separating out the others as a group which was essentially noncriminal before addiction makes their increase in crime after addiction even clearer. Among the 180 men who were not professional criminals, 19 men were given a total of 35 sentences before addiction. After addiction, 63 of these 180 men were given a total of over 163 sentences.

The analysis also throws some light on criminal acts which are not reflected in official records of arrests and sentences. Almost all of the 32 professional criminals, by their own statements, had been guilty of criminal acts before their addiction, and yet 56 percent had no arrests and 69 percent no sentences before addiction. It is clear that some of their crimes are not included in official records. This does not necessarily mean, however, that a large number of unrecorded offenses were committed. Twelve of these men became addicts in their teens, and 13 more in their 20s. Their addiction followed the start of their criminal careers, but frequently by a short interval. Since early offenses, even when detected, are sometimes overlooked by law-enforcement officials, and it is rare that a person's first offenses are detected, the age of these subjects largely accounts for the fact that their preaddiction crimes do not appear in official records.

After addiction, only two of these 32 avoided arrest and only eight avoided sentences, but as only about half of them had three or more sentences, it may seem that they did not pay the full price that their criminal careers could have justified. This is true for some of them, who had few arrests and sentences despite frequent offenses. For most, however, the number of sentences does not show their difference from other men as much as does the amount of time served. The total number of months served by the 32 was almost as high as the total served by the remaining 180. The 180 served, on the average, 16 months each; the 32 professional criminals, on the average, 77 months each.

These facts tend to support the assumption made in earlier sections. The official record of arrests and sentences, even though it is known to be an incomplete record of offenses, is sufficiently accurate to separate subjects into groups which differ to a meaningful degree on criminal behavior.

Crime and Other Variables

There is a strong association between criminal record and the measure of involvement in the drug subculture which was described in the previous chapter, but this is partly artificial, since several items in the measure of involvement relate to criminal behavior. One item, however, use of the intravenous route of administration, can serve as an indication of involvement, and carries no implication of criminal behavior.

Those men who used the intravenous route were much more likely to have arrests and sentences after addiction. Of the men who used it, 80 percent had arrests and 57 percent had sentences after addiction began, compared with 45 and 28 percent for the men who used other routes. In addition, many more of them had numerous arrests and sentences.

It may be inferred, therefore, that there is a direct relationship between involvement in the drug subculture and crime. If it may be postulated that this is a causal connection, its direction is from involvement to crime. Some subjects were involved at the start of addiction, as evidenced by the fact that their first route of administration was sniffing, smoking or intravenous injection of the narcotic. These were more likely to have later arrests and sentences than those whose first use was by another route.

Criminal record was found to be mildly predictive of posthospital drug pattern: The greater the number of sentences after addiction, the greater the likelihood that men would show a pattern of continued addiction to narcotics. Similarly, a pattern of addiction to substitutes was more frequent among men with several postaddiction sentences. Abstinence was found mainly among the men with no sentences, or with only one or two sentences.

Summary

In this sample about 15 percent of the male subjects can be classified as professional criminals whose criminal careers started before their addiction, though half of them had no arrests, and two-thirds no sentences, before addiction. About a quarter of the remaining men had been arrested once or more before addiction, but only 10 percent of them had been given a sentence. Prior to addiction, therefore, the majority of the men had no criminal record. This, however, has been changing over time. Of those men who became addicted in the early decades of this century, few had a prior record. An increasing proportion had such a record in each ensuing decade, reaching half of those who became addicted in the 1950s.

There was a large increase in the number of arrests and sentences, and in the proportion of men with arrests and sentences, after addiction. This increase was found to be greater for the professional criminals, for others with criminal records before addiction, for those addicted in earlier decades, and for those who were younger at the beginning of addiction.

This increase occurred in two ways. Offenses against the drug laws appeared after addiction, and there were more income-producing crimes after addiction than before. There was no increase, but also there was no decrease, in crimes against persons.

One variable which seemed to determine in part whether or not there was an increase in arrests and sentences after addiction was the source from which subjects obtained their narcotics. The increase was greatest for those who obtained all or most of their narcotics from illegal sources, least for those who obtained drugs from stable legal sources. There was some increase, however, for all groups, even for those who always obtained narcotics by prescription from one physician at a time.

Some items used in the measure of involvement in the drug subculture are closely related to criminal behavior, and no conclusions are justified on the basis of the strong statistical association which was found between the measure of involvement and crime after addiction. One indicator of involvement, however, the use of the intravenous route as the usual method of administering narcotics, is conceptually independent of criminal behavior, but empirically was closely associated with it. This association, and the fact that crime increased after addiction, therefore suggest that involvement in the drug subculture is directly related to criminal behavior, and that the causal connection is from the former to the latter. But involvement in the drug subculture does not necessarily lead to crime; some men who were involved had no recorded or suspected criminal record.

The women differ from the men in that they showed almost no criminal behavior before addiction, and only a few showed it after addiction. The general pattern of an increase after addiction was the same as for the men, but much less marked. Because it was less marked, there were too few cases to examine the effects of the variables found to have an effect on crime among the men. The most that can be said is that there is no reason to believe that these variables operate any differently for the women.

Comparison of the findings in this study with those of previous studies makes it possible to offer plausible answers to some of the questions which have been raised about the connection between addiction and crime. The cumulative evidence of all studies supports the conclusion that in recent decades addicts have increasingly been recruited from criminals. Further, there is an increase in crime after addiction begins, and this increase is greater than would have been expected for the persons in whom it is noted. The increase is not due to any direct effect of narcotics on the personality or behavior of addicts, but is due to the way of life associated with addiction under current laws and in the current climate of attitudes toward drug use.

Crimes against persons are relatively less frequent after the onset of addiction, but this study suggests that the change is due to the increase in other crimes, rather than to a decrease in the number of crimes against persons.

The number of sentences after addiction was found to predict posthospital drug pattern to a slight extent, in that those subjects with patterns of complete abstinence or much abstinence are found mainly among men with no sentences, less often among men with one or two sentences, and only rarely among men with three or more. These latter more often show patterns of addiction, either to narcotics or substitutes. These differences are statistically significant, and of some practical and theoretical importance, but their magnitude is not great enough to make them useful as practical predictors of posthospital drug pattern.

Footnotes, Chapter 7

[1] Faris, Robert E. L., and Dunham, H. Warren. *Mental Disorders in Urban Areas.* Chicago: University of Chicago Press, 1939. p. 170.

Dai, Bingham. *Opium Addiction in Chicago.* Shanghai: The Commercial Press, 1937. pp. 88–89, 189.

Finestone, Harold. Narcotics and criminality. *Law and Contemporary Problems.* 22:72, Winter 1957.

Chein, Isidor; Gerard, Donald L.; Lee, Robert S.; and Rosenfeld, Eva. *The Road to H.* New York: Basic Books, 1964. pp. 11, 57–65.

[2] Meyer, Alan S., ed. *Social and Psychological Factors in Opiate Addiction.* New York: Bureau of Applied Social Research, Columbia University, 1952. pp. 82–91. This annotated bibliography summarizes the findings of about 20 studies reporting empirical data on addiction and crime.

[3] Anslinger, H. J., and Tompkins, William F. *The Traffic in Narcotics.* New York: Funk and Wagnalls, 1953. p. 194.

[4] Eldridge, William Butler. *Narcotics and the Law.* New York: American Bar Foundation, 1962. p. 28.

[5] Anslinger and Tompkins, *op. cit.* pp. 189–190.

[6] Lindesmith, Alfred R. *Opiate Addiction.* Bloomington, Indiana: Principia Press, 1947. pp. 192–93. See also: *Drug Addiction: Crime or Disease?* Interim and Final Reports of the Joint Committee of the American Bar Association and the American Medical Association on Narcotic Drugs. Bloomington, Ind.: Indiana University Press, 1961. Volume 8. pp. 45–50, 64–68.

[7] Anslinger and Tompkins, *op. cit.* pp. 268–270, 277.

[8] Dai, *op. cit.* p. 67.

[9] PESCOR, MICHAEL J. A statistical analysis of the clinical records of hospitalized drug addicts. *Public Health Reports,* Supplement No. 143, Washington: U.S. Government Printing Office, 1943. p. 25.

[10] Finestone, *op. cit.* p. 76.

[11] Chein, *op. cit.* p. 11.

[12] VAILLANT, GEORGE E. A twelve year follow-up of New York City addicts: I. The relation of treatment to outcome. *American Journal of Psychiatry,* 122:727–737, January 1966.

[13] Meyer, *op. cit.* pp. 82–91.

[14] Chein, *op. cit.* pp. 57–65.

[15] *Ibid.* p. 11. Finestone, *op. cit.* p. 76.

[16] KOLB, LAWRENCE. Drug addiction in its relation to crime. *Mental Hygiene,* 9:74–89, January 1925.

[17] GLASER, DANIEL. *The Effectiveness of a Prison and Parole System.* New York: Bobbs-Merrill, 1964. p. 469.

[18] *Ibid.* pp. 467–74. See also: TAFT, DONALD R. *Criminology,* 3rd ed. New York: Macmillan, 1956. pp. 112–13. CLINARD, MARSHALL B. *Sociology of Deviant Behavior.* New York: Rinehart, 1957. pp. 198–200. CAVAN, RUTH SHONLE. *Criminology.* 2nd ed. New York: Thomas Y. Crowell, 1956. pp. 41–49. Almost any text on criminology makes the point, though none known to the writer makes it in terms of the probability of first arrest for given offenses at given ages. In this connection, it has also been stated "that drug addiction results in a large and permanent increase in the volume of crime" because the addiction constrains the addicts to continue in a criminal pattern which otherwise would have been abandoned with increasing maturity. See: *Drug Addiction: Crime or Disease?, op. cit.* pp. 66–67.

[19] BALL, JOHN C. Two patterns of narcotic drug addiction in the United States. *Journal of Criminal Law, Criminology and Police Science,* 56(2): 203–211, 1965.

[20] Several students of addiction have suggested that narcotics should be made available to addicts legally and cheaply, and that this would reduce crimes by addicts because it would reduce their need to commit crimes. The reasoning is logical, and the data here are consistent with it, in the sense that most addicts probably resemble those studied here in that they would be less likely to steal money for expensive illicit drugs if cheap legal drugs were at hand. But the desirability of such a policy depends not only on its effect on crime, but also on its effect on the prevalence of addiction, the other effects of addiction on addicts and on society, and on moral considerations. These will be discussed in later chapters, but it may be stated here that the writer, while recognizing that the arguments for the proposed policy have some force, does not support the proposal.

CHAPTER 8

Postaddiction Employment

It was shown in chapter 5 that prior to the onset of addiction male subjects had achieved occupational levels comparable to those of the 1960 Kentucky population, and therefore equal to or higher than the average level of their contemporaries. Almost 30 percent of the men who could be classified achieved more than the sales and clerical level, and 10 percent achieved major professional or executive status.

After these subjects became addicted, there was a trend toward a lower level of employment status, but only to a minor extent. The physicians continued to practice medicine, with the exception of two who eventually lost their licenses. Those who were salesmen or skilled workers usually continued to work at these occupations, and the general level of employment status declined only a little. What did happen, however, in a large proportion of cases, was that periods of unemployment became more frequent and longer, or work was interrupted by periods of treatment or incarceration.

Chapter 5 described a three-point measure of work pattern, which was applied to three periods of time, before addiction, during addiction, and for those to whom it applied, after the end of addiction. Table 8.1 uses the measure to compare the pattern before addiction with the pattern during addiction.

The preaddiction pattern was surprisingly poor. Only 97 men—less than half of the subjects—showed a steady work pattern before addiction.

Table 8.1. Pattern of employment during addiction compared with pattern prior to addiction, male subjects

Pattern During Addiction	Male—Preaddiction Pattern				
	Steady	Less Than Steady	Little Or None	Unknown	Total
Steady	36	--	--	--	36
Less than steady	32	40	2	2	76
Little or none	26	29	32	2	89
Unknown	3	--	--	8	11
Total	97	69	34	12	212

Despite this low starting point, table 8.1 shows a definite deterioration in employment during addiction. Of the 97 men whose employment had been steady before addiction, only 36 maintained this level during addiction. Some deterioration was seen for 32, and 26 more had little or no legitimate employment during their addiction. Of the 69 who had been in the middle category before addiction, none improved, and 29 dropped to the lowest level during addiction. Of the 34 who began at the lowest level, only two showed improvement.

It might be expected that, for men who ceased to be addicted, their work pattern would then improve. Some improvement was seen, but there were also cases in which further deterioration occurred. About one-third of the men who could show improvement on a three-point scale did so, but almost half of those who could show further deterioration did show it.

Examination of the case material suggests that the improvement was real, while some of the deterioration was only apparent. Where improvement was found, it meant that a subject who had not worked, or worked sporadically during addiction, had worked steadily after addiction ended. Failure to improve or deterioration were accounted for partly by the fact that so many subjects merely shifted to alcohol when they gave up narcotics use, with few other changes in their way of life. In other cases the age at which the subjects gave up their use of narcotics, or the physical condition which made it impossible for them to continue to obtain narcotics, also would explain why they could not work, or could not work steadily.

Employment, Involvement and Crime

The level of employment status before addiction determined, to some extent, the later involvement of male subjects in the drug subculture. Forty-four percent of the 18 farmers had no involvement; this dropped to 21 percent of the 53 men who had worked at higher than the clerical level, and to 15 percent for all other men. But a more significant association is seen in table 8.2, which groups occupations as follows:

1. The health professions include 14 physicians, 3 pharmacists, 3 dentists and one owner of a drugstore who was not a pharmacist. These men could acquire narcotics legally.
2. "Other high levels" include 2 lawyers, 3 ministers or priests, 3 teachers, and an owner of a large business concern.
3. "Other legitimate" includes the remaining men, except for those in the next category.
4. "Illegitimate" refers to the 32 men who were classified in the previous chapter as professional criminals, who included persons in classifications such as the following: carnival workers, beggars, gamblers, thieves, and a race track tout.

Table 8.2. Involvement in drug subculture by type of occupation before addiction, male subjects (percentages)

Type of Occupation Before Addiction	Involvement In Drug Subculture				
	Much	Some	None	Total	No. of Subjects
Health Professions	29	48	24	[1] 100	21
Other High Levels	44	33	22	[1] 100	9
Other Legitimate	40	39	21	100	150
Illegitimate	66	28	6	100	32
No. of Subjects	91	81	40		212

[1] Figures do not add to 100 due to rounding errors.

The men differ widely in the percentage with much involvement in the drug subculture, depending on the type of preaddiction occupation, with the health professions showing the lowest percentage and professional criminals the highest. It is noteworthy that the "other high level" occupations resemble the "other legitimate" occupations closely, and both of these are intermediate between the extremes. This suggests that it was not the level of employment or the social status associated with it that determined the degree of involvement, but the access to narcotics which was associated with level of employment. But it is also to be noted that the first three types are almost equal in the percentage with no involvement; the type of occupation seems to have had little effect on whether or not men became involved, though it did affect the degree of involvement for those who became involved.

The deterioration which was found in employment pattern during addiction is not affected to the extent that might be expected by subjects' involvement in the drug subculture after addiction, There is a tendency, significant at the .05 level, for men with much involvement in the subculture to show less often a steady pattern of employment during addiction. The difference is not great, however. Among those men whose preaddiction employment pattern was steady, the deterioration during addiction is somewhat greater for those who were much involved in the subculture, but similar deterioration is shown by half of those with some involvement and 58 percent of those with none. The change in pattern from the "during addiction" to the "postaddiction" period is almost identical for the three degrees of involvement during addiction.

Another negative finding of interest is that the deterioration in employment pattern is not associated with the different sources from which subjects obtained their narcotics. It might have been expected that men with stable and legal sources would show less deterioration in employment pattern, but such a difference is not found. About two-thirds of the men in each classification worked less steadily after addiction than before; even the physician subjects, for whom it would presumably have been easiest to maintain a stable pattern, show deterioration in half the cases.

The fact that employment patterns deteriorated to almost the same degree for men whose source of drugs varied so widely needs explanation. Case material on the men was reviewed to see if it would suggest one, but no simple or clear-cut explanation was suggested by this review. It does appear that the deterioration among men who obtained all of their narcotics from a physician sometimes was attributable to the fact that an illness which led to addiction also impaired their ability to work. Even among these men, however, there are suggestions of other factors. The record of one such man, for example, suggests he left the work he had been doing, and the city where he had been successful, because he could get morphine there only occasionally for the pains due to locomotor ataxia, but could get it regularly from a physician (who himself was an addict) in his home town in Kentucky.

No clear differences among men who obtained drugs from other sources were found. Many had been alcoholics before addiction, and were alcoholics between periods of addiction; deterioration in their work patterns may have been due to the alcoholism rather than to addiction. A factor which applied to all groups was the interruption of employment by "cures." In no case did trouble with the law precede the deterioration in work pattern.

Addicts With Stable Employment

The literature occasionally refers to addicts who are able to maintain a stable pattern of employment while they are addicted, or even to addicts who are able to function better while they are addicted than when abstinent. If such addicts exist, they are not well represented in this sample.

This does not necessarily mean that they do not exist. If they do, presumably they are persons who are physically able to work, and whose source of narcotics is both stable and such that they are not likely to have trouble with the law. In this sample, subjects with a stable legal source of narcotics were likely to have an illness, or to perceive themselves as having an illness, which might interfere with employment. The employment difficulties of others could be due to difficulties associated with the obtaining of drugs, and conceivably they might have worked steadily if they had had a stable legal source.

The few cases which may resemble the hypothetical addicts who work steadily when addicted are to be found among those subjects who were addicted when located. It will be recalled that 14 of these 21 subjects were receiving their narcotics from physicians, so their source was stable and legal. In addition, more data are available on them than on most subjects, so their employment at the time of the interview can be contrasted with their earlier patterns of employment in more detail than is possible for other subjects.

The six women who were addicted when located include four who received all drugs from one physician each. Two of these were in their 60s, and unable to work because of age and illness; another, aged 50, was a housewife. The fourth was unemployed, supported by welfare and possibly some illegal liquor sales. Of the two women whose drugs came from other sources, one probably and the other certainly was a prostitute.

Fifteen men were addicted when located. Five were unemployed because of illness, four of them receiving drugs from physicians. Five more were unemployed. Only one of these received his narcotics from a physician, and he was 71 years of age. The other four obtained drugs from other or unknown sources, mostly using exempt narcotics; two were in their early 60s, the others 39 and 43.

The remaining five men were self-supporting, and all had a steady source of narcotics from a physician. Two were gamblers, and had been all of their adult lives. Only the remaining three men, therefore, can be seen as maintaining steady, legitimate employment during addiction, and the case material on them suggests that their employment pattern was better than it had been during earlier years of addiction when their drugs came from other sources.

> One (No. 179) was in his mid-70s, but still actively and successfully engaged in business. He had been a successful businessman before his addiction began, at age 51. He was continually addicted after that, with the exception of brief periods during and for a few days after hospitalizations. This subject used morphine, most of it bought on the illicit market, some from physicians who were themselves addicts; he estimated he had spent over $100,000 for morphine. Because of the difficulty of obtaining it, particularly during the war years, he had to travel a good deal, and his business suffered, though he was never arrested or charged with an offense. As he approached 70, his family physician began to prescribe three grains of morphine per day, gradually increased to about five grains, with the knowledge and what the subject considered to be the consent of the Federal narcotics agents. For the past 5 or 6 years, therefore, his source was stable, and in his own opinion he was functioning better than in the earlier years of illicit use.
>
> The second man (No. 114) was 67 when he was interviewed. His addiction began at age 32, after years of alcoholism, and had continued since then, with occasional brief periods when narcotics could

not be obtained, and he substituted alcohol. He usually bought illegal narcotics. Much of his adult life was spent in hospitals, for addiction or alcoholism, and when not in a hospital he was nominally employed in one of several businesses owned by relatives. This employment was not only frequently interrupted by hospitalizations, but also usually involved stealing money from the business.

For several years before the interview, however, he had been receiving three-quarters of a grain of morphine per day. During this time, despite his age, the subject worked more steadily than ever before. He was still employed by a relative, however, and the earlier pattern suggests that the fact of his being employed did not necessarily indicate he was a satisfactory employee.

Finally, one man (No. 33) was 57 when interviewed. He first used narcotics at age 21, became addicted within a few years, and since then has been abstinent only while institutionalized. His initial source of drugs was the illegal market, and while he claims to have worked fairly steadily (unverified) in the early years of addiction, he admitted supplementing his income by gambling and stealing. This was during the depression years, and his eventual loss of his job, at semiskilled labor, could have been due to economic conditions. The breakup of his first marriage, about the same time, he attributes to his addiction.

With the loss of his job and wife, he left the metropolitan area where he had been living, and in the early 1930s returned to his home in a small town in Kentucky. For about the next 10 years he was, for practical purposes, dependent upon his mother. During this period of dependence most of his narcotics were obtained from physicians, but at least occasionally he used illicit drugs.

He married again, began to work on a farm his wife owned, and his relationship with her seems to have been much like the earlier one with his mother. For 8 years before he was interviewed a physician supplied two grains of morphine daily, and for 6 years prior to the interview, the subject was steadily employed at one job, at an unskilled labor level. He had become truly self-supporting for the first time in 25 years.

In the last two cases, unsatisfactory employment performance was associated with unstable and at least partly illegal sources of narcotics. In all three, an improvement in work pattern followed the securing of a stable legal source. This can be interpreted as suggesting that the change in source of narcotics caused or permitted the improvement in employment. The data are not, however, sufficient to establish a causal connection.

In the third case it is known, and it may be true of the others, that the improvement in work pattern followed the acquiring of a stable source by about 2 years. In the second, the readiness of the subject's relatives to accept any level of performance means that the improvement may have been minimal. In all three cases, the improvement came when the subject was middle-aged or elderly, and may be attributable to maturation or to some "burning out" process as much as to the drug history.

It is notable that in all three cases the daily dosage of narcotics was far below what they had used in the earlier years of their addiction. There are, therefore, a number of other factors which might contribute to the improvement in work patterns, and it would be rash to assume it is explained solely by the stable source of narcotics.

Employment and Posthospital Drug Pattern

Among male subjects, those in the health professions showed the lowest percentage with a pattern of narcotic addiction, by far the lowest percentage addicted to substitutes, and the largest proportion in the abstinent patterns. At the other extreme, showing most relapse and least abstinence, are the illegitimate occupations. Other high level occupations—the lawyers, ministers, and businessmen—resemble the criminal occupations in relapse and abstinence rather than the health professionals.

This finding suggests that it is not the occupational status of the addict, but the availability of narcotics, which is more important in affecting the relapse rate. When a physician, dentist or pharmacist is found to be addicted, his license to possess narcotics is usually taken away, or the probability that his records will be checked frequently makes it less likely that he will use narcotics from his own supply. His major source of narcotics is effectively blocked. Other professional and executive workers are not affected in this way, and they have larger financial resources than other workers, so that they can continue to obtain drugs by their usual method, whether through legal or illegal channels. They thereby resemble the criminal occupations whose access to illicit sources continues.

Those men whose work pattern had been "steady" before addiction were slightly more likely to show a posthospital pattern of abstinence, and to be currently abstinent. They were about as likely, however, to show a posthospital pattern of addiction as the others, and showed the highest percentage of current addiction to narcotics. It is the fact that they were not as likely to be in an institution, or to have shifted from narcotics to barbiturates or alcohol, which differentiates them from the men with other preaddiction work patterns.

Summary

Even before addiction began, less than half of the men showed a pattern of steady work. Their work patterns deteriorated markedly after they became addicted, and did not improve much after addiction ended, among those for whom addiction did end. The latter finding, however, may be attributable to the fact that addiction ended for many in middle age or later, or was followed by alcoholism. It may well be that if an addict gives up his use of narcotics while he is still young enough and healthy enough to work, and does not substitute other drugs for narcotics

335-199—69——10

but becomes completely abstinent, and if he was not a professional criminal before addiction, his work pattern would improve. This does appear to be true for the few individuals in the sample who meet all of these conditions.

After they became addicted most men were involved in the drug subculture. The degree of involvement seems to have been less for the men at the higher employment levels, but this in turn is more probably explained by the fact that health professionals had easier access to narcotics than by status *per se*.

A warning note against over-interpretation of these findings may be in order. It may be true, as it is plausible, that higher-status men are less likely to become involved in the drug subculture, or any delinquent subculture, before or after their introduction to narcotics. If it is true, one may speculate that some such men in Kentucky were introduced to narcotics, quickly learned that addiction would require involvement in the subculture, and gave up their use of drugs to avoid the involvement. If such cases exist, they had little chance of being selected into this sample, because they would not have been admitted to the hospital. Involvement in the drug subculture after addiction may, in short, be probable only for those men who continue to be addicted for some length of time, not for all who become addicted.

A finding of some interest is the fact that deterioration in work patterns was about equally probable for all men, regardless of their source of narcotics. A stable legal supply of narcotics did not protect subjects from this deterioration in employment patterns as it was found, in a previous chapter, to protect them from criminal behavior.

If there are addicts who maintain stable and productive employment patterns during addiction, or who function better while addicted than when abstinent, they did not exist or were not identified in this sample. There are no more than three cases in the entire sample who might fit this pattern. In these three, a recent stable employment pattern was associated with a newly-acquired legal and stable source of narcotics, though earlier and less stable work patterns had been associated with illicit and unstable sources. In all three, however, there are other factors than the source of narcotics which might explain the improvement. Even one such case, of course, is sufficient to establish that deterioration in work pattern is not an inevitable result of narcotics use. Like criminal behavior, deterioration in work pattern after addiction cannot be seen as a direct result of drug use, but appears to be partly a result of the way of life involved in addiction, and partly the continuation and development of tendencies discernible before the onset of addiction.

Finally, as with previous variables, the posthospital drug pattern was found to be very weakly associated with preaddiction employment.

CHAPTER 9

Narcotics and Alcohol

Previous chapters have established that alcohol use is prominent in the history of the subjects in this study. For over one-third of male subjects, and a few of the women, the onset of narcotic addiction was in the context of treatment for alcoholic excesses. When narcotics became difficult to obtain, many subjects substituted alcohol. In this chapter the relationship between alcohol and narcotics use will be examined in more detail.

Table 9.1. History of alcoholic excesses, by sex

	Male	Female	Total
History Before Addiction	141	11	152
History Before First Admission	15	2	17
History After First Admission	7	5	12
No History	38	35	73
Unknown	11	1	12
Total	212	54	266

In table 9.1 the subjects are classified by what is known of their alcoholic excesses. For 141 men, two-thirds of the male sample, it is known that there were some alcoholic excesses before their addiction to narcotics. This does not mean that all of them could have been regarded as alcoholics; in a few cases there may have been only occasional excesses. But these 141 include the 75 men who were first given narcotics for alcoholic excesses, and in many other cases the excesses were established by records of arrests for drunkenness. In still others, drinking had led to marital difficulties, or had adversely affected employment. For most subjects, therefore, their drinking had led to some difficulties in social adjustment. At the minimum, these men had shown some readiness to abuse one drug, alcohol, before they became involved with narcotics.

In 15 more cases, the earliest excesses could not be dated prior to narcotic addiction, but had occurred before their first admission to Lexington. In seven more, excesses could not be documented until after the first admission. In 38 cases there is confirmation of the claims of subjects that they never used alcohol excessively. As far as a negative can be said to be established, these men had no history of alcoholic excesses at any time in their lives. Finally, in 11 cases no excesses could be documented, but the confirmation of this was weak or absent for periods in their lives, and it is more conservative to say that it is not known if they ever used alcohol excessively.

Only 11 of the women—one-fifth of the sample—had a history of alcoholic excesses before addiction, and only seven more had a later history. Two-thirds of the women never used alcohol to excess. Alcohol, therefore, was much less frequently abused by the women in the study. But this is true for women in general, and was even more true in the years when these women were young than it is today. If figures on alcoholic excesses in Kentucky were available for comparison, it might be that the women in the sample exceeded other women in their abuse of alcohol to an extent greater than that by which the male sample exceeded the male Kentucky population.

In the following paragraphs, the 141 men with alcoholic excesses before addiction will be called alcoholics, for the sake of brevity, and will be contrasted with the 38 men who never drank excessively, and therefore had had no excesses before addiction. The second and third groups and the unknowns will not be used.

There are two reasons for not using the second and third groups. It is not so certain for them, as for the fourth, that there were no excesses before addiction. The earlier excesses may not have been recorded for some of them and some may belong in the first group. Second, almost half of the men in the second and third groups became narcotic addicts before they were 20 years old, which is true for very few in the group of alcoholics, and for only a small minority of those who never used alcohol excessively. By omitting these groups, at the cost of only about 10 percent of the sample, it becomes possible to compare two groups which are alike in that they had equal opportunities and roughly equal lengths of time to use alcohol before addiction, and for which there is firm evidence that the first group used it excessively and the second did not.

The circumstances surrounding the first use of narcotics indicate that the alcoholics were then already more in contact with addicts than were the others. This contact would be indicated by receiving the first narcotic from an addict, or using it by addict-taught routes like smoking, sniffing or intravenous injection, or using heroin or opium, available only from addicts. One or more of these indications was found for 31 percent of the male alcoholics and for only 18 percent of the others. It is significant that this difference is even greater for the women, 55 percent of the alcoholics showing such contact, to 14 percent of the non-alcoholics. The excessive use of alcohol was more deviant for women than for men, and the greater contact with addicts indicated for the women suggests that they were already more involved in a deviant subculture than were the male alcoholics.

After addiction began, those subjects who had been alcoholics became much more involved in the drug subculture than did the others. Among the separate indices of involvement, the alcoholics were much more likely to learn to use the intravenous route. Larger percentages of the alcoholics also got all or most of their narcotics from illegal sources. In both of these respects, the differences for the women were even greater than for the men.

For both sexes, more of the alcoholics had arrests before and after the onset of addiction, and more of them had sentences, though the latter differences are smaller than for arrests.

Preference for Narcotics

Case material makes it clear that almost all subjects preferred the effects of narcotics to those of alcohol. The normal pattern was to give up the use of alcohol as an intoxicant once addiction to narcotics began. The use of alcohol for other purposes—in social settings, or the drinking of a salesman with his customers—did not completely disappear, but even this was greatly lessened because of the common belief of subjects that alcohol "works against" narcotics.

> The pattern is best seen in one man (Case 004) who had been drinking heavily since age 24 in 1936. Each evening he drank from a pint to a quart of whiskey with friends. In his dry county, the whiskey was bought from bootleggers, who began selling narcotics too in the early part of 1938. The hospital record on his single admission, late in 1938, says:
>
> "One morning in March the patient awoke feeling quite ill. He thought he would be unable to go to work. These neighbors were selling liquor also, and he went to their house to get a drink. He was persuaded, however, after he got there, to take a shot of morphine. He was told how it would straighten him out immediately, and make him feel perfectly well. They prepared a half-grain shot and gave it to him intravenously . . . He did feel quite sleepy, but did not lie down, feeling 'too good to sleep it off.' He says that after the first shot, he knew that morphine was something that he wanted. He never felt so completely satisfied in his life. In about a week he went back for another shot. He had not been drinking this time and has drunk practically no alcohol since then. He says 'whiskey doesn't taste right after you start taking morphine.' "

The last two sentences of the above description are a refrain running through many cases. Another subject (Case 115) who received his first shot for a hangover considered himself addicted from that first shot.

> 'It made me feel so much better. It didn't make me sick. It would brighten up your mind and take all your worries away from you.' He also quit drinking with his first dose of morphine. Asked if he had ever tried going back to liquor, for example after one of his many periods of treatment, he replied, 'I tried it, but I had to quit it, too bad a hangover.

> It will fix you up right now and it's gone in a little bit, and you really do get into terrible shape then. You'd better get you some drugs somewhere. Alcohol won't go ever, if you've ever used drugs, won't work.'

The usual attitude expressed was not that the addict had little or no desire for alcohol when narcotics were available, but that he positively avoided using alcohol. Nor was this the attitude only of subjects, perhaps explainable as an expression of their preference for narcotics. It was also the inference of informants from observed changes in subjects' behavior. One widow of a subject spontaneously mentioned her husband's avoidance of alcohol when addicted because "alcohol works against narcotics." The sister of another subject stated she could always tell when he was on drugs, because he would not eat, drank tremendous amounts of coffee, and also he was not drinking alcohol.

A physician, writing to the hospital at the time of a subject's admission, explained that the latter had been using morphine irregularly, and alcohol regularly, up to four years before admission. Then he was having symptoms of acute gastritis, jaundice, liver trouble and possibly heart disease. "At the time I decided that these symptoms were due to overuse of alcoholic drinks, and that an alcoholic cirrhosis was developing. The subject would not drink whiskey when he had morphine, and as he already had a habit for morphine I decided that by prescribing morphine for him, he would get along better. This has been true, and the patient has had only a few attacks in the past four years of acute pain in the epigastrium and these occurred when the subject was short of morphine."

This avoidance of liquor during addiction was so frequently described that for a time it was thought that it might be universal within the sample. Only one clear exception was found, a subject who stated that he continued to drink while addicted, and that the drinking was occasionally excessive. His drinking was with friends who were not addicts, and it appears likely that it was companionship, rather than the effects of alcohol which he sought. But the fact remains he did not regard the alcohol as something to be avoided.

The only other possible exceptions to the rule were in cases where both the drinking and addiction were referred to in various records in the past tense, and it was not possible to determine if they referred to the same past time, or to different times. Whenever similar statements were made by current informants, and it was possible to focus questions on whether or not the drinking and narcotics use were simultaneous, such use was reported in only two situations. In one, the subject had shifted to alcohol, and was still given an occasional shot to help him sober up. In the more frequent, the subject was having difficulty in obtaining narcotics, and used alcohol when he could not get narcotics. With the single exception cited above, there was no case in which subjects were receiving regular doses of narcotics, and used alcohol too.

It should be added that no inference from the above should be generalized beyond this study. It is clear that subjects in this study would have used narcotics in preference to alcohol if the two had been equally available. There may well be other persons, however, whose preference would be the reverse. If such persons existed in Kentucky, they would not have been admitted to the hospital, could not have been in the sample, and their preference could not have been observed in this study.

The question of simultaneous use of narcotics and alcohol is not only of theoretical importance, but was of practical importance in this study, and probably will be found to be so in others. It was sometimes difficult to establish that a subject was not using narcotics during some past period, but easy to establish from records of arrests or hospitalizations that he was using alcohol to excess regularly. This could be taken as evidence that he was not then using narcotics more than occasionally, if simultaneous use is rare.

Unfortunately, the literature on alcoholism and addiction rarely touches on this point. Two studies, however, do. In his study of criminal addicts in British Columbia, Stevenson reports the same avoidance of alcohol, while on heroin, which was found in Kentucky.[1]

Hubbard, however, writing in 1881, states that while his addicts usually avoided alcohol during the first few years of their addiction, many then began to use alcohol in fairly large quantities.[2] But it is to be noted that the situation he describes differed in one important respect from those in Vancouver and Kentucky. In 1881 addicts could acquire any quantity of narcotics they desired, and in the case histories Hubbard gives, his subjects were using 15 to 30 grains of morphine per day. They used alcohol to counteract the excessively narcotic effect of these large doses. Heroin users in Vancouver, and in recent decades morphine users in Kentucky, did not have this problem; they had difficulty in getting as much narcotics as they wanted, and the counteraction of alcohol was not desirable.

Further study of this relationship between narcotics and alcohol is needed, but tentatively it would seem plausible to conclude that an addict using up to about 10 or 12 grains of morphine per day will rarely use alcohol at the same time. Evidence of regular excessive use of alcohol therefore can be regarded, as it was in this study, as partial confirmation that the drinker was not then addicted.

Effects of Alcoholism and of Addiction

This study, unfortunately, throws no light on a question of even more importance, the relative effects of alcoholism and narcotic addiction on the social performance and adjustment of subjects. There are reasons, in the physical effects of addiction and alcoholic intoxication, to believe that in a social climate where the two were equally approved or disapproved, and where the drugs were equally available, narcotic addiction would be less disruptive than alcoholism. But the condition of equal approval and availability did not hold during the time period covered by this study.

As a matter of objective fact, the addict whose drugs came from a stable medical source was no great problem to his community. If he tried to obtain narcotics from several physicians, he became a nuisance to them, but hardly more. He became a serious problem only if he engaged in illegal activities to obtain narcotics. The alcoholic was more visible, and his arrests more frequent, though each individual offense was a relatively minor one. But the community attitude was generally more accepting of the alcoholic. He might be seen as useless, and in that sense a burden on his family and on the community, but there was never the overtone of seeing him as a threat to the community, which was frequent when informants spoke of addicts.

From the viewpoint of his family, there might seem to be little to distinguish the alcoholic from the addict. Both were burdens to the family, dependent, unproductive, and sources of embarrassment and disgrace. But most relatives expressed some relief, and regarded it as some improvement, when subjects shifted from narcotics to alcohol. This may have been because they shared this embarrassment with more people, or because alcoholism was less likely to lead to headlines, trials which evoked public interest, and prison sentences. But the major reason seems to have been that families shared the general attitudes which disapproved of addiction more than of alcoholism. Even when subjects had received all narcotics from a physician, so that these could be seen as medications needed for an illness, spouses of subjects frequently described the addiction as an unmitigated disaster, as the worst thing that had ever happened, or could have happened, to the family.[3]

It is well known that addicts usually regard themselves as superior to alcoholics, and addiction as inherently less undesirable than alcoholism. But among those subjects who gave up narcotics use, most—whether or not they had become alcoholics—came also to see addiction as worse, and described their later alcoholism as an achievement for which they deserved some credit. In Kentucky, addiction seemed to be more disruptive than alcoholism, but this may have been the result of the stronger condemnation of addiction as well as of the effects of the drug.

Posthospital Drug Pattern

As might be expected, a history of alcoholic excesses before addiction was associated with post-hospital drug pattern. Men with no such history showed patterns of addiction to narcotics or of complete abstinence.

Those with a history of alcoholism before addiction, and to a lesser extent those with such a history before first admission to the hospital, were no more or less likely to show a pattern of abstinence, but they were more likely to show patterns of addiction to substitutes than to narcotics.

The same difference was found on the current addiction status of the living men. Of those who had been alcoholics before addiction, only 7 percent were found addicted to narcotics, while 30 percent were alcoholics again, or addicted to barbiturates. The corresponding percentages for men who had not used alcohol excessively before addiction were 41 and 7 percent. The differences seem to be similar for the women, but are less clear-cut because of the smaller numbers involved.

Summary

Two-thirds of the male subjects, and one-fifth of the women, had a history of alcoholic excesses before they became addicted to narcotics. In most cases this use of alcohol had been serious enough to lead to some difficulties in marriage and employment, and in about half of these cases the alcohol abuse led directly to the addiction, in that the first narcotic was administered in the treatment of alcoholic excesses.

With only one clear exception, the subjects in this study strongly preferred narcotics to alcohol, and avoided the use of alcohol while they could obtain narcotics. Even in the one exceptional case, the continued use of alcohol was sporadic, while the narcotic addiction was steady.

Those subjects who had been alcoholic before addiction tended more often than others to become involved in the drug subculture after addiction, to learn from addicts such things as the intravenous route of injection, and to obtain narcotics from illicit sources. This was even more true for the women than for the men, suggesting that deviant women become, or are forced to become, more deviant than their male equivalents.

When narcotics became harder to obtain, this difficulty was greater for the alcoholics than for the others, because they had been more dependent on illicit drugs and were less likely to have some medical pretext for narcotics. Those who had not been alcoholics before addiction tended to remain addicted or to become completely abstinent when narcotics were unavailable. Those who had been alcoholics tended more often to shift to substitutes, either alcohol or barbiturates. Eventually, however, they showed about as much complete abstinence as the others.

The study does not furnish enough data to compare the effects of alcoholism and narcotic addiction on the behavior and social adjustment of subjects. The direct effects of narcotics use might have been less disruptive. But public attitudes were more negative to narcotics, and communities, families and some subjects themselves regarded narcotic addiction as worse than alcoholism.

Footnotes, Chapter 9

[1] Stevenson, George H., *et al. Drug Addiction in British Columbia.* Vancouver: University of British Columbia, June 1956. pp. 83–84. (mimeo.)

[2] Hubbard, Fred Heman. *The Opium Habit and Alcoholism.* New York: A. S. Barnes & Co., 1881. pp. 12–13.

[3] There was one apparent exception to this rule. In case 33, outlined in Chapter 8, several informants stated that the wife of the subject had been married before, to an alcoholic, and regarded an addict as a great improvement over an alcoholic. This, of course, could have been due to other differences between the two husbands.

CHAPTER 10

Marital History

Lemert has pointed out the "basic incompatibilities between undisciplined drinking and the demands of married existence," citing as evidence the high divorce rate of alcoholics, and the fact that many alcoholics never marry, or are separated from their spouses.[1] It may be asked if similar incompatibilities exist between addiction and marriage. Are they reflected there too in high divorce rates, and a high proportion of single and separated persons?

It is known that narcotic addiction is, to a large extent, spread by "contagion" from addicts to others whom they introduce to drugs.[2] That this contagion can operate within a family, as from parent to child, is evident from passing references in the literature.[3] Few associations are as close as that of marriage, so one may ask to what extent the spouses of addicts become addicted too. It has been noted that some wives of alcoholics begin drinking to help control their husbands' drinking, and wind up as alcoholics themselves. Does something similar occur with respect to addiction?

One may also ask if addiction in one spouse is likely to be associated with other forms of deviant behavior in the other spouse. If it is, is this because addiction produces the other deviant behavior, or because addicts tend to marry spouses who are already deviant?

Marriages and Children

The number of marriages of subjects is shown in table 10.1 The figures include 28 "common-law" marriages, as well as 367 formal marriages. In the following paragraphs, these data will be compared with data on marriages for Kentuckians, age 40 to 64, from the 1960 census.[4]

Thirteen percent of the men never married, as compared with 6.7 percent of men in Kentucky. Of those who did marry, 40 percent married more than once, against 16.6 percent of male Kentuckians. Reversing the comparison, one would expect 78 percent of male Kentuckians to have married once and only once, and the figure in the sample is 52 percent.

The pattern is slightly different for the women, in that only 2 percent of the sample, as against 6.3 percent of women in Kentucky, age 40 to 60, never married. Of the women who did marry, 51 percent in the sample, as against 16.4 percent in Kentucky, married more than once. One would expect 78 percent of Kentucky women to have married once and only once, and the figure in the sample is 48 percent.

Table 10.1 Number of marriages, by sex

Number of Marriages	Male		Female	
	No.	Percent	No.	Percent
Never married	28	13	1	2
1	110	52	26	48
2	51	24	9	17
3	17	8	13	24
4	3	1	3	6
5	3	1	2	4
Total Cases	212	[1] 100	54	[1] 100
Total Marriages	290		105	

[1] Percentages do not total to 100 due to rounding.

Table 10.2 shows how these marriages terminated. Looking only at those marriages which have terminated, and where the manner of termination is known, two-thirds ended by divorce or separation, for each sex. Of the remainder, ended by death, for male subjects it was the death of the subject twice as often as the death of the wife. For female subjects, it was the death of the subject in only 40 percent of the cases.

Twenty-eight of the men never married, and for 14 more the number of children is unknown. The remaining 170 men had a total of 367 children, an average of 2.2 children for this group, or an average of 1.9 for all on whom the number of children is known. No strictly comparable data on Kentucky males are available.

One woman never married, and the number of children is unknown for six more. The remaining 47 women had a total of 102 children. Since only two of the living women are under 35 years of age, and one

Table 10.2 Manner of termination of marriages of subjects, by sex

	Male	Female
Still married	37	20
Ended by death of subject	54	10
Ended by death of spouse	27	16
Ended by divorce or separation	163	58
Ended, cause unknown	9	1
Total	290	105

more under 40 it is unlikely that many more children will be produced. The number of children for the 47 women, then, can hardly rise to much more than the present average of 2.2. Directly comparable census data are available; in 1960 the average number of children born to women who had ever been married was almost exactly 3.0 for the age groups from 35 to 59, and 3.5 or more for women in the age group beyond 59.[5] It is clear, therefore, for the women subjects, and almost equally certain for the men, that they have produced fewer children than would be expected, and it may be estimated that they have produced about two-thirds the expected number of children.[6]

It is well known that one of the effects of narcotics use is to reduce the sex drive, but this is not likely to be the explanation of the reduced number of children. The median age at first marriage for the men was 24, for the women 18. The corresponding median ages at first addiction were 31 and 30. For both sexes, therefore, but especially for the women, the years in which they were most likely to produce children predated their addiction.

There are several factors which probably contributed to the reduced number of children born to sample subjects. Because of the frequency of broken marriages, many of the child-producing years of sample subjects were spent without a spouse. For some subjects, much time in married status was spent in prisons or hospitals, rather than with the spouse. When addiction was associated with illness the illness is not likely to have reduced the probability of producing children; in such cases the illness usually began after age 40, after numerous children could have been born.

Deviance in Spouses

Information was collected on four kinds of deviant behavior in the spouses of subjects: narcotics use, alcoholism, prison record, and mental illness. Narcotics use clearly constituted addiction in only 20 of the spouses, those who were also hospitalized and for whom a diagnosis of addiction was made. It is possible that in some of the remaining cases the use was short of addiction, but for brevity all such spouses will be called addicts in the following discussion. Alcoholism was defined by informants; if they called a spouse alcoholic, he was so counted. The third type of deviance does not refer to criminal behavior, but to having been imprisoned for such behavior. The fourth was sought by questions about mental illness, further described as "nervous breakdown" or "extremely nervous" when necessary, but these seem to have elicited information only on those who were hospitalized for a mental illness.

The data on deviant behavior in spouses are subject to the limitations implied by the above definitions, and to the usual limitations of historical data obtained by retrospective interviews—the possibilities of faulty memories, of deliberate falsification, and of variation among informants in the degree of knowledge about the data sought. Such limitations make dubious any estimate of the true frequency of deviant behavior in the spouses of subjects. On the other hand, there is no known or suspected reason why these limitations should operate differentially within the sample, why data on some subjects should be less accurate than on others. The following analysis, therefore, will emphasize within-sample differences.

Table 10.3. Number of deviant and addicted spouses, by sex of subjects

Subjects	Deviant Spouses	Non-deviant Spouses	Total	Addicted Spouses	Non-addicted Spouses	Total
Male	48	242	290	26	264	290
Female	43	62	105	17	88	105
Total	91	304	395	43	352	395
Chi-square	24.528			3.437		
P	<.001			<.10		

Table 10.3 shows that spouses of female subjects were deviant far more often than spouses of male subjects—41 percent to 17 percent. Spouses of female subjects were also more likely to be addicts—16 percent to 9 percent. The first difference is clearly significant, and the latter is by the .10 criterion.

Such findings might simply reflect a statistical fact of life, that men are more likely than women to be deviant, or to be labelled as deviant in the four ways here counted. Male alcoholics outnumber females, more men than women go to prison and, at least in recent years, more men than women are addicts. One would therefore expect more women than men to find themselves married to a deviant spouse.

No data exist to rule out this explanation of the difference in the number of deviant spouses. It seems unlikely that among Kentuckians of marriageable age 41 percent of men and 17 percent of women have histories of one or more of the four forms of deviance here considered, but the count has never been made. Available estimates of the prevalence of addiction, however, even though less than exact, are sufficient to rule out prevalence among the general population as an explanation of the difference between the sexes in the number of addicted spouses.

If the finding had been of the order of 1 percent addicts among husbands of female subjects, and half as many among wives of male subjects, one might accept the difference as reflecting the probabilities of a Kentuckian marrying an addicted person. But it is incredible that the prevalence of addiction in Kentucky adults has ever approached 16 percent of men or 9 percent of women. That more husbands than wives are addicted, in short, would not be surprising. But that this relative difference is maintained, when the number of addicted wives is at least 10 times as large as it could be by the chance operation of prevalence factors, must be significant in more than the statistical sense. The number of spouses who were addicts or otherwise deviant is large enough to require explanation, and five hypotheses may be suggested as possible explanations.

1. Subjects tended to marry spouses who were already addicted.
2. Subjects tended to marry spouses who were already deviant.
3. Marriage to an addicted subject somehow produced addiction in the spouse.
4. Marriage to an addicted subject somehow produced deviance in the spouse.
5. Spouses who were deviant before marriage to subjects were more likely than non-deviant spouses to become addicted.

Table 10.4 can be used to test these hypotheses. In the left stub subjects are divided by sex, and within sex by the onset of addiction in relation to time of marriage. Looking at the marriages of male subjects in column 1, 104 were contracted when the subject had been addicted before the marriage, and continued to be addicted during all or part of the marriage. In 108 more, the subject was not addicted at the time of the marriage, but became addicted during it. In the remaining 78 marriages of male subjects, their addiction did not begin until after the marriage had terminated.

The marriages thus divided by the time of onset of addiction in the subject are broken down, in columns 2 through 7, by the status of the spouse. Column 2 includes those spouses who were addicted at the time the marriage occurred. Column 3 and 4 include spouses who were not addicted but were otherwise deviant at the time of the marriage; column 3 shows those who became addicted after the date of the marriage, and column 4 those who never became addicted. Similarly, columns 5, 6 and 7 include spouses who were neither addicted nor otherwise deviant at the time of the marriage; column 5 those who became addicted (and possibly showed other forms of deviance too), column 6 those who did not become addicted, but did become deviant, and column 7 those who never showed any form of deviance.

Table 10.4 Number of spouses addicted or otherwise deviant before and after marriage to subjects, by onset of addiction in subjects before, during and after marriage, and by sex

Onset of Addiction in Subject	Number of Spouses	Spouses Addicted Before Marriages	Spouses Not Addicted Before Marriage				
			Other Deviance Before Marriage		No Deviance Before Marriage		
			Addicted Later	Never Addicted	Addicted Later	Deviant Later	Never Deviant
	(1)	(2)	(3)	(4)	(5)	(6)	(7)
MALE							
Addicted Before Marriage (A)	104	4	2	6	10	7	75
Addicted During Marriage (B)	108	1	1	2	7	3	94
Addicted After Marriage (C)	78	--	--	2	1	2	73
Total (D)	290	5	3	10	18	12	242
FEMALE							
Addicted Before Marriage (E)	32	5	--	8	1	1	17
Addicted During Marriage (F)	39	7	--	3	1	4	24
Addicted After Marriage (G)	34	2	1	7	--	3	21
Total (H)	105	14	1	18	2	8	62

The hypotheses will be tested by combining appropriate cells in table 10.4. The combinations will be described in the text, and for convenience the resulting fourfold tables are shown in table 10.5, with chi-square and p values.

1. The first hypothesis is that subjects tended to marry spouses who were already addicted. The relevant cells in table 10.4 are D2 and H2; 5 of 290 spouses of male subjects, and 14 of 105 spouses of female subjects, were addicted at the time the marriage took place. The percentages are 2 percent and 13 percent, supporting the hypothesis, since there is no reason to believe that the prevalence of addiction among Kentucky women and men has ever been as high as these percentages.

Further light can be thrown on this hypothesis by forming a fourfold table from cells D2, D3–7, H2 and H3–7, in table 10.4. The difference by sex of subject in percentage of spouses addicted before the marriage is significant (hypothesis 1a). The women subjects were much more likely than the men to marry partners who were already addicted.

Table 10.5. Tests of hypotheses

Hypothesis	Fourfold Table		Chi-square	P
1a	5	285		
	14	91	20. 23	<. 001
1b	5	21		
	14	3	14. 15	<. 001
2	18	272		
	33	72	41. 40	<. 001
3a	20	187		
	1	77	4. 66	<. 05
3b	2	57		
	1	31		N.S. (.72 [1])
4a	27	169		
	3	73	4. 44	<. 05
4b	7	41		
	3	21		N.S. (.56 [2])
5a	3	10		
	18	254		. 06 [1]
5b	1	18		
	2	70		N.S. (.51 [1])

[1] Probability value by Fisher's Exact Test.
[2] Binomial probability test on left column, taking right marginals as expected proportion.

Two additional points may be made. Of the 26 addict spouses of male subjects, only five were addicted before the marriage, but of the 17 addict spouses of female subjects, 14 were addicted before the marriage. Table 10.5 shows that this difference is significant (hypothesis 1b). Second, for male subjects it may be noted that four of the five spouses already addicted were married by subjects who also were addicted at the time of the marriage. Female subjects, on the other hand, were equally likely to marry men already addicted whether or not they themselves were then addicted.

335–199—69——11

The first hypothesis, then, is supported. Subjects did show a tendency to marry spouses who were already addicted at the time of the marriage. But the tendency was much more marked for female subjects. Further, it existed for female subjects regardless of their own addiction status at the time of marriage, while for male subjects it held only for subjects who were addicted at the time of marriage.

2. The second hypothesis is that subjects tended to marry spouses who were already deviant. The table shows that 18 (D2–4) spouses of male subjects and 33 (H2–4) spouses of female subjects—6 vs. 31 percent—were deviant, by addiction or in other ways, prior to the marriage. The median age at marriage was under 22 for wives of male subjects, and under 26 for husbands of female subjects. Since addiction and alcoholism, which account for two-thirds of the deviance in spouses, normally occur, or are recognized, much later in life, percentages this high must mean that subjects selected spouses disproportionately from the small group of Kentuckians who were deviant so young.

The observed percentages are so high as to give reason to accept that both sexes tended to marry already deviant spouses. But the tendency is clearly much more marked for female than for male subjects, and table 10.5 shows that this difference is significant (hypothesis 2). The appropriate cells are D2–4, D5–7, H2–4 and H5–7.

As with the first hypothesis, it may be noted that of the 18 already deviant spouses of male subjects, 12 (A2–4) were spouses of subjects who were already addicted. Female subjects, on the other hand, were almost equally likely to marry already deviant men regardless of their own addiction status at the time of marriage.

3. For the third and fourth hypotheses, rows A and B, and E and F, represent subjects who were addicted during the marriage, and may be contrasted with rows C and G, the subjects whose addiction did not begin until after termination of the marriage.

The third hypothesis is that marriage to an addicted subject produced addiction in the spouse. From the 212 spouses of male subjects in A1 and B1 must be subtracted the 5 (in A2 and B2) who were already addicted. Of the remaining 207 spouses, 20 (A3, A5, B3, B5) later became addicted. But of the 78 (C1) spouses of not-yet-addicted male subjects, only 1 (C5) later became addicted. The difference is significant (hypothesis 3a in Table 10.5).

The parallel figures for female subjects can be located in rows E–G. Fifty-nine female subjects who were addicted during the marriage had married men who were not addicted before the marriage; of these, two later became addicted. Thirty-two not-yet-addicted female subjects had married non-addicted spouses, of whom one later became addicted. This difference is not significant (hypothesis 3b).

The third hypothesis, therefore, is supported for male subjects, but not for female. Marriage to an addicted male subject is associated with later addiction in the wife, but marriage to an addicted female subject does not lead to addiction in the husband.

4. The fourth hypothesis can be tested by columns 5 through 7 of table 10.4. Of 196 spouses (A5–7, B5–7), not deviant before marriage, of male subjects addicted during the marriage, 27 (14 percent) became addicted or otherwise deviant. Of 76 (C5–7) similar spouses of male subjects who were not addicted during the marriage, only three (4 percent) became deviant later. The difference is in the direction predicted by the fourth hypothesis, and is significant (hypothesis 4a).

Of 48 (E5–7, F5–7) similar spouses of female subjects addicted during the marriage, seven (15 percent) became deviant, as against three (12 percent) of 24 spouses of female subjects whose addiction began after the marriage. Again, the difference is in the predicted direction, but clearly is not significant (hypothesis 4b).

The fourth hypothesis, then, like the third, is supported for male subjects, but not for female, in the sense that increased deviance after marriage to an addicted subject is found for the wives of male subjects, but not for husbands of female subjects. But the conclusion, so stated, is misleading. Of 72 non-deviant husbands of addicted and not-yet-addicted female subjects, 10 later became deviant. This is 14 percent, just as high as the percentage of later deviants among wives of addicted male subjects, and much higher than the percentage among wives of not-yet-addicted male subjects. It is not that addiction in the subject produced deviance in non-deviant wives, and failed to produce it in non-deviant husbands. Rather, husbands of female subjects became deviant, whether or not the subject was addicted during the marriage; wives of male subjects became deviant only if the subject was addicted.

5. The fifth hypothesis is that spouses deviant before marriage were more likely than non-deviants to become addicted after marriage to subjects. So stated, the appropriate cells for testing are D3, D4, D5 and D6–7. Of thirteen spouses of male subjects, deviant before marriage, three (23 percent) became addicted later; of 272 non-deviant spouses, 18 (7 percent) became addicted later. The hypothesis is therefore supported for spouses of male subjects (hypothesis 5a). If the test is restricted to rows A and B, thereby shifting the hypothesis to the effect of marriage to a male subject addicted during the marriage, 27 percent of deviant and 9 percent of non-deviant spouses later became addicted. This difference also is significant, at the .08 probability level.

For female subjects, however, the hypothesis is not supported. One (5 percent) of 19 deviant spouses and two (3 percent) of 72 non-deviant spouses became addicted later, an insignificant difference (hypothesis

5b). If the comparison is restricted to rows E and F, then none of 11 deviant, and two of 48 nondeviant spouses became addicted later, with the difference opposite to the direction predicted.

The fact that the hypothesis does not hold for female subjects does not, as with the previous hypothesis, mean that their husbands were likely to become addicted regardless of the subject's addiction status. The percentages are lower than for the men. Female subjects were more likely than male to marry addicts; they were more likely to marry deviants; their non-deviant spouses were equally likely to become deviant; but neither deviant nor non-deviant spouses were likely to become addicts after the marriage.

The findings suggest that the hypotheses can be modified and connected to form a coherent explanation of the frequency of addiction and other deviance in spouses of subjects. Subjects did tend to marry persons who were already addicted or otherwise deviant, with both tendencies much stronger for female than for male subjects. Spouses who were not deviant before marriage showed some tendency to become deviant after it, wives only if subjects were addicted during the marriage, husbands regardless of the addiction status of subjects.

There was also a tendency for wives of addicted male subjects to become addicted, and addiction was more likely in those wives who had been deviant before marriage than for the non-deviants. But these statements do not hold for the husbands of female subjects. With only slight over-simplification, the pattern of findings is this: male subjects show only a slight tendency to select deviant women to marry, but a moderately strong tendency to make their wives addicts or deviants after the marriage; female subjects showed a marked tendency to select addicted or otherwise deviant men as husbands, a moderate tendency to make deviants of the non-deviants, but little or none to make them addicts later.

One implication, then, is that addiction was transmitted more often from husband to wife than from wife to husband. This is supported by column 2 in table 10.4. Fourteen husbands of female subjects were addicted before marriage, and in at least 9 cases, the subject's addiction began later; 5 wives of male subjects were addicted before marriage, and in only one case was the subject's addiction clearly later.

Characteristics of Subjects With Deviant Spouses

The previous discussion has been in terms of the spouses of subjects, and therefore does not reflect the extent to which some subjects had several deviant spouses. In the following, the discussion shifts to the subjects, and examines the differences between those who had, and those who did not have, deviant and addicted spouses.

No male subject had more than two deviant wives, but three female subjects had three deviant husbands each, and one had four deviant husbands out of five marriages. The 48 deviant wives were married to 40 different male subjects, while 43 deviant husbands were married to 26 different female subjects. Of married male subjects, 22 percent had at least one deviant wife, while 49 percent of married female subjects had at least one deviant spouse.

If the number of marriages is controlled, there were 161 men with one or two marriages, and 19 percent of these had at least one deviant spouse; of 23 men with three to five marriages, 43 percent had at least one deviant spouse. Corresponding figures were 35 women with one or two marriages, of whom 34 percent, and 18 women with three to five marriages of whom 78 percent had at least one deviant spouse.

Of the men, 161 were married either once or twice, for a total of 212 marriages; 34 (16 percent) of those spouses were deviant. For the 23 men who were married three or more times, for a total of 78 marriages, 14 spouses (18 percent) were deviant. This difference is insignificant. Yet deviance in the wives of male subjects seems to have been more probable if it was a later marriage; 14 percent of first wives, 18 of second, 26 of third, and 33 percent of fourth and fifth wives were deviant. These differences do not quite reach the level of statistical significance, but the increase is so regular that it may indicate a real trend.

The picture is reversed for the women; 35 were married once or twice, for a total of 44 marriages, and 13 (30 percent) of these husbands were deviant. For the 18 women married three or more times, for a total of 61 marriages, 30 (49 percent) of husbands were deviant. This difference is just short of statistical significance at the .05 level (chi-square=3.30, 1 d.f.). Later husbands, however, were no more likely than first husbands to be deviants. Whether it was the first or a subsequent marriage for the women, 41 percent of husbands were deviant.[7]

In short, those men with more than two marriages may have been somewhat more likely to choose deviant spouses in their third and later marriages, but in the main their greater probability of having at least one deviant spouse was explained by the increase in number of spouses. For women, however, third and later husbands were no more likely than first or second husbands to be deviant, but those women who were to have three or more marriages were more likely than others to choose deviant spouses, even in their first and second marriages.

An increased probability of having a deviant spouse is therefore, for female subjects, partly attributable to some new selective factor, as well as to the two factors which apply to both sexes, an original tendency to select deviant partners, and an increase with number of marriages.

Table 10.6. Subjects with and without addict spouses compared on selected characteristics

	Male			Female				
	With Addict Spouse 1	No Addict Spouse 2	p[1] 1 vs 2	With Addict Spouse 3	No Addict Spouse 4	p[1] 3 vs 4	p[1] 1 vs 3	p[1] 2 vs 4
Number of subjects	23	161	----	12	41			
Mean number of marriages	2. 1	1. 5	<. 01	3. 0	1. 7	<. 01	<. 05	N.S.
Before start of addiction:								
History of arrests	15%	32%	N.S.	9%	----	N.S.	N.S.	<. 001
History of sentences	9%	15%	N.S.	---	----	N.S.	N.S.	. 004
At start of addiction:								
Mean age	30. 0	34. 1	<. 10	22. 7	37. 0	<. 01	<. 05	N.S.
Use for pleasure or alcoholism	57%	53%	N.S.	50%	5%	. 001	N.S.	<. 001
Contact with addicts	39%	25%	N.S.	75%	10%	. 000	<. 10	<. 05
After start of addiction:								
History of arrests	76%	54%	<. 10	64%	12%	. 001	N.S.	<. 001
History of sentences	59%	39%	N.S.	33%	----	. 002	N.S.	<. 001
All drugs from one physician	9%	28%	N.S.	8%	65%	<. 01	N.S.	<. 001
Involvement in drug subculture	91%	77%	N.S.	92%	41%	<. 01	N.S.	<. 001

[1] Differences between means by t-test; others by chi-square or, when exact probability given, by Fisher's Exact Test. N.S. means >.10.

In this sample, 23 male subjects had a total of 26 addicted wives, and 12 female subjects a total of 17 addicted husbands. Table 10.6 compares married subjects who had at least one addicted spouse with those who had none, on a number of attributes or characteristics. Differences are compared within sex, between subjects who had and who did not have an addict spouse (column 1 vs. column 2; column 3 vs. column 4), and between the sexes, for subjects who had (column 1 vs. column 3), and who did not have, an addict spouse (column 2 vs. column 4).

While there are many differences in table 10.6 which deserve discussion, the major implication of the table may be seen in a glance down the probability columns. With the exception of mean number of marriages, there are no differences between men with and without addict spouses which might not be attributed to chance. The women with addict spouses, on the other hand, differ markedly from the women who had no addict spouses, on almost every characteristic. Comparing columns 1 and 3, the men vs. the women with addict spouses, only three differences are significant. Between columns 2 and 4, however, almost all differences are large and significant.[8]

The table uses criminal record to compare the groups before addiction. There are no differences within sex, but the women are less likely than the men to have arrests or sentences before addiction.

Three variates are used for comparison at the time addiction started; the subjects' age, whether or not the first narcotic was taken for pleasure, or in the treatment of alcoholic excess (as against treatment for illness) and whether or not the circumstances of the first use indicated contact with addicts. Such contact might be indicated by receiving the drug from illicit sources, using heroin, or using the intravenous route.

The male subjects who had an addict wife do not differ on these variates from those with no such wife, except that they were slightly younger. Among the women, however, all differences are large. The women with addict husbands began their addiction 14 years younger than the others, were much more likely to give pleasure or alcoholism as the reason for starting on narcotics, and almost all of them were in contact with addicts at the time narcotics use began.

After addiction began, the male subjects with addict wives were more likely to have a history of arrests, more likely to be sentenced, more likely to obtain drugs from sources other than a physician, and more likely to be involved in the drug subculture. The pattern is consistent, and probably meaningful, but of the individual differences only the first can be regarded as statistically significant. The pattern for the women is exactly the same, but much more marked, and all four differences are significant.

Not only do the two groups of female subjects differ from each other, but their differences are such as to place them at the two extremes, with both groups of male subjects between them. Thus at the start of addiction, women with addict spouses were significantly younger than the corresponding men, while the other women tended to be slightly older than the other men. Female subjects with addict spouses were more likely than corresponding males to be already in contact with addicts, while other women were less likely than other men to have such contact.

This tendency is visible even when the statistical differences are not significant. Comparing criminal records before and after the start of addiction, all groups show an increase in the percentage with arrests, but the increase is by far largest for the women with addict spouses, and smallest for the women without such spouses, with the increases for both groups of men falling between. The women without addict spouses were much more likely than the corresponding men to obtain all drugs from one physician, and to avoid involvement in the addict subculture; but those women with addict spouses obtained drugs from other-than-medical sources, and were involved in the drug subculture, even more often (though by only a percentage point) than the men who correspond to them.

The table must be interpreted cautiously; the list of characteristics is incomplete, and the fact of having or not having an addict spouse may be attributable more to the number of marriages than to other characteristics. But the table and previous findings would be consistent with the following interpretation:

Among male subjects, those with addict spouses were not distinguishable from those without such spouses by preaddiction characteristics. They were, however, slightly younger at the start of addiction, later became slightly more involved in the drug subculture, and showed more criminal behavior. Among women subjects, those with addict spouses are markedly different from the others, both before and after addiction. Only 9 percent had a history of arrests, but this was before age 22, while none in the other group, at an average age of 37, had been arrested. They were much more in contact with addicts at the start of addiction, and began for hedonistic reasons more frequently. After addiction they became as involved in the drug subculture as the most involved men, and their criminal records approached those of the men.

Female subjects, in short, fall into two distinct subgroups. A few had youthful contacts with deviants, became addicted early, and then became even more involved in a deviant subculture. Perhaps by choice, but probably for lack of alternatives, they selected husbands from among deviant men. Most of the women, on the other hand, had no early contacts with deviants; their addiction began years after their choice of husbands had been made, and then led only to slight or moderate involvement in the drug subculture, and to little or no criminal behavior.

The male subjects fall between the two groups of women in the respects discussed. Like the second group of women, their addiction started after the age at which most first marriages occur; like the first group, however, many of them had been in contact with a criminal subculture, and—as alcoholics—with a deviant group. But these facts did not greatly affect their choice of wives. Those who had addicted wives did tend to have been somewhat more involved with deviants, and as an effect of this may have more often selected wives who were or would become addicts. But men involved with deviants were clearly not restricted to these in choosing wives, as the first group of women may have been in choosing husbands.

The way in which marriage was enmeshed in an almost totally deviant way of life for the first group of women, and a few of the others, may be shown by a few examples.

> Little information is available on the adjustment of one (Case 79) of these women before she first married at age 20. The first husband was not an addict, but was an alcoholic. During this marriage, or after her separation, she became addicted at age 22, introduced to narcotics by friends. She had been, or soon became, a prostitute. At 25, she married again. Her second husband, also a subject in this study, had been married before, and was an alcoholic before this second marriage. She introduced him to narcotics, and it seems probable that this was done deliberately, so he would help her in the "making" of physicians and forging of prescriptions which were her methods of obtaining narcotics. Some years later she formed a common-law relationship with a third man who had a prison record and had been addicted before they met. He is now serving a long sentence, and she has formed another relationship with a fourth man, who had been addicted and a patient at Lexington.

> The second case is that of the one woman who was involved with addicts before her addiction, and much involved in the drug subculture after it, but who is not classified as having married a man with a history of narcotics use. She (Case 189) was married at 15, to an alcoholic. The marriage ended in separation very quickly, and she became a prostitute and an addict by age 16. At 18 she formed a brief relationship with an addict, which she described as a common-law marriage on her admission to Lexington, but which was not counted as a marriage because it was so brief, and because later she did not count it as a marriage. At 20 she formed a lasting common-law relationship with a man who had a prison record, and who was serving another sentence when she was interviewed years later. This man was a Negro and the interracial marriage violated local norms, as evidenced by the fact that the woman avoided all contact with her family in order to conceal the marriage.

> Another woman (Case 228) first was married at age 18, and her husband, as far as is known, was not deviant in any way. This marriage terminated, and at age 25 she became addicted, in the course of

medical treatment, but very soon she began to get narcotics from illegal sources. She used opium, heroin and cocaine, and became a prostitute to support her addiction. After this process, at age 29, she was married again, to a man who was an ex-convict, and got him started on narcotics.

It may be noted that in two of these cases the women are said to have deliberately introduced their spouses to addiction, and in each case informants believed that the motive was to make it easier to maintain the subject's addiction. In this sample, though there were more cases in which wives of male addicts became addicted, there was no evidence in any of these that the man intended to addict his wife. These cases of transmission were usually described as giving her the drug for some illness, or complaint of pain.

This difference in attributed motives may reflect some real difference, but the evidence is not sufficient even to suggest it strongly, much less to establish it. It may be that when a woman deviates, she goes further astray than do most men; what is certain is that most of the informants interviewed believed this to be true, and therefore were ready to ascribe almost any evil to those women who were clearly deviant.

It is impossible to estimate how general the deliberate addicting of spouses may be, because the only certain source of information on motives is the person who acts on these. While addicts are much more ready than most persons would be to admit that they have behaved in ways which are generally disapproved, very few will admit deliberately introducing another person to narcotics. This denial may well be accurate in many cases. There are other factors sufficient to explain why the spouse of an addict is likely to become addicted. The drugs are easily available, their effects are observable, and the addicted spouse is seen to regard these effects as desirable.

Summary

About twice as many as expected of the male subjects never married. The more striking fact about the marital histories, however, is that both men and women had multiple marriages much more often than the base Kentucky population. Marriages were likely to end in divorce or separation. Subjects had only about two-thirds the number of children that would have been expected.

Data were collected on four kinds of deviant behavior in the spouses of subjects—addiction, alcoholism, prison record, and mental illness. The total number of deviant spouses, and the number of addicted spouses, were so much beyond chance expectancy as to establish that some selective factors must have been operating. Five hypotheses were suggested to account for the frequency of addiction and other deviance in spouses.

Some support was found for all, but in each case the pattern for female subjects was found to differ from that for the males.

In general, male subjects showed a slight tendency to select addicted or otherwise deviant women as wives, but a moderately strong tendency to make their wives deviant, especially in the form of addiction, after marriage. Female subjects showed a marked tendency to select addicted or otherwise deviant men as husbands; the non-deviants they married became deviant fairly often, but not addicted.

Male subjects had as many as two deviant wives in very few cases, and multiple marriages increased the probability of having a deviant wife only in proportion to the number of marriages. But women with a deviant husband tended to have more than one, and the men they married were much more likely to be deviant for women with three or more marriages than for women with only one or two marriages.

With reference to addiction in the spouse, those male subjects who had such a wife differed little from those with no addicted wife. What difference existed seems to have been somewhat greater involvement in a deviant subculture for those with addict wives. The female subjects with addicted husbands, on the other hand, differed markedly from those with no addict husband, and the difference is associated with greater involvement in the drug and criminal subcultures. Men involved in a deviant subculture were somewhat more likely than others to choose a deviant woman as wife, but their choice was clearly not restricted to such women, and many married non-deviants. But women involved in the same subculture chose deviant men as husbands so consistently as to suggest that their choice was largely restricted to these men.

The data indicate that the transmission of addiction in marriage was from husband to wife much more often than from wife to husband. There is also a suggestion, but no more, that when transmission was from wife to husband this represented a conscious act of making the man an addict, for utilitarian reasons—though in these cases the man was clearly deviant before his use of narcotics, and the use was but a short step further along a familiar road. When transmission was from husband to wife, the drugs were said to be given for illness or pain, with no suggestion of intended benefit for the giver.

This difference, however, may establish little more than the readiness of informants to attribute any evil to women who were unmistakably labelled as deviants. Perhaps the more interesting finding is that in most cases where both husband and wife were addicted, all subjects and other informants insisted that they became addicted independently, or refrained from assigning the responsibility to one of them. Addicts, more ready than most people to admit to disapproved actions, rarely admit to one—making an addict of another person.

Footnotes, Chapter 10

[1] LEMERT, EDWIN M. *Social Pathology.* New York: McGraw-Hill, 1951. p. 378.

[2] TERRY, CHARLES E.; AND PELLENS, MILDRED. *The Opium Problem.* New York: Committee on Drug Addiction and Bureau of Social Hygiene, 1928. pp. 94–136.

[3] *Ibid.* p. 106.

[4] U.S. Bureau of the Census. *U.S. Census of Population: 1960. Detailed Characteristics, Kentucky.* Final Report, PC(1)–19D, Table 105.

[5] *Ibid.* Table 113.

[6] The census asked, for women ever married, "How many babies has she ever had, not counting stillbirths?" The question could not be asked in exactly this form in follow-up interviews. It was usually, "How many children did she have by that husband" or ". . . in that marriage," or "How many children were born to the marriage?" It is possible that deceased children, particularly if they died as infants, were omitted from the count more often than they were omitted in response to the census inquiry, but extremely unlikely that such a difference could account for the large difference observed.

[7] This statement contradicts one made in the writer's paper: Marital history of narcotic addicts. *International Journal of the Addictions,* 2:32, Spring 1967. The earlier statement incorrectly inferred, from the fact that women with three to five husbands had more deviant husbands, that third and later husbands were more likely to be deviant. A later check showed that this was not correct.

[8] Part of the difference between the two columns on the right might be due to sample size; identical differences in percentages might be nonsignificant when 23 men are compared with 12 women, and significant when 161 men are compared with 41 women. Visual comparison of the differences from column 1 to 3, and from 2 to 4, will satisfy the reader that this possible explanation can be ruled out.

Attention might also be called to the fact that usually the differences from column 1 to 3 and 2 to 4 are in the same direction, but this is not true of "Contact with addicts" at start of addiction. Among subjects with addict spouses, many more women than men had such contact; among those with no addict spouse, many fewer women had it. The two probabilities in the right columns seem close, but they apply to differences opposite in direction.

CHAPTER 11

Hospital Treatment

Neither this chapter nor any other part of the report should be interpreted as evaluating the effectiveness of treatment in the Lexington hospital. An evaluation of treatment ideally requires comparison of treated patients with a matched group of addicts who were not treated, or received another type of treatment, and no data are available on any such control group. Even an evaluation of the relative effects of aspects of hospital treatment, such as length of hospitalization or participation in psychotherapy—by separating subjects on such variables and comparing them on outcome—logically requires that the groups compared be shown, or assumed, to be matched on all other relevant variables.

This matching cannot be shown within this sample, but some such comparisons will be made. When findings are negative, they weaken the plausibility of some hypotheses about treatment effects. But the data of this chapter are best regarded as describing part of the natural history of addiction; treatment is a recurrent event in the lives of most addicts.

Data are reported only for objective measures, like length of hospitalization. Other variables of more importance, like participation in psychotherapy, are omitted because hospital records do not furnish a sufficient basis to measure or categorize the variable reliably.

Some subjects were hospitalized a number of times and, especially if they were prisoners, a very large amount of information about them was recorded. Others were hospitalized only once, leaving against medical advice after only a few days, before the usual psychiatric and other studies were started, so the hospital records on these contain much less information. Another factor making for unevenness in the records is that the admissions of subjects ranged over a 25-year period. There were turnovers in personnel, fluctuations in the number, training and interests of staff members, wide variations in the number of annual admissions, with consequent variations in the amount of staff time available per patient, changes in the emphasis on various kinds of treatment, and variations in how completely these were recorded. For these reasons, this study did not attempt to classify subjects on many of those variables which, from psychiatric theory or experience, might be expected to produce different outcomes.

Information on some variables, however, was recorded on all or most subjects, and has descriptive value. In addition, relating some findings of the followup to variables recorded on all patients may be the beginning of making the hospital data useful for projecting estimates for cohorts of patients other than the group studied here.

Admissions and Readmissions

Table 11.1 shows the number of admissions to the Lexington hospital for the subjects in the study. The number of admissions of male subjects, from the opening of the hospital in May, 1935 to September 30, 1964 ranges from 1 to 24. For the women, who were first admitted in 1941, the range is from 1 to 6. The mean number of admissions for the men is almost three, for the women, almost two. It is clear, however, that a small minority of subjects accounts for a large proportion of total admissions. Nine men, who have more than 10 admissions each, account for a total of 155 admissions; thus 4 percent of the men account for 26 percent of male admissions. The 27 men who have more than five admissions account for a total of 292 admissions; 13 percent of the men with 48 percent of male admissions. Slightly over half of the men had no readmissions, and almost two-thirds of the women had no readmissions.

Table 11.1. Number of admissions from 1935 to September 30, 1964, by sex

Number of Admissions	Male	Female
1	114	34
2	35	8
3	19	3
4	12	5
5	5	2
6	4	2
7	6	--
8	4	--
9	1	--
10	3	--
11	1	--
12	1	--
13	1	--
14	1	--
15	1	--
21	1	--
22	1	--
23	1	--
24	1	--
Total Admissions	606	101
Number of Subjects	212	54

Table 11.2. First admissions, total admissions and percent of subjects readmitted, by year of first admission and sex

Year of First Admission	First Admissions	Total Admissions	Number with One or More Readmissions	Percent Readmitted
	Male			
1935–39	67	234	35	52.2
1940–44	31	134	18	58.1
1945–49	56	155	26	46.4
1950–54	43	66	17	39.5
1955–59	15	17	2	13.3
Total	212	606	98	46.2
	Female			
1940–44	7	14	3	42.9
1945–49	18	43	9	50.0
1950–54	22	35	6	27.3
1955–59	7	9	2	28.6
Total	54	101	20	37.0

Table 11.2 separates these first admissions and readmissions by the five-year periods within which subjects were first admitted. This breakdown shows that, as might be expected, the total number of admissions varies roughly with the length of time within which readmissions were possible. The 67 men first admitted in 1935–39 have a mean of 3.5 admissions; the 31 first admitted in 1940–44 have a mean of 4.3 admissions. The mean then drops regularly for the next three 5-year periods.

Of more significance, however, is the fact that as of September, 1964, only 52 percent of the men first admitted in 1935–39 had been readmitted. It is highly unlikely that men who have not had a second admission in 25 years will have one in future years, so the 52 percent may reasonably be taken as the highest figure this percentage will reach. Similarly, 58 percent of those who were first admitted in 1940–44 have had a subsequent admission, and it is not likely that many of the others will be readmitted after this 20-year period. From these two percentages, it is plausible to conclude that a figure of 55 to 60 percent is the ceiling which readmissions, in groups comparable to that studied here, are likely to approach. The ceiling for the women would appear to be not much below this.

It should not, however, be assumed that the 40 percent of the 1950–54 male first admissions who have had a second admission, or the 13 percent of 1955–59 first admissions, will eventually increase to 55 or 60 percent. It will be seen below that there are reasons to expect that the more recently admitted subjects will show a smaller proportion with readmissions than those admitted in the early years of the hospital.

With exceptions infrequent enough to justify ignoring them, the fact that a patient is readmitted to Lexington means that he has relapsed to use of narcotics. If he is not readmitted, this fact cannot be taken as an indication that he has not relapsed; he may have a stable source of drugs, or be in treatment elsewhere, or he may be dead. Still, patients who have not been readmitted include those who have not relapsed. The possibility therefore exists that the readmission rate of discharged patients bears some constant relationship to their relapse rate.

If this relationship could be established, the readmission rate could be used as an index of the relapse rate. It would constitute a valuable tool, since the former rate is easily determined from hospital records, while the latter can be established only with difficulty, in a followup like the present study. It might become possible, for example, to evaluate different treatment approaches, within tolerable limits of error, from differences in the readmission rates of the groups which received the differing treatments. The data of this study can be used as a beginning point to study the relationship between readmission and relapse. The approach is to answer questions of the following form: given a cohort of patients who were discharged from their first admission *x* years ago, and who have not been readmitted, what percentages are dead, using narcotics, abstinent by virtue of being institutionalized, or otherwise abstinent?

Table 11.3. Survival and addiction status, by number of years since first discharge, in hypothetical cohorts (of 1000 in size) of white male patients who have not been readmitted to Lexington

Year After First Discharge	Dead	Addicted	In Institutions	Off Narcotics
1	101	428	78	393
2	133	351	118	398
3	187	268	129	416
4	217	269	97	417
5	262	252	89	397
6	320	190	72	418
7	361	174	72	393
8	407	134	66	393
9	478	112	47	363
10	504	114	41	341

Table 11.3 has been constructed to answer such questions. (The data and logic on which the construction are based are presented in Appendix D.) If one identified a group of patients who had been discharged 10 years earlier, and of whom nothing is known except that they had not been admitted a second time, he could infer from the table that half of the group are dead, 15 percent either addicted or in some institution, and 34 percent are off narcotics, though in a situation in which they could be using narcotics. Such an inference, of course, involves a number of assumptions, among these that the group is so similar to the Kentucky sample that findings on the latter may be applied to it.

Such an assumption would not be justified for most groups, and there are other reasons why inferences could not now be made from table 11.3 with confidence. It was noted above that relapse and readmission behavior of the Kentucky sample are changing over time. In addition, the table does not take into account variables which are already known, or must be assumed, to have an effect on relapse and readmission behavior, like age of subjects, their involvement in the drug subculture, and so on. The table is not presented here as being of any current use, but as an example of how future followup studies can be analyzed. When the relapse behavior of several different samples is related to their readmissions, it may be that the findings will be similar enough to each other to establish that readmissions furnish a reasonably accurate index of relapses. If the findings are not similar, and it is shown that readmissions do not constitute a useful index, the effort will not have been wasted, since the differences between the samples will then point to probable explanations of the differences in relapse or readmission behavior.

One finding in table 11.3 will be especially interesting if it is paralleled in future studies. This is the fact that the percentage living and off narcotics is so stable; for eight years after first discharge it fluctuates only between 39 and 42 percent.

Age at First Admission

It may be seen in Table 11.4 that there has been a trend toward increasing age for Kentucky addicts at the time of their first admission to Lexington, over the first 25 years of the hospital's existence. The men with first admissions in 1955–59 were 7.5 years older than those who were first admitted in 1935–39, and the mean age of the women at first admission had increased 9.1 years from 1940 to 1959. Further, for each sex the largest increase occurred after the first 5-year period of admissions, though these related to different points in time because women were not admitted during the first 5 years of the hospital's existence.

This finding is striking because it is the opposite of what one might have expected. From the description of one county in the next chapter, and

335–199—69——12

Table 11.4. Age at first admission by five-year periods and by sex

Year of First Admission	Male			Female		
	n	Mean Age	s.d.	n	Mean Age	s.d.
1935–39	67	38.7	12.5	--	--	--
1940–44	31	43.8	10.5	7	37.9	10.1
1945–49	56	43.1	10.1	18	43.8	16.3
1950–54	43	41.2	11.4	22	41.9	13.6
1955–59	15	46.2	13.4	7	47.0	14.1
Total	212	41.6	11.6	54	42.7	14.1

from other data throughout this report, the expectations might be as follows. Since there were more addicts in the State before 1935 than later, and many of these were elderly, and since persons who became addicted in recent decades could be admitted to Lexington soon after addiction began, while those addicted before 1920 or 1930 necessarily had to wait until 1935 (or 1941 for the women) to be admitted, the early admissions to Lexington should show larger numbers, a higher mean age, and a longer length of addiction.

In rough terms, the larger number of admissions is noted in table 11.4 for the earlier five-year periods, but mean age was lowest in the first five-year period. The expectation of a longer length of addiction for early admissions is also belied. The mean length of addiction for male patients in 1935–39 was 10.1 years; means for the following periods were 13.0, 8.0, 6.6, and 9.5. Beginning with the 1940–44 period for the women, the mean length of addiction was 13.1 years, and in the subsequent periods 10.2, 6.0, and 8.6. For the men, therefore, there is the question why the length of addiction was less in 1935—39 than in the subsequent period. For both sexes, why did the length of addiction increase in 1955–59 after a steady drop for 15 years?

The next two tables suggest an answer to the first question. Table 11.5 shows that the hospital status of male subjects, on their first admission, has varied with the year of that admission. In 1935–39, almost half of the subjects were prisoners or probationers. The proportion dropped to one-fourth in the next 5-year period, one-eighth in the next, and about one-twentieth in the last two periods. In 1935–39, in short, almost half of the male subjects entered the hospital on the decision of a court, not on their own initiative.[1]

Table 11.6 shows that hospital status, in turn, was associated with the age of the subject at the time of admission. Those who were sent to the

Table 11.5. Hospital status of male subjects on first admission by year of first admission (percentages)

Year of First Admission	Prisoner or Probationer	Voluntary	No. of Subjects
1935–39	43	57	67
1940–44	26	74	31
1945–49	12	88	56
1950–54	5	95	43
1955–59	7	93	15

Table 11.6. Hospital status of male subjects on first admission by age at first admission (percentages)

Age at First Admission	Status		
	Prisoner or Probationer	Voluntary	No. of Subjects
Under 30	30	10	31
30–39	32	27	60
40–49	30	30	64
50–59	8	23	42
60 or over	--	9	15
	100	[1] 100	
No. of Subjects	47	165	212

[1] Figures do not total to 100 due to rounding.

hospital as prisoners or probationers were much more likely to be the younger men; 62 percent were under age 40, while only 37 percent of voluntary patients were so young. Even among the prisoners and probationers, those admitted in 1935–39 were 8 years younger, on the average, than later court commitments. Almost two-thirds of all prisoner and probationer patients were admitted in the first of five equal time periods; since men with these statuses were younger, and especially so in 1935–39, the mean age of male admissions in the 1935–39 period was lower than in later years.

Only three women were first admitted as prisoners or probationers, so the same kind of interaction among hospital status, age, and year of admission cannot account for the lower mean age of the women first admitted. But their sex may have had an effect like that of older age among the men, and the following may be advanced as a plausible, internally consistent explanation of the findings in tables 11.4 through 11.6.

Prior to 1935, and for women prior to 1941, a sizeable backlog of addicts had built up in the state. When it first became possible for them to enter the Lexington hospital, these addicts ranged widely in age and included a large number of elderly persons. They also ranged widely in the length of time they had been addicted; in this sample one man admitted in 1935–39 had been addicted for forty years. If admissions to Lexington in any given year had represented random selections from the existing addicts at that time, the earlier admissions would have been older and would have had longer histories of addiction. They would also have been more numerous, if admissions represented some constant proportion of the number currently addicted.

But first admissions were not randomly selected. Some were selected, mainly in 1935–39, to a lesser extent in 1940–44, and to a negligible extent after that, by being prosecuted, convicted and committed to the hospital. The law enforcement officials who chose to prosecute some addicts decided, it is apparent, not to prosecute women or elderly men, but to make cases only among younger men. This selection did make the number of admissions in 1935–39 higher than in succeeding periods, but brought the mean age and mean length of addiction down.

What of the women and the elderly men who were not prosecuted? Some of them entered the hospital voluntarily. But from 1935 to about 1944 many of them must have avoided hospitalization. The description of a county in the next chapter and abundant case material in other counties establish that the elderly addicts, and women addicts, remained in their communities and in almost all cases remained on narcotics. There was probably no formal or conscious policy decision on the part of any specific persons or agencies, but in effect there was a decision to allow elderly addicts to remain on drugs until they died, while efforts were being made to force younger addicts to abstain, and prevent the appearance of new cases of addiction.

Admissions to Lexington did not represent a constant proportion of the number of currently addicted persons in Kentucky. In 1935–39 the percentage of existing addicts who were admitted to Lexington was certainly much less than 100 percent; the writer would estimate that less than one-half of the addicts who would have been eligible for admission were actually admitted. It will be argued later in this chapter that in later years this percentage rapidly increased, so that after 1945, and certainly after 1950, almost all Kentucky addicts were admitted to Lexington.

Whether or not the above explanation of findings is accepted, it is evident from table 11.5 that the law-enforcement process which sent prisoners and probationers to Lexington for the first time was concentrated in the very early years of the hospital's existence. One may ask why prisoners and probationers did not constitute as large a proportion of first admissions in the 1950s as in earlier years.

The answer is not that law enforcement efforts became relatively slack in later years, after an initial drive against addiction. Indeed, enforcement of narcotics laws increased over the years, with the appointment of State as well as Federal agents with specific responsibility for drug laws. Kentuckians continued to be sent to Lexington as the result of court action, but as readmissions. Thirty-eight men had admissions as prisoners or probationers in 1935–39, 24 percent of these being readmissions; there were 32 such admissions in 1940–44, and 32 more in 1945–49, of which 75 percent and 78 percent were readmissions. Only in the 1950s was there a drop in the number of prisoner and probationer admissions, and this, it will be shown later, was the result of factors other than changes in law enforcement.

It is clear, then, that the findings of table 11.5 apply only to first admissions; it is not that in later years fewer men were committed by courts, but that most so committed had had a prior admission as a voluntary patient. Case material makes it clear that two factors were operating. In some cases, enforcement officials refrained from pressing charges if addicts would enter the hospital voluntarily; in others, addicts aware that arrest was imminent would enter the hospital in the hope of avoiding prosecution, or of persuading the court later that the motivation shown by voluntarily seeking treatment justified a lenient sentence.

The fact that men admitted in 1935–39 were younger can be taken as the explanation for the shorter length of addiction noted in those years. The decline in mean length of addiction in the 15 years after 1940, described a few pages earlier, can be interpreted as due in part to a tendency to seek treatment earlier in the drug history, to avoid prosecution or for other reasons. But not too much emphasis should be placed on this tendency; another explanation is needed for the rise in length of addiction for 1955–59 admissions. Further, even in the 10 years from 1945 to 1954, when the mean length of addiction was at its lowest, it ranged up to more than 30 years for some first admissions. In no 5-year period did the percentage of male first admissions with histories of over 20 years of addiction fall below 12 percent.

But the changing nature of the addiction problem, and the changing characteristics of addicts in Kentucky, do suggest why fewer prisoners and probationers appear among the first admissions and readmissions of recent years, and why the length of addiction increased for recent first admissions. In recent years there were fewer addicts who might be prosecuted. Those first admitted after 1950 were older, were more likely than earlier admissions to have some medical justification or pretext for use of narcotics, were more likely to be obtaining the narcotics from a legitimate source, were less likely to be involved in the drug subculture, and were less likely to be involved in crime. When the addiction of such subjects came to the attention of enforcement agencies there was less reason to perceive it as an illicit activity, and if an investigation was made, it was less likely to uncover a legal offense.

The same factors operated to increase the length of addiction at time of first admission for subjects first admitted in 1955–59. Legal pressures toward treatment were almost absent, and addiction could continue for a number of years before other pressures led to hospitalization. While first admissions in 1955–59 included fewer subjects with over 20 years of addiction than in previous periods, and none with over 30 years of addiction, they also included fewer with less than 5 years of addiction. The mean length of addiction therefore increased, though the variance continued to decrease.

These factors also furnish the reasons for the statement made earlier that readmissions, for subjects first admitted in recent years, are not likely to reach the 55 to 60 percent noted in 1935–39 and 1940–44. The recent subjects were older at first admission, and therefore had lower life expectancies within which readmissions could take place. They felt fewer of the pressures which led to readmissions for earlier subjects. Finally, more of them fell in the "medical addict" type; they were likely to be addicted continuously if a physician prescribed, and to be abstinent if none would prescribe. In neither case was readmission necessary. The readmissions of medical addicts are discussed in more detail in the later section on length of hospitalization.

Prognosis on First Admission

In the following sections of this chapter, several variables usually or always recorded in the hospital record will be examined to see to what extent they predict three variables; total admissions, posthospital drug pattern, and current addiction status for the subjects who were interviewed. Comparisons will be based on the male subjects only, because the number of women is too small for the necessary breakdowns.

Until recent years, hospital staff formally recorded a prognosis for each patient on whom studies were completed. This prognosis was intended to predict something about the patient's future use of narcotics, but there can be no certainty that the many staff physicians who recorded prognoses were all predicting the same thing. Prognoses were recorded on the first admission for only half of the male subjects. Almost all of the cases where there is no prognosis were voluntary patients, and among these, the prognosis was most frequently missing for those who left the hospital before completing the recommended period of treatment.

The formal prognoses can be grouped in five classes: very poor, poor, guarded, fair, and good. Some estimates were made more informally, using such words and phrases as "dismal," "hopeless," "doubtful," "slightly better than average" or "well above average." For use here, these estimates were assigned to one of the five classifications from very poor to good, and several psychiatrists on the hospital staff checked these assignments to be sure that no serious errors of classification were made. The breakdown was 7 very poor, 34 poor, 26 guarded, 27 fair and 12 good. The first pair and the last three were grouped for chi-square measures.

Those men who were given guarded, fair or good prognoses were no more likely to be currently abstinent, or to have post-hospital drug patterns of "much abstinence" or "complete abstinence," than those with poorer prognoses. There is a slight, but not statistically significant, tendency for them to be less frequently found using substitutes for narcotics, both at the time of interview and for the entire posthospital period.

It might be expected that subjects with the better prognoses would be less likely to have readmissions to the hospital. This was not so, and the opposite was true to a significant extent. Of 65 men with guarded to good prognoses, 54 percent were readmitted, against 32 percent of the 41 men with poor or very poor prognoses.

Hospital Status

On first admission 149 of the men were voluntary patients, 16 were committed voluntarily, 16 Federal probationers, and 31 were prisoners. For purposes of comparison the 149 voluntary patients were treated as one group, as were the 31 prisoners. The committed voluntary and probationer patients were combined into a third group. These three were then compared on readmissions, current addiction status and post-hospital drug pattern. No significant differences were found.

Length of Hospital Stay

The length of hospitalization might be related to the outcome variables. Length of stay, however, is related to status, with the voluntary patients having shorter stays, committed voluntaries [2] and probationers longer, and prisoners still longer. Comparisons therefore must be made within status. Within status, the selection of cutting points along the length of hospitalization time-scale was arbitrary, to facilitate comparison.

Of the male subjects who were voluntary patients on their first admission, 58 remained less than 10 days, 36 more left before the 30th day,

28 more left before the 100th day, and 27 remained 100 days or more. Looking first at total admissions, a significant difference is found. Of 122 subjects who had under 100 days of hospitalization, 34 percent were readmitted; of 27 who remained 100 days or more, 59 percent were readmitted.

The group of committed voluntary and probationer patients can be divided into three sub-groups on length of hospital stay, with eight remaining less than 100 days, 11 for 100 to 199 days, and 13 for 200 days or more. These sub-groups do not differ in the percentage readmitted.

The prisoners fall into three sub-groups, with ten remaining under 400 days, 13 for 400 to 599 days, and eight for 600 days or more. Those with longer hospital stays tended to have more readmissions, with four, seven, and seven subjects readmitted in the respective groups. For the male subjects, therefore, controlled on hospital status, in two of the three comparisons those subjects with shorter stays tend to have fewer readmissions.

Making the same comparisons on posthospital drug pattern, no clear-cut findings emerge. Differences between sub-groups are not statistically significant, and suggest no consistent trend.

With respect to the current addiction status of those subjects who were interviewed, those who had been voluntary patients on first admission were more likely to be found completely abstinent if they had stayed under 30 days than if they had stayed longer. Only 13 male subjects who had been committed voluntary patients or probationers on first admission, and only 18 who had been prisoners, were interviewed and classified on current addiction status. These numbers are too small for comparisons on length of stay to be meaningful, but it can be said that in neither group is there any indication of more abstinence among those who stayed longer in the hospital.

The findings in this section can best be summarized negatively; there is no support for the hypothesis that a longer period of hospitalization, in itself, decreases the probability of readmissions, or increases the probability of later abstinence, either at the point in time when subjects are located, or for the entire posthospital period. Those findings which are statistically significant point in the opposite direction, but it would not be correct to conclude that shorter periods of hospitalization lead to better results, because there are alternative explanations of the findings.

One alternative relates to sub-types of addicts. A "medical addict" has been defined in chapter 6 as a subject who began narcotics use in the context of treatment by a physician and who had obtained all narcotics from one physician at a time. Such subjects can be contrasted with all others, and are found more often to be voluntary patients. Also more often than others, they left the hospital in less than ten days.

On the outcome variables, only 4 of 38 medical addicts had readmissions, while half of the other addicts did. Ten of the medical addicts were alive and located in the followup study. Five were then addicted to narcotics and four were completely abstinent. Nine of the ten, in short, were at one of the two extremes, while other addicts were distributed more evenly over the five categories of the classification of current addiction status. The distribution of posthospital drug pattern is similar; the medical addicts show patterns of narcotic addiction and of complete abstinence more often than the others, and show patterns of addiction to substitutes and of occasional use less often. It seems more reasonable to conclude that factors associated with being a medical addict made the subjects leave Lexington quickly, and then kept them abstinent or returned them to addiction, with no later admissions, than to see brief hospitalizations as the cause of fewer readmissions.

The reasons why medical addicts left the hospital quickly, and the explanation for their posthospital drug patterns, have been suggested earlier. Their self-concept was one of having been given a medicine for illness, rather than of taking a drug for pleasure. They were frequently disturbed by the other addicts they met in the hospital; many of the latter had criminal histories, and had values and attitudes more characteristic of a criminal than of merely a drug subculture. The hospital was an alien and frightening situation, and this contributed toward their decisions to leave quickly. But whether they left the hospital early or late was less likely to determine their future drug use than was the attitude of their physicians when they returned home.

> One such medical addict (Case 213) was first hospitalized in 1950, leaving against medical advice on the fourth day. He remained abstinent for 18 months, then was again given narcotics by a physician who had the reputation of prescribing narcotics too freely, to the extent that addicts from other States visited him for occasional prescriptions. He remained on narcotics until 1963, when he returned to the hospital because this physician was retiring and would soon stop prescribing for him. He had gone to the other physicians in his community and found that none of them was willing to prescribe. On this second admission, he left on the third day. One would not wish to predict his future use of narcotics, however, on the basis of this fact. From his past pattern it seems evident that he will be addicted again if a physician will prescribe for him, and probable that he will be abstinent if none is willing to prescribe.

Psychiatric Diagnoses

The Lexington hospital is a psychiatric hospital, and all addict patients who remained long enough were given a psychiatric examination. This normally resulted in one or more psychiatric diagnoses, in addition to the diagnoses specific to drug addiction. Psychiatric terminology has changed since 1935, and there have been changes in diagnostic practices. The diagnoses recorded for the subjects in this study were coded to fit the major classications of "Mental Disorders" in the 1959 International Classification of Diseases.

These diagnoses are not useful for statistical analysis, because the large majority fall in a single classification, Personality Disorders. Within that classification, a breakdown into its subheadings was not found to be useful, because of the unreliability of the assignment to the more specific diagnoses. It frequently happened, for subjects with two or more admissions, that the diagnoses made on these occasions fell into different subclasses of Personality Disorders, though the distinction between this and other major classifications was maintained with a high degree of reliability. All of the Personality Disorders are therefore grouped in table 11.7 with the exceptions of Alcoholism, which denotes a condition of special interest in this study, and Transient Situational Disorders.

Table 11.7. Psychiatric diagnoses, by sex

Diagnosis	Male		Female	
	Primary Dx First Adm.	Dx Made on Some Adm.	Primary Dx First Adm.	Dx Made on Some Adm.
Brain Disorders	--	2	--	--
Mental Deficiency	1	5	--	--
Psychoses	1	6	2	2
Psychophysiologic, Autonomic and Visceral Disorders	--	1	--	--
Psychoneurotic Disorders	5	15	7	13
Personality Disorders	54	114	11	19
Alcoholism	28	51	--	1
Transient Situational Personality Disorders	1	1	--	--
No diagnosis recorded	122	78	34	27

Table 11.7 shows the first psychiatric diagnosis made on the first admission, and those diagnoses which were ever made on any admission. Half of the women and over one-third of the men never had a formal diagnosis made and the proportions without a diagnosis are even higher for the first admissions, which would be of most interest for predictive purposes.

Most diagnoses fall into the Personality Disorders. Alcoholism is the next most frequent, and in most cases this diagnosis was made in association with one of the other diagnoses in the Personality Disorder classification. The only other diagnostic category appearing with noteworthy frequency is that of Psychoneurotic Disorders. These diagnoses were relatively more frequent among the women than the men. More than half of them were made on subjects who were also diagnosed, on the same or on other admissions, in the Personality Disorder classification.

It is worth specific mention that psychoses were infrequently diagnosed. Even among the eight subjects with such a diagnosis, seven were also diagnosed in the Personality Disorder category. The modal picture is of subjects who were basically in the Personality Disorders group, but who were in a psychotic state during one of their admissions. It is also worthy of note that in only one case was the personality disorder considered to be a Transient Situational Disorder.

When a formal psychiatric diagnosis was made, in short, the subjects were perceived as being characterized by serious and long-standing mental disorders. Almost all of these fell into, or were associated with, one of the major sub-classes of mental disorders, that of Personality Disorders. There was no case in which a psychiatrist regarded a subject as a "normal" person, though of course this description might have been applied to some of the subjects for whom no diagnosis was recorded, if psychiatric studies had been completed on them.

Lexington Admissions as a Sample of Kentucky Addicts

Inferences about the history of addiction in Kentucky, which will be made in following chapters, depend on a judgment as to how well patients admitted to Lexington, who could have been selected as subjects in this study, represented all addicts in Kentucky. It was shown earlier that women and older men were under-represented in the early admissions to Lexington, but it was stated that more recent admissions included almost all Kentucky addicts. The evidence for the latter statement was an unplanned by-product of one of the procedures used in the study.

Field staff were not to reveal to anyone that a subject had once been an addict, or had once been treated in the Lexington hospital. In rural counties and small towns it was expected that certain persons, including the physicians, Health Department officials, police, sheriffs, and court officials, could furnish information about several different subjects. A common element for these subjects would be that they had been addicts and hospital patients, and if an informant knew this, he could infer that other subjects about whom inquiries were made had been addicts and patients too. In the initial contacts in a community the only safe procedure was to give no names. The purpose of the study was explained, and the informant was asked if he knew or had known of any addicts there.

Under these circumstances, if the subjects treated at Lexington had been, for example, about one-half of the addicts in the county, one would expect that about half of the addicts named by informants would be identifiable as subjects, and the others would not have been patients in the hospital. This was what in fact happened, for persons named as having been addicted before the 1940s. It will be seen in a description of one county, in the next chapter, that informants identified about 20 persons who were addicted during the 1920s and 1930s. Of these, nine had been admitted to Lexington and were subjects in the study. Of those who were named as having been addicted in the 1940s or 1950s, however, all were subjects in the study; all had been admitted to the hospital. It is difficult to imagine an explanation for this except that the ten recent subjects represented all of the known addicts in the county in these recent decades.

This fact, that for recent decades all addicts named were subjects, while for earlier decades some were not, was not true of this county alone, but held for all of the State. It was most clear-cut in another county, which eventually was included in the sample, but was chosen for a pilot field trip before the sample was selected. At that time the major concerns were with the practicability of the study design; field experience might require re-designing the study, or even show it was impractical. A pilot field trip was therefore planned as soon as a sufficient number of subjects was identified as having come from one county.

Two interviewers visited the county and spent a week there, with a list of the 19 subjects who had been identified. All of their questions about the feasibility of the study were satisfactorily answered. The point relevant here is that they were given information not only on the subjects they knew about, but on 14 more addicts who were not on their list.

Of the 23 subjects who were eventually identified as residents of this county, 16 had their first admission by 1945, in the first 10 years the hospital was open. All were named by one or more informants in the county and they also named 10 others, using drugs at about the same time, of whom only one had been admitted to the hospital. (He was not a subject because his first admission had been from another county, not included in the sample.)

The remaining seven subjects from the county, first admitted after 1945, were also named by informants. But they named no other person in the county as having been addicts during these recent years, except for early subjects who had continued to be addicted.

In still another county, the two independent checks of hospital records failed to identify one man as a subject. He was identified when several informants, mostly in his county but even in another county, named him as an addict and as having been to Lexington. The pattern was the same across the State; if a list of addicts had been drawn up from names given by informants, it would have included almost every subject in the study. In addition, it would have included a large number of others as having been addicted in the 1930s, who were never admitted to Lexington. But it would have included only a handful whose addiction began in the 1940s or later, and who were not admitted to the hospital.

These facts indicate that almost all known addicts in recent decades have been admitted to Lexington, while in the late 1930s and early 1940s only some—probably about half—were admitted. Other explanations cannot be completely ruled out, but seem highly improbable. One might be that informants knew of other recent addicts, and chose not to name them to interviewers. If this were so, it would imply that they knew of addicts' histories in enough detail to be sure which had been treated at Lexington, and which had not, and named only the former. But there were normally indications that most informants did not have such specific knowledge.

Another explanation might be that some recent addicts have been able to conceal their addiction so successfully that informants did not know they were addicts. This would include concealing their addiction from their physicians, since physicians were among the best informants, and the general pattern in most counties, where there were only a few physicians, was that each knew of the addicts among his colleagues' patients. Successful concealment of addiction, in all but the metropolitan counties, would therefore mean that the addicts were maintaining their addiction on illicit narcotics. It would also mean that they were successfully concealing the illegal activities which would normally be needed to raise money for illicit drugs. Further, it would mean concealing these activities not only from the police, but also from other addicts, who were among the best informants the study used.

Such an explanation cannot be disproved, but this arises from the notorious difficulty of proving a negative. There is literally no indication, in all of the data of the study, that such concealment of addiction exists.

The argument is somewhat less firm for the metropolitan counties. In large cities all of the physicians do not know each other and the police officials, and they do not compare notes among each other to the extent that occurs in smaller cities. It is therefore possible that in Louisville, for example, the small proportion of physicians interviewed might not have known addicts who do exist. If so, these would almost certainly be addicts who get narcotics from other physicians, since they are not known to the addicts and ex-addicts in the sample, most of whom knew each other or knew of each other. If there are many unreported addicts in Louisville who do not get admitted to Lexington, there would be two major possibilities. One would be that they get narcotics from physicians, and that for some reason the great reduction in this source, to be documented in later chapters, did not occur in Louisville. The other would be that a completely new pattern of narcotic addiction has appeared, in which users of illicit drugs do not know of each other or do not talk about each other, and in which their criminal activities to raise money are never or rarely traced back to them. These are not impossibilities, but there is no shred of evidence to suggest they are real.

Summary and Discussion

Internal evidence from the characteristics of subjects admitted to the Lexington hospital, and experience in the field with informants who named addicts, strongly suggest that in recent years—since about 1945—almost all known Kentucky addicts have been admitted, and subjects are therefore fully representative of the State's addicts in recent years. Admissions prior to 1945, however, represented only about half of the known addicts. But it is known that they were selected from younger male addicts, and older men and women were underrepresented. Since the bias in selection is known, it can be allowed for, and inferences from the sample to the State can be made with little likelihood of error.

Most of the subjects in this study had only one admission to the Lexington hospital, but those who had readmissions tended to have several, with a small minority showing so many readmissions that the mean total admissions is almost three for men and two for women. Even among the subjects who were first admitted in the first 10 years of the hospital's existence the proportion who eventually had a second admission only slightly exceeded one-half.

Readmissions indicate relapse, and those patients who are not readmitted include the abstinent, though they are not restricted to the abstinent. In this study, the percentage abstinent among subjects without a second admission is stable at 40 percent for the first 8 years after first discharge. If future followup studies find a pattern comparable to this, it may become possible to use readmission rates as an index of relapse rates, and as a criterion on which different treatment groups can be compared.

Data recorded on patients during their first admission to Lexington reliably enough to be potentially useful as predictors of posthospital outcome variables were not found to be, in fact, useful. Neither prognosis, hospital status, nor length of hospitalization was found to predict the outcome variables consistently, and subjects did not differ enough in psychiatric diagnoses to permit testing diagnosis as a predictor.

Such findings should not be interpreted as indications that the hospital treatment programs have been a failure. They do point to a need, in studies aimed at evaluating treatment programs, of specifying in advance what kinds and degrees of observable effects can reasonably be expected from successful treatment. Both the predictor variables and outcome variables need to be specified in terms of some theory about treatment and its effects. One cannot simply use variables which are at hand, like length of hospital stay, or status on admission, and assume they are meaningful parameters of treatment; similarly, one cannot take a measure like posthospital drug pattern over a long period of time, during which many variables are operating on a subject, and use it as if one expected it to be completely or largely determined by the treatment given during hospitalization.

To put such considerations into concrete terms, the subjects in this study had lived, on the average, about 42 years before their first hospitalization in Lexington. They had been addicted almost 10 years, on the average, at that time. In many cases they were then hospitalized for only a few days, and in most cases for no more than a few months. It would be unreasonable to expect that anything which could conceivably be done in so short a time would have a perceptible effect on posthospital patterns for an average of about 10 years, and in some cases up to 24 years, after discharge.

If one looks only for effects which could reasonably be expected, it is not difficult to demonstrate from case material that the hospital did help many of the subjects in this study. As one example, if patients remained even a few months the hospital normally succeeded in withdrawing narcotics and demonstrating to the patients that they could live in equal or more comfort without narcotics. The hospital could, in short, end the physical dependence on narcotics and start the patient on a period of abstinence which could last indefinitely, if other factors operated to maintain abstinence. Most patients remained abstinent at least briefly after a period of hospitalization. In 28 cases, patients remained abstinent from all drugs from the time of their discharge on first admission to death or to the time of the followup interview. In additional cases, such a period of complete abstinence to death or followup began with discharge from a readmission. It would not be justified to regard these "cures" as a result of the hospitalization alone, but it would be equally wrong not to recognize that the hospital made an essential contribution to them.

Another benefit of hospitalization is seen most clearly in the records of subjects who had several readmissions. On each admission some of these subjects were seriously ill, but were restored to good physical condition by the time of discharge. It is likely that the hospital prolonged life, sometimes by many years, for many patients. Since these extra years of life were often spent unproductively, in states of addiction or alcoholism, this benefit may not count for much on any relative scale of values. But in medicine the preservation of life is an absolute value, so by medical standards the hospital achieved much. Even from a viewpoint which would regard abstinence as the only relevant criterion, some subjects became abstinent many years after their first hospitalization, for reasons which may have had nothing to do with any treatment they received. But the hospital (together with Veterans Hospitals and State Hospitals) can claim credit for having kept the subjects alive long enough for these other reasons for abstinence to take effect.

Footnotes, Chapter 11

[1] It is true that some voluntary admissions are the result of pressure from the police or others, but voluntary admissions represent some choice on the part of the patient, while the prisoner or probationer has no choice. Committed voluntary patients appeared in a court, and technically were found guilty of a misdemeanor, but in actual fact these patients went to the court voluntarily, to arrange for pressure to keep them in the hospital when they would be tempted to leave. The 16 men in this status are therefore grouped here with the 149 voluntary patients.

[2] Committed voluntary patients have been treated differently in different sections of this chapter. In an earlier section, they were grouped with the voluntary patients because in both statuses the patient had exercised some choice in entering the hospital, in contrast to prisoners and probationers. Here the concern is with length of hospitalization, in which the committed voluntary and probationer patients resemble each other closely, while voluntary patients had much shorter, and prisoners much longer, hospitalizations.

CHAPTER 12

Urban-Rural Differences

Previous chapters have focussed on the characteristics of subjects as individuals and, with the exception of their marital histories, not on their relationships with other persons and social institutions. Even involvement in the drug subculture has so far been treated as characterizing the individual, and no description of that subculture has been given. But there have been numerous indications that social relationships were important. The practice of medicine determined the availability of narcotics for many subjects. For others, contact with addicts led to the onset of drug use and to the learning of techniques of obtaining and using drugs. In this and the following chapters the focus will shift to these considerations, to the social context within which drug use took place.

Urban-Rural Status

It will be recalled that the sampling procedure used in this study selected counties rather than individuals, and that the selection was from counties stratified on an urban-rural continuum. Further, the procedure was designed to over-represent the more rural counties. But rural counties contain towns and urban counties contain farming areas, so the distribution of subjects by counties does not necessarily represent accurately the urban-rural status of the places in which individuals lived at the time of their first admission.

Table 12.1 relates the urban-rural classification of the counties used in sample selection to the size of the community in which the subject lived at the time of his first admission to Lexington. The 1960 Census data were used to classify size of communities; changes in size over the 25-year period of admissions have not been great enough to affect the broad classifications which will be used in the following analysis.

The striking fact in the table is that even a sampling procedure which was designed to maximize the number of rural subjects identified only five as having lived on farms at the time of their first admission, and only a minority—90, or 34 percent of the sample—as having lived in a rural environment.

In 1960, 57.5 percent of the white population of Kentucky lived in rural areas, as against the 33.8 percent of the subjects admitted from such areas. Within rural areas, in 1960 only 7.5 percent of the rural residents of Kentucky lived in places of 1,000 to 2,500 population,[1] while 47.8 percent of the 90 rural subjects in the sample lived in places of that size.[2]

Table 12.1. Subjects classified by size of community (1960 data) and urban-rural classification of county of residence at time of first admission

1960 Census Classification of Community	Rural-Urban Classification of County					
	Most Rural	Rural	Less Rural	Urban	Metro-politan	Total
RURAL						
Farm	--	--	--	5	--	5
Under 1,000	12	19	4	6	1	42
1,000–2,500	25	7	7	4	--	43
URBAN						
Under 2,500	--	2	8	--	1	11
2,500–10,000	--	25	10	14	3	52
10,000–25,000	--	--	9	6	--	15
25,000–100,000	--	--	--	34	22	56
100,000–500,000	--	--	--	--	42	42
Number of subjects	37	53	38	69	69	266

The conclusion is clear; even within the most rural counties in the State those addicts who were admitted to the Lexington hospital came from towns and small cities, not from farms. Addiction in Kentucky, as in the nation, has been an urban problem.

For the following analysis of urban-rural differences, the Census classification will be used, and will be reduced to three categories, defined as follows:

1. Village: includes the three "rural" classifications of the Census—farm, places under 1,000 and 1,000–2,500.
2. Town: the next three census classifications, urban communities up to 25,000 in size.
3. City: the remaining census classifications, urban communities over 25,000 in size.

These terms are used in preference to other possibilities—e.g., rural, city, metropolitan—for two reasons. They describe this sample accurately, and they avoid the usual connotations of other terms. Ninety subjects legitimately could be called rural, and by the Census would be so designated. But it has been shown that very few rural Kentuckians live in places over 1,000 in population, while almost half of the subjects who could be called rural live in places that large. To call them villagers calls attention to the fact that few subjects were rural in the usual meaning of the word.

At the other end of the scale, most subjects from places over 25,000 in size could be called metropolitan residents, since they lived in Standard Metropolitan Statistical Areas. But even the largest cities in Kentucky do not approach the size of the giant metropolitan areas where addiction is most prevalent today, and the danger of unjustified generalizations is minimized by avoiding the word "metropolitan" for this sample.

Using "village" and "city" for the two extreme categories makes "town" an appropriate choice for the middle category. Two-thirds of the subjects in this classification lived in urban places from 2,500 to 10,000 in size.

Among men, city subjects tended to become addicted in earlier years than the others. Nineteen percent became addicted before 1920, against 7 percent of the village and 5 percent of the town subjects; 43 percent were addicted before 1930, against 25 percent of the village and 16 percent of the town subjects. These differences were reversed from 1930 to 1949, and all three showed about the same percentage in the 1950s. The pattern for the women is different; by far the largest percentage addicted before 1930 is found for the village subjects.

This finding for the men parallels and probably is largely accounted for (through differences in life expectancy) by the fact that the city subjects were much younger when they became addicted. Twenty-two percent were addicted before age 20, and 64 percent before age 30; the corresponding figures are 1 percent and 29 percent for the village, and 10 percent and 42 percent for the town subjects. The women, on the other hand, showed no association between age at addiction and urban-rural status.

A complementary pattern is found with respect to the reason for first addiction. For male subjects, 51 percent of the villagers began in the course of medical treatment, with 42 percent beginning in the treatment of alcoholism, and only 7 percent for pleasure. For town subjects the percentages are 48, 33 and 18; for city subjects 35, 34 and 31. Among the women only eight subjects began through alcoholism or for pleasure; two were town dwellers and six from cities.

For the men, therefore, a clear pattern emerges. Those who lived in villages began addiction at an older age, in more recent years, for illness or for alcoholism. The subjects from cities began much younger, in earlier years, and as many started for pleasure or for alcoholism as for illness. The town subjects fell between the other two groups on all three variables. The women resemble the men in the association between urban-rural status and reason for addiction, but not on the other two variables.

Once addiction began, table 12.2 shows that urban-rural status was associated with involvement in the drug subculture. Involvement was more likely, and much involvement more likely than only some, the larger

Table 12.2. Involvement in the drug subculture after addiction by urban-rural status as of time of first admission and by sex (percentages)

Involvement in Drug Subculture	Male			
	Village	Town	City	No. of Subjects
Much	26	40	62	91
Some	46	44	26	81
None	28	16	12	40
Total	100	100	100	
Number of subjects	76	62	74	212
	Female			
Much	--	19	25	9
Some	50	31	29	19
None	50	50	46	26
Total	100	100	100	
Number of subjects	14	16	24	54

the community in which subjects lived. This was true for women as well as for men, though to a lesser degree. It should also be noted, however, that almost three-fourths of the men in villages showed at least some involvement in the drug subculture, and that a few of the city subjects avoided all involvement.

In view of the associations between variables which have been established, one would expect that the major source of narcotics would also vary with urban-rural status, and table 12.3 shows that it does. The men from villages were more likely to receive all narcotics from one physician at a time, and were much less likely to depend on illegal sources of narcotics. This association does not hold for the women. The percentage of women whose narcotics came mostly or entirely from illegal sources is highest for those from villages. But the differences for women are not statistically significant; the table is to be interpreted as showing, for women, no association between urban-rural status and major source of narcotics.

Some of the variables treated in other chapters are also related to urban-rural status. With respect to employment, the higher-level occupa-

Table 12.3. Major source of narcotics by urban-rural status as of time of first admission and by sex (percentages)

Major Source of Narcotics	Male			
	Village	Town	City	No. of Subjects
One physician	38	19	11	45
Multiple physicians	14	15	6	22
Own supply	10	8	2	12
Medical; some illegal	11	21	17	30
Most or all illegal	27	38	65	82
Total	100	[1] 100	[1] 100	
Number of subjects	73	53	65	[2] 191
	Female			
One physician	62	56	46	28
Multiple physicians	8	6	17	6
Own supply	--	--	--	--
Medical; some illegal	--	31	12	8
Most or all illegal	31	6	25	11
Total	[1] 100	[1] 100	100	
Number of subjects	13	16	24	[2] 53

[1] Figures do not add to 100 due to rounding.
[2] Twenty-one men and one woman unknown on source.

tions were found more often in villages and towns than in cities. Of 14 physicians, for example, six practiced in villages, seven in towns, and only one in a city. The illegal and marginal occupations, on the other hand, were far more frequent among city subjects; 28 percent of men from cities, 13 percent of men from towns, and only 4 percent of men from villages were classified as having such occupations prior to addiction.

Similarly, about 21 percent of men from towns and cities had little or no legitimate employment before addiction, against 10 percent of village men. The percentage of men with a steady preaddiction employment pattern drops from village subjects to town subjects, and drops again to city subjects. But even for the village men, only 56 percent had a steady pattern before addiction.

Before addiction the differences on criminal record were not great. The men from towns showed a higher percentage with arrests than the other groups, though they were slightly exceeded by city men in the percentage with three or more arrests. The town and city subjects were equal in the percentage with sentences before addiction, and in the percentage with three or more sentences. The village subjects had fewer arrests and sentences, but not by much.

Table 12.4. Sentences after addiction, by urban-rural status as of time of first admission, male subjects (percentages)

Number of Sentences After Addiction	Village	Town	City	No. of Subjects
None	71	60	44	122
One or two	20	21	18	41
Three to five	7	14	21	29
Six or more	3	5	17	17
Total	[1] 100	100	100	
Number of subjects	76	62	[2] 71	[2] 209

[1] Figures do not add to 100 due to rounding.
[2] Three men unknown on number of sentences.

These urban-rural differences in criminality became greater after addiction. Table 12.4 shows that over half of the city men then had sentences, while most of the village and town men had none. The number of sentences also increased with the size of the community.

Finally, there was at most a slight relationship between urban-rural status and posthospital drug pattern. Among men, the city dwellers were slightly more likely to show a pattern of addiction to narcotics, and less likely to show a pattern of much or complete abstinence. The latter difference was also found for the women. It may be, therefore, that in a larger sample this difference would be statistically significant. Here the chi-square value fell short of the .05 level, though it did reach the .10 level.

The Drug Subculture in Rural Kentucky

The concept of a drug subculture is normally applied to metropolitan areas where there are hundreds or thousands of addicts. Whatever other elements may enter into the definition of a subculture, contact among its members is essential. In this study, some subjects came from areas where there were few or no other addicts, and it may be asked in what sense these had, or could have had, contact with other addicts.

Table 12.2 showed that the probability of involvement in the drug subculture was greater as the size of the community in which the subjects lived was larger. The explanation is, in large part, the obvious one; the number of addicts tended to increase with community size, and so in the larger cities there were more addicts with whom a subject could be involved. When involvement was tabulated against the total number of addicts admitted from each county, there was a clear increase in the extent of involvement as the number of addicts admitted from the county increased. But even in counties from which only one or two addicts were admitted, the majority of subjects showed at least some involvement.

Fewer than 10 percent of the sample came from counties with only one or two admissions, and for most of these involvement meant only that the subjects had had cures for addiction before their first admission to Lexington. They had met other addicts once, or a few times, for relatively brief periods. This was sufficient, however, for them to discover how addicts regard themselves and how they are regarded by others, and to define themselves as addicts. In some cases, these cures or other contacts with addicts were enough to lead to further involvement, through learning the intravenous route, new narcotics which could be used, or new sources of drugs.

In general, such isolated addicts did not show "much involvement," but it is instructive to note that they could. The possibility is also illustrated by subjects from counties with several addicts, who were not at all involved with the other local addicts, but were in regular contact with addicts or drug peddlers in other States. This pattern of involvement seems to have existed mainly for the first 10 or 20 years after the passage of the Harrison Narcotic Act. In several cases, it involved regular trips to a source of supply out of the State, and in at least one case the supplier travelled regularly through the subject's town, stopping off to sell him—and him alone, as far as the subject knew—a supply of narcotics. These subjects could score positive on enough of the seven indices to be classified as "much involved" in the drug subculture though they had infrequent contact with other addicts, and little or none with those in their communities.

At this extreme, there were six counties in which one subject was the only known addict, and these had no regular contact with other addicts. There were four or five more subjects who avoided all contact with other local addicts, but were nonetheless in contact with the drug subculture, as described in the above paragraph. At the other extreme, in one city there was a large enough number of addicts to constitute a drug subculture in the usual sense of addicts in regular contact with each other.

Most addiction fell between these extremes. Addiction was not evenly scattered over the State, but occurred in pockets, in small concentrations of addicts, for the most part in communities of a size where all addicts knew each other, and the whole town knew them as addicts. In such situations two patterns were found.

The much less frequent pattern was that the addicts did not form a group in any sense, as far as the procedures used in this study could detect. In two counties, in each of which all addicts obtained their narcotics from the same physician, each of five or six addicts had a separate relationship with the physician, and each knew of the others' addiction, but no other connection between them was found. These seem to have been the last surviving examples of what probably was, prior to 1914, a common pattern in the State.

The much more frequent pattern was that when there were a number of addicts in a community, they came to depend on each other, and may have been pushed together by the growing disapproval of drug use in the community. These subjects spent more time with each other than with any equal number of nonaddicts. They learned from each other, supplied each other with narcotics and information, teamed up in techniques for obtaining money or drugs, and to some extent shared in the nationwide argot of addiction.

Addicts in a Rural County

This latter pattern, the one that applies to most of the subjects in this study, can best be pictured by a detailed account of addiction in one county. The one used as an example here is chosen because it is rural, had a relatively large number of addicts, and because due to several unusual informants more cross-checks on information were available than for most counties.[3] Its addiction pattern was typical of other counties, up to the most urban, with the exception that the number of addicts was higher than for counties of comparable population, and with certain other differences which will be specified below.

It is one of the most rural counties in the State; in 1960 the Census classified all of its population as rural. Few Kentucky counties have a smaller population. The county seat has ranged between 1,000 and 2,000 in population for the past 30 years, and is the only community of appreciable size in the county.

Nineteen addicts, all male, were admitted to the Lexington hospital from this county between 1935 and 1959. All but one were residents of the county seat, and the exception was from a community of about 100 people. All, therefore, were classified as "villagers" in the first section of this chapter, and all came from two places which together contained, in the years of their admissions, from one-tenth to one-fifth of the county's population.

Just as the addicts were concentrated in the county seat, so were the county's physicians. Some 20 different physicians practiced there between 1906 and 1965. Up to the First World War as many as 8 or 9 were in practice at the same time, one or two in very small communities, and the rest in the county seat. After World War I all physicians had their offices in the county seat, and the number in practice at a given time dropped to four or five until about 1950; since that time the number has been two or three.[4]

There was a high prevalence of addiction in this county prior to the passage of the Harrison Act in 1914. The fathers of two subjects, and an uncle of another, were addicts. One of these was repeatedly mentioned as a morphine addict who had introduced many to drug use. Several physicians were addicts, and as in other counties this meant that they addicted others. One of the still-living subjects can remember when morphine could be and was bought freely in the country stores, though this was a few years before he himself became addicted. The same subject could remember, name and describe some 20 addicts who died shortly before or after the Lexington hospital opened, and were never treated there. These included a few who were locally prominent and successful people. That this is a generally correct picture was confirmed by other informants, including an elderly physician from a neighboring county, and by one physician who entered practice in this county in the 1930s. He knew of about twenty addicts who had been addicted by his older colleagues, named three older physicians as definitely having been addicts, and two others as probably addicts.

The 19 addicts from this county who were treated at the Lexington hospital fall into two groups. Nine became addicts between 1917 and 1932, and will be referred to as the early, or older, addicts. The other 10 became addicts between 1941 and 1952, and will be referred to as the recent addicts. There are at least 12 important differences between these two groups which require explanation.

1. Between 1917 and 1932, when onset of addiction occurred for the early addicts, it also occurred for a number of other persons in the county, who never were treated at Lexington. In this 15-year period, the number of new addicts was about one per year. But between 1932 and 1962 the 10 recent addicts seem to have been the only new addicts. The incidence of addiction had dropped to one-third of its earlier rate.

2. The nine early addicts were all classified as much involved in the drug subculture, while none of the recent 10 was so classified. The measure of involvement was based on seven indices; the nine men addicted

before 1933 could have a total of 63 positive scores, and had 44, while the 10 addicted after 1940 could have 70, and had only 22.

3. The nine early addicts had a mean age at onset of addiction of 27; the 10 recent had a mean age of 34. Part of this difference could be due to the fact that early addicts represented a selection of youthful addicts for hospitalization, but there was another factor operating. Eight of the nine early addicts were addicted by age 30 or earlier, and the ninth at age 31. Only two of the recent addicts had begun so early, at 27 and 29.

4. Among the early addicts, narcotics were first used to treat gonorrhea in two cases, and alcoholic excesses in the other seven. Six of the recent addicts first had narcotics prescribed for medical reasons—nerves, gunshot wound, "ulcers and bum blood," ulcer, rectal fistula, and asthma. One more received the drug for a medical reason, stomach trouble, but from a friend rather than a physician. In the remaining three cases onset was in treatment of alcoholic excesses. For neither group was pleasure-seeking given as a reason, but the relative importance of medical treatment and alcoholism had reversed for the two groups. Even though the prescription of narcotics for the recent group represented questionable medical judgment, there was at least some pretext of medical need more often than for the early addicts.

5. The first narcotic was supplied by physicians in 7 of the 9 early cases, and in 8 of 9 recent (one first source is unknown). This represents no change, but that there was a change in medical practice is indicated by the fact that none of the recent addicts (except possibly the unknown case) received drugs from a physician for alcoholic excesses, against five of the early cases. Physicians were no longer treating alcoholism with narcotics.

6. Of the nine early addicts, only one completed less than eight years of school. Six had 8 to 12 years of education, one was a college graduate, and one a physician. Only one appears to have been below average in intelligence with a mental age of 12.4. Of the recent addicts, five had three years or less of school, two completed the fifth grade, and three the eighth. Three were described by psychiatrists as mentally deficient or of borderline intelligence, including two of those who reached the eighth grade. Two more were described as illiterate or barely literate.

In short, the early addicts might have been expected to achieve average or superior status in the community had it not been for their alcoholism and addiction. The recent addicts were unlikely to achieve average status in the best of circumstances.

7. The early addicts also were superior in occupational achievement and social status. The man with a fifth grade education became a barber, owned his own shop, and acquired some property before addiction began. Of the six with 8 to 12 years of school, half worked at skilled labor,

clerical, or minor managerial positions. The college graduate was a teacher and the last a physician. Two married into the wealthiest families in town.

Among the recent addicts, six never worked above the unskilled labor level, and two achieved the skilled labor level for short times, as painter and construction equipment operator. The ninth had operated a poolroom and later a service station, but was back at unskilled labor before his addiction started. The tenth was a farm worker before and during his addiction, eventually owning and successfully operating a small farm after his addiction ended.

8. The older addicts had less serious criminal records prior to addiction. Only 2 of 9 had as many as two arrests before addiction, while 5 of 10 recent addicts had this many.

9. Both groups had more serious criminal records after the onset of addiction, and this increase was greater both in absolute and relative terms for the older addicts. All of the older addicts, and only five of the recent, had two or more arrests following the onset of addiction. For seven of the older addicts the number of post-addiction arrests was from three to five (and these were on serious charges, narcotics offenses or offenses against property). Of the recent addicts three had no post-addiction arrests, two had only one, and the remaining five had five or more ranging up to fairly large numbers, greater than for any of the older addicts. But almost all of these were for minor offenses, mainly drunkenness during periods when narcotics were not available. Five of the older addicts, and three of the recent, served sentences after addiction.

The increase in criminality after the onset of addiction was, therefore, greater and more significant for the older addicts than for the recent. The older group, with one or two possible exceptions, had been essentially law-abiding prior to addiction. But after addiction all were arrested and most were sentenced, mainly on narcotic charges, though four also served time for other offenses. The recent addicts, on the other hand, got in about as much trouble with the law after onset as before, and it was not much more serious after than before.

10. It was mentioned above that the recent addicts showed less involvement in the drug subculture than the older. This is reflected in the methods they used to get drugs. Of the early addicts one was a physician who used drugs he could legally order, and needed no other source. A second had used some illegal drugs early, then established a connection with a physician who was willing to dispense narcotics, learned to be satisfied with this amount, and needed no other source. The remaining seven all obtained narcotics in at least three different ways (of the 10

described in chapter 6), with the total number of methods ranging up to eight.

Among the recent addicts, however, only four got narcotics in as many as three ways, and none in more than three ways. Over the entire history of narcotics use, six of the recent ten got drugs only from legal sources, while this was true for only one of the early nine, the physician.

11. Seven of the nine older addicts had admissions to Lexington as prisoner or probationer patients, against none of the recent ten.

12. On the whole, the recent group spent far less time in addiction status than the older. The older men averaged 12 years of addiction prior to their first admission, the recent addicts only four years. The first admission to Lexington among the recent addicts was in 1945, and the second in 1948, more than 10 years after the older addicts had had their first admissions. Yet in the next 10 years they accumulated almost as many readmissions as did the older group; periods of addiction were even shorter and more frequently interrupted for the recent group.

What accounts for these differences? No rigorous answer in terms of statistical associations can be given, but a plausible and internally consistent answer can be given in terms of historical changes in the county.

When the Lexington hospital opened in 1935 the nine early addicts had been using narcotics steadily from three to 18 years, an average of 10 years. Their addiction was common knowledge, to law enforcement officers as well as to others, but only one had been charged with a narcotics offense. Yet by 1938 seven had been sent to Lexington as prisoners or probationers, and the other two were voluntary admissions in 1938 and 1942.

Before 1935, if an addict was convicted he could be sent only to prison. It was probably due to this, though the connection cannot be demonstrated, that only flagrant violations, and not all of them, were prosecuted. With the opening of the specialized hospital, and the natural hope that addicts sent there would be cured, it must have seemed a favor to the addict to prosecute and convict him. It seems reasonable that this explains, in part, why the police drive against addiction so closely followed the opening of the hospital. Up to 1935, in short, addiction was regarded as unfortunate, but nothing perceived as appropriate could be done about it; when the hospital opened, something could be done.

But this involved arrest, trial and sentence, and the usual connotations of these carried over to the addicts who were convicted. Addiction had been redefined as criminal, and it now involved serious risks of punishment. The vaguely negative attitudes of the community towards addiction crystallized, and both these attitudes and the fear of prison must have made some potential addicts think twice when they had opportunities to try narcotics.

So much is speculation, though plausible; it is more than speculation that opportunities to try narcotics were simultaneously reduced. The nine older addicts, while obtaining some narcotics from non-medical sources, had until 1935 obtained most of their supply from the physicians in the county seat, or from physicians in nearby counties who were equally free in prescribing or dispensing narcotics. Several of these physicians, including one subject, were themselves convicted on drug charges. They could no longer order and dispense narcotics, and other physicians suddenly became much less ready than before to prescribe or dispense narcotics. Other factors were also operating, and will be discussed in a later chapter on physicians, but the effect was that in the late 1930s the small group of physicians who had been responsible for creating and maintaining most of the addiction in the county were prevented from, or became fearful of, supplying narcotics.

The county was atypical in that one physician continued to dispense narcotics freely. Dr. Smith (a pseudonym) said that he himself created no addicts, but that he inherited about 20 from the older physicians in town. Once, before the Lexington hospital opened, he persuaded some of the younger men to go to a State hospital for treatment, but he accepted their quick relapses as proof that they could not get along without morphine. He professed to believe that after an addict has used narcotics for some number of years, abstinence is dangerous to life, and adhered to this belief to the extent that in one case, when the subject had been treated at Lexington and had been off narcotics for four months before discharge, he began dispensing morphine to the subject immediately after his return home. Dr. Smith stated, when interviewed, that he was "just about out of the morphine business now," but that in prior years he used to dispense 500 grains of morphine a week.

When the first nine men admitted to Lexington returned home in the late 1930s or early 1940s, most were able to get narcotics from Dr. Smith. These supplies, if inadequate to what subjects felt they needed, could still be supplemented on occasion. But except for the two to five or six grains of morphine per day supplied by Dr. Smith, and except for the addicts to whom he was willing to dispense narcotics, the old pattern of addiction in the county was dead. It was no longer possible for a man to use morphine day in and day out for years, in amounts of 10 grains a day or more.

Most of the first nine addicts were not, at least initially, satisfied with the relatively small amount of narcotics Dr. Smith was willing to dispense. They tried to supplement it by forging prescriptions, "making" other physicians, especially the elderly ones in nearby counties, and by seeking bootleg narcotics, which were available but increasingly expensive in several cities in nearby States. But now their addiction was frequently interrupted by arrests, or by voluntary hospitalizations when money gave out, when the dosage had increased to a level the addict could not maintain, or when his physical condition deteriorated as a result of malnutrition or other forms of neglect. The long-range adjustments of these early subjects fell into one of three patterns.

One is exemplified by a still living subject, who had used morphine steadily for 18 years before his first admission to Lexington in 1937, except for two brief hospitalizations. From 1937 to 1964, however, he had a total of 23 admissions to Lexington, at least 12 admissions to Veterans Administration Domiciliary Homes or Hospitals, and one prison term. His addiction was interrupted on an average of more than once a year, with many periods of institutionalization lasting for months, and some for a year or more. He spent more than half of the past 27 years in one institution or another. While he used morphine all of the time he was not in institutions, each period of use was six months or less in length, and some periods were so short he could scarcely have developed physical dependence on the drug. Two more of the first nine subjects followed a similar pattern.

Two others accepted the several grains per day the physician was willing to dispense, did not seek more from other sources, avoided trouble with the law, and had only one or two interruptions of their addiction by institutionalization. A third pattern was followed by the other four; they began using paregoric, barbiturates and alcohol as substitutes for morphine. While they still used what narcotics they could obtain, these formed a minor part of their intake.

Up to 1935 the community had regarded these addicts as weak and ineffectual but essentially harmless individuals. They were problems to themselves and their families, but not to the community as a whole. After the first wave of arrests and convictions, however, there was a marked deterioration in their adjustment, in addition to the deterioration in work and marital adjustment which had taken place after the onset of addiction but prior to first arrest. Through their efforts to obtain narcotics they became a nuisance and a threat to the physicians in practice; they stole from their families and others; they worked less regularly or not at all; and their repeated relapses to drug use after periods of treatment dashed the initial hopes of their families and others. The community attitudes toward them changed; they began to be perceived as a burden on the community as well as on their families. They were regarded as hopeless cases because of their relapses, and since abstinence from narcotics was generally regarded as requiring no more than an act of willpower, were seen as weaklings or as having chosen evil instead of good.

It is impossible to specify the sequence and causal connection of the changes. In all probability there was a spiral causation in which a number of factors reacted on each other: the availability of a treatment center; the drive to enforce the drug laws; reduced supplies of narcotics; relapses and deterioration in behavior of the addicts; and an increasingly negative attitude toward addiction in the community. However it developed, by the late 1930s the pattern of addiction for the older addicts had changed markedly from the pre-1935 pattern.

These factors would explain why the incidence of new cases of addiction dropped after 1935, and why the 10 recent addicts differed so much from the early nine. The image of the addict had changed. He was now seen as a useless or evil person, engaged in criminal activities which could lead to serious punishment. When an opportunity to try narcotics was offered, the more adequate and less delinquent were now less likely to accept it, which would account for the lower educational and occupational achievements of the recent addicts, and their higher number of preaddiction arrests.

Perhaps more important, the usual sources of narcotics had been largely blocked. Existing addicts had difficulty in obtaining the amounts of narcotics they wanted, and presumably were less ready than before to supply it to friends. Physicians were much more careful about prescribing narcotics, and would not do so at all for alcoholics. There had to be at least a reasonable pretext for drug use, which would account for both the older mean age at onset for recent addicts and the preponderance of medical reasons given for them.

The physician who prescribed the first narcotics would also be reluctant to continue prescribing when the original reason for use disappeared and it became obvious that the person was continuing drug use because of physical dependence only, or because he enjoyed the use. His refusal to continue prescribing would lead the recent addicts to seek hospitalization much more quickly after onset than had been the case for earlier addicts.

This appears to be one reason why all of the recent addicts were voluntary patients on their first admissions to Lexington, against only two of the nine early addicts. It does not seem to reflect a difference in law enforcement practices over time, a closing of eyes to narcotic offenses after the initial enforcement drive in 1935–37. There were fewer prisoner and probationer admissions in later years, but this can be explained on the basis that there was no legal offense which could be charged.

In 1935 and 1936 the early addicts were using large quantities of narcotics, buying most of the drugs from a few unethical physicians and selling part to each other. They were thereby guilty of illegal possession and sale, could be charged, and were. These unethical physicians were no longer selling, or were much more careful in their sales, when the recent group became addicted. The recent addicts committed no offense when they used drugs prescribed by a physician, and when he discontinued prescribing they could not buy illicit drugs, because these were rarely available. There was therefore no offense with which they could be charged.

One of the reasons they used fewer ways of getting drugs, then, was because fewer ways were open to them. Another reason may have been a different self-concept among recent addicts, arising from the fact that they had started use in the context of medical treatment. If they perceived themselves as patients using medicine, they would have been less likely to seek new sources when the physician terminated prescriptions. Further, the decline in number of addicts and in involvement in a drug subculture, to be discussed below, may have meant less group support for criminal drug-seeking behavior.

For this particular county, though not for the State as a whole, there is an additional explanation for the facts that recent addicts used fewer ways to get drugs, and were less likely to be sentenced on narcotics charges. They were less competent addicts than the earlier ones.

When narcotics become difficult to obtain, it requires initiative, ingenuity, skills of various kinds, and money to maintain addiction. To travel around to where narcotics can be bought takes money; to "make" physicians requires some histrionic skill, and money for travel; to forge prescriptions requires at least literacy and a little imagination. These methods were in effect closed to most of the recent addicts. They could stay on drugs while a physician was willing to supply them, and if no physician was willing, could only abstain or use substitutes.

Not only did the recent addicts have lower learning capacities than did older ones for criminal skills, but they also had fewer learning opportunities because the drug subculture had become much smaller. In the 1920s and early 1930s there were at any given time from 15 to 20 addicts in the county seat among whom interaction could, and did, take place. But in the 1940s and 1950s some of the older addicts had moved away or died, fewer new addicts were being produced, and of the active addicts at any one time several were away in a prison or a hospital. Rarely were more than two or three addicts in town and using narcotics. Interaction with other addicts was less possible than in earlier decades.

There was also less motivation to interact with other addicts. One function the subculture had served in early decades was to distribute narcotics; an addict whose usual source was temporarily blocked could buy from another. But now no other addict was likely to have an extra supply from which he would be willing to sell.

Indeed, there was now positive reason to avoid other addicts. Since there was only one possible regular source of drugs, the physician who was prescribing (or Dr. Smith, if he agreed to accept the addict as a patient when the first physician discontinued drugs), it was in the addict's interest to have his physician regard him as an individual patient receiving medication, not as one of a group seeking pleasure from narcotics. To be identified with a group of addicts could thus threaten the best source of drugs, without any compensating advantage.

This dependence on the physician can be seen in the four subjects who were still residents of the county at the time of followup. Dr. Smith was willing to dispense morphine regularly to two, and both of these continued to be addicted. He would not supply it to the other two, largely because they got drunk and annoyed him. One of these was a confirmed alcoholic, the other an alcoholic with fairly regular barbiturate use, and occasionally some narcotics from physicians in other counties.

There were four other living addicts from this county, now residents in other States. One was addicted to paregoric rather than to the original morphine. Another had been abstinent from narcotics from 13 years, with occasional alcoholic excesses. The others had been abstinent from all drugs for 10 and 14 years respectively.

Of the nine older addicts, who had had fairly long addiction histories prior to first admission, none ever achieved complete abstinence. Only two of them were still alive at time of followup, and these were the two still maintained on narcotics by Dr. Smith. Of the six recent addicts still alive, one was addicted to paregoric and three were alcoholics. Only two had shown long periods of complete abstinence up to the time of followup.

Nothing much can be inferred from such small numbers, but it may be more than coincidence that these two men were also the only two among the recent addicts who had achieved beyond the labor level, by ownership of small businesses and a farm, before addiction. It may be suggested, not as a conclusion established by these data, but as an hypothesis worth investigation, that the probability of abstinence after hospitalization is fairly high for men who have shown a period of good social adjustment before addiction and whose addiction is interrupted within a few years, but not for those who meet only one of these conditions, or neither of them.

There was agreement among all informants that the two older subjects who were still addicted were, and for years had been, the only addicts in the community. The physician who supplied their morphine still dispensed and prescribed narcotics much more freely than do most physicians; this was clear from the frequent and detailed checks which State narcotic agents made of his and pharmacy records. But it was equally clear from these checks, and possibly due to them, that Dr. Smith avoided addicting any patients, by controlling the amount prescribed, or the time period over which narcotics are prescribed, or both.

335-199—69——14

Dr. Smith was due for retirement soon, and neither of the addicts was likely to live more than another decade. Then it is likely that addiction will have disappeared from the county.

Summary

Even a sampling procedure which was planned to overrepresent rural addicts was found to have selected subjects from small towns and cities, not from farms. In Kentucky as in the nation, addiction is an urban problem, and has been urban for at least the past 40 or 50 years. But some differences of importance were associated with residence in small villages or towns rather than in larger cities.

The city dwellers began drug use at an earlier age, in earlier years, and the onset of addiction was attributed in about equal proportions to pleasure-seeking, alcoholism and the treatment of illness. In villages, at the other extreme, addiction began at an older age, in more recent years, and was attributed mainly to medical treatment, but almost equally as much to alcoholism and only negligibly to pleasure-seeking. The subjects from intermediate-size towns fell between these extremes. This pattern was clear-cut for the men, but for women urban-rural status was associated only with the initial reason for addiction.

Once addiction began, involvement in the drug subculture increased with the size of the community in which subjects lived, though some involvement characterized even the most rural subjects. For men, but not for women, obtaining narcotics from illicit sources was more frequent in the larger communities, but again was not completely absent in the smallest. The increase in criminality after addiction was greater in the larger communities. Urban-rural status was not found to predict posthospital drug pattern, though there may be a tendency for subjects from smaller communities to show more abstinence.

Somewhat more than one-quarter of the sample, but about 40 percent of all Kentuckians admitted to the Lexington hospital, were residents of Louisville and other large cities in the State. Here the number of white addicts was sufficient, up to about 1950, to make possible a drug subculture smaller than, but in most respects similar to, those that existed at the same time in the largest centers of addiction. At the other extreme, about 10 percent of the sample, and a lesser proportion of all addicts in the State, were isolated in their addiction, and could have had no frequent interaction with other addicts. Even among these, however, some had regular, infrequent interaction with one or a few addicts or suppliers of narcotics in other communities or other States.

For about two-thirds of the sample, representing slightly over half of all addicts admitted from Kentucky, the pattern was that addicts were clustered in small numbers in small towns. In each community the total number of addicts was too small for them to restrict their contacts wholly or largely to other addicts, as would be conceivable, for example, in New York or Chicago, but they did know each other, and usually developed mutually supportive relationships. The onset of addiction can often be traced from one to another, it is clear that newer addicts learned from older ones, and frequently they teamed up in illegal activities to obtain narcotics or money.

This pattern was examined in detail for one rural county, reasonably typical of the State as a whole. Addiction was prevalent there before and for some 20 years after the passage of the Harrison Act, with new addicts being recruited by old ones or being produced through highly questionable administration of narcotics by physicians, several of whom were addicts themselves. One of the major routes to addiction was through the administration of morphine in the treatment of alcoholic excesses. Addiction could be maintained steadily for years, at high dosages, with some morphine available fairly cheaply through illegal channels, but most of it supplied even more cheaply by physicians.

In the late 1930s this pattern was abruptly broken by the almost simultaneous prosecution of most of the then active addicts, and of several of the physicians who had supplied them with narcotics. After this, most of the continuing addiction in the county was maintained by one physician. New cases of addiction were produced at perhaps one-third of the old rate, and now were attributable to medical reasons much more often than before. Alcoholism continued to lead to addiction, but less frequently, and now it was no longer through treatment of alcoholic excesses by physicians, but the treatment by addict friends. Addiction was interrupted more frequently than in earlier decades, rarely reached high dosage levels, and in many cases addicts were forced to shift from morphine to paregoric. They also shifted to barbiturates and alcohol, and eventually most of them were no longer narcotic addicts, but alcoholics who might or might not also use paregoric when it was available, and who were likely to use more barbiturates than narcotics.

Of those men who had had a long run on morphine before their addiction was interrupted, none ever achieved a completely abstinent status. Of the more recent addicts, whose addiction was interrupted within a few years after onset, those two men who had shown some capacity for success before addiction, by achieving ownership of a farm and a small business respectively, were the only two who became completely abstinent. The others were alcoholics who also used what paregoric and barbiturates they could obtain.

From such facts one can advance plausible hypotheses about individual characteristics of addicts which may be predictive of later relapse or abstinence. But the major impression derived from a study of addiction in this county was that the later course of the natural history of addiction depended less on individual characteristics of addicts than on whether or not one physician was willing to supply them with narcotics.

Footnotes, Chapter 12

[1] This and the other comparative figures in the discussion are based on *U.S. Census of Population,* 1960, PC(1)–19B, Table 14.

[2] The difference may be somewhat less. On a few subjects, the only fact available was the address given on first admission, and sometimes this was only the name of a small town. It is possible, therefore, that these subjects lived on farms outside the community. For the large majority of subjects, however, the address was clearly within the city limits, or within the densely populated fringe.

[3] Thirty-four individuals were interviewed, in relation to subjects from this county, during the follow-up period. These included the eight subjects from the county who were still alive, six widows or ex-wives, twelve parents, siblings or children, four law enforcement officials (one also counted as a relative of a subject), four physicians, and a subject from another county. One of the living subjects supplied varying amounts of information on 17 others, and other subjects on up to 8 others. The law enforcement informants supplied information on up to fifteen subjects, and one physician on fourteen of them. There was an average of 5.5 informants per case during the follow-up period alone. In addition, information was available from the Lexington hospital records and the other record sources discussed in Chapter 1. While the focus in interviews and records was on information about each subject as an individual, the extent of overlap is such that some inferences can safely be made about addiction in the county as a whole, and about the relationships of the subjects with each other.

[4] Based on the first (1906) through twenty-third (1965) editions of the *American Medical Directory.*

CHAPTER 13

Availability of Narcotics

Previous chapters found that a number of variables were associated with posthospital relapse and abstinence. Abstinence from narcotics was found to be more frequent among women and among those who had less involvement in the drug subculture; had fewer prison sentences; were employed in health professions; or had steady employment patterns before addiction. But these associations, while statistically significant, were not strong. Neither separately nor in combination, as far as combinations can be tested within a sample of this size, do they furnish practically useful predictors of abstinence.

On the other hand, no associations were found between abstinence and a number of other variables which, on various theoretical grounds or on the basis of clinical impressions, might have been expected to predict abstinence. Examples of such variables are: age at onset of addiction; year of addiction; reason for addiction; major source of narcotics; urban-rural status; and such facts about the first admission to Lexington as hospital status, length of hospitalization and the prognosis recorded by psychiatrists.

Such variables refer mainly to characteristics of the subjects as individuals, or to facts about their histories as individuals. It is the thesis of the present chapter that these variables had weak or no associations with abstinence because one factor was of such overriding importance in producing abstinence that other variables had little chance to show an effect. The major factor was the availability of narcotics. Overstating the conclusion to some extent, most subjects would have continued to be addicted if narcotics had been available to them. They quit the use of narcotics only when they could no longer obtain narcotics, whatever their personal characteristics were. Once they had quit its use, these personal characteristics do explain to some extent why some became addicted to substitutes, and others became and remained completely abstinent.

One aim of this chapter, therefore, is to present evidence that decreasing availability of narcotics largely explains the abstinence found in this sample. Much of this evidence also supports the conclusion mentioned in previous chapters, and discussed in detail in chapter 15, that there has been a decrease in the incidence and prevalence of narcotic addiction in Kentucky over the past three or four decades, and that this decrease is attributable, in large part, to the decrease in availability of narcotics.

Table 13.1. Reasons given for abstinence from narcotics, between last discharge and interview or death, by sex and survival status of subjects

	Male			Female			Total
	Living	Dead	Total	Living	Dead	Total	
Number of Subjects	88	124	212	34	20	54	266
Number with no known abstinence	20	70	90	5	12	17	107
Number with abstinence, no reason given	7	27	34	3	1	4	38
Number with reasons given	61	27	88	26	7	33	121
REASONS							
Narcotics not available	25	19	44	13	5	18	62
Money not available	5	1	6	3	--	3	9
Will power	39	8	47	12	--	12	59
Responsibility to family	8	--	8	3	--	3	11
Recognition of losing control	2	--	2	1	--	1	3
Disappearance of medical need	8	1	9	7	2	9	18
Absence of addict associates	11	1	12	3	--	3	15
Effect of hospital	5	5	10	5	--	5	15
Supportive therapy	6	--	6	4	--	4	10
Other	11	2	13	4	--	4	17
Total Reasons Given	120	37	157	55	7	62	219

"*Reasons*" *Given For Abstinence*

Table 13.1 reports the reasons given for abstinence from narcotics, by subjects and other informants, for those cases in which there was a period of abstinence.[1] The reasons do not form a logically constructed or mutually exclusive set, but adhere as closely as possible to the words used by informants. Most of them are self-explanatory, but explanations may be needed for two. "Effect of hospital" means, in one or two cases, that the subject attributed his abstinence to the fact that the hospital withdrew him from narcotics, and he never resumed their use. In all other cases it refers to a feeling that he learned something at the hospital which made him decide not to use drugs again. Most of these were subjects who had had little or no previous contact with addicts, saw many at the hospital, and decided they did not want to be like this group of people.

"Supportive Therapy" does not refer to formal psychiatric treatment, which none of these subjects received after their treatment in

Lexington, but to any clearly supportive relationship, usually with physicians but occasionally with friends or employers, which existed after hospitalization and which the subjects saw as having helped them achieve or maintain abstinence.

The reasons fall into two groups, which are separated in the table. The first two reasons, that narcotics were not available or that money to buy narcotics was not available, indicate that abstinence was attributed to factors beyond the subject's control. All other reasons attribute it, in whole or in large part, to an act of choice by the subject. All of the second group might be subsumed under "will power," but some of the specific reasons are more persuasive and more revealing.

It would be unwarranted to accept these reasons as the "real" reasons for abstinence, or the figures in the table as indicating the relative importance of the reasons. There is, indeed, internal evidence in the table of selective perception of factors which might explain abstinence. For example, the reasons given for living subjects include reasons given by subjects themselves, and these assign one of the will power reasons about three times as often as one of the availability reasons. Subjects, in short, tended to claim some credit for their abstinence. The reasons given for dead subjects, on the other hand, are necessarily reasons given by informants other than the subjects, mainly by relatives and physicians. Their more objective or more jaundiced eyes saw unavailability of narcotics as the reason for abstinence more often than they credited subjects with an act of will.

But, whatever its relative importance, the table makes clear that unavailability of narcotics was perceived as an important explanation of abstinence. One or more reasons were given for 121 subjects. In 62 cases, almost exactly half, unavailability of narcotics was given as one reason. For another nine subjects (with an overlap of three subjects for whom both reasons were given) lack of money to buy narcotics was given as a reason for abstinence. Even when one looks only at the reasons given for living subjects, unavailability of narcotics or of money was mentioned for almost half of the men and over half of the women. There is no apparent reason why subjects should disclaim credit for what might be regarded as a laudable achievement unless they felt no praise was due them. There is, on the other hand, some reason to believe that many people would claim credit for abstinence even when it had been forced on them, and it will be seen below that there are specific reasons to conclude that this happened in individual cases.

Table 13.1 may therefore be interpreted as showing that subjects themselves, and other informants even more frequently, perceived the unavailability of narcotics to be a major reason for the abstinence found in this study. The proportion of cases in which it was the major reason is a matter of guesswork, but one-half is more likely than not to be an underestimate. The first evidence, then, that unavailability of narcotics was a major cause of abstinence is the fact that the people who were in the best position to weigh causes said that it was an important one.

Credibility of Informants

The second major basis for accepting unavailability as a major cause is the plausibility of the detailed statements which are coded as "narcotics not available." Lack of availability may have been, in a few cases, only a rationalization, a generalization offered when no other reason was apparent, reflecting the belief (a common one among both subjects and other informants) that an addict will continue to use narcotics if he can get them, so that abstinence must indicate he could not get them. But such cases are few. The explanations were usually offered in enough detail, and the details rang so true, that project staff felt they must be literally correct in most cases.

The most frequent explanation of how narcotics became unavailable was that the physician who had supplied narcotics to the subject became unable or unwilling to continue.

> One subject (Case 050), according to his own story, and that independently given by his wife, was abstinent from 1955, after his eighth discharge from Lexington, to 1963, with the exception of one 4-month period when he was using cough syrups regularly. The wife credited their physician for this abstinence. The physician confirmed the story, and explained that the subject's father, who was a physician and an addict himself, had addicted both his wife and his son, the subject. After the father died, another physican continued to prescribe for the subject's mother, and the subject used some of the mother's narcotics, plus what he could occasionally get from other sources. This physician left town about 1955, leaving only one physican, the informant, in practice. The latter then simply refused to give the subject any narcotics, and took steps to see that he could not get them from his mother, telling the subject that if he wanted to stay on narcotics he would have to leave town, because he was not going to get any there.

> One woman (Case 242) had had morphine prescribed for about 5 years by an old physician, but in 1948 an investigation by the narcotics agents led to his losing his narcotics license, and to her hospitalization. When she returned home she went to a new physician, who knew her history, and who refused to prescribe or administer narcotics, except once, after a gall-bladder operation. The account was verified by her husband and the physician.

Many more examples could be cited, but the subject of physicians as a source of narcotics is important enough to deserve detailed discussion, which will be given in the next chapter.

Another group of cases have in common the cessation of drug use when the subject became physically unable to seek narcotics, and the previously ineffective efforts of his family to prevent him from obtaining drugs became effective.

One man (Case 035) had used narcotics from about 1907 to 1949, obtaining them first from a drugstore he owned and later from physicians. His widow thought he might have used some for about a year after his discharge from Lexington, getting them from physicians, but was sure he used none from 1950 to his death in 1961. In 1949 he began to lose his sight, and by 1950 he could not leave the house without her. He could not go to physicians, and she would not get narcotics for him. This account was confirmed by the subject's son, and by a physician.

Another subject (Case 177), according to his son, was abstinent in the latter years of his life because, due to arthritis, he was bedridden. All medications were controlled by his family, and they could make sure that no narcotics were used.

Another (Case 183), a physician who first used narcotics from his own supply and later obtained them from other physicians, was taken to Lexington when these physicians refused to continue prescribing. He was then 65, senile, and restricted to a wheel chair. His widow stated that he was abstinent from his discharge to his death. His daughter confirmed this story, adding that if he could have obtained narcotics he would have used them, because his last words were a request for morphine.

Another subject (Case 193) claimed abstinence for 10 years up to the time of followup, attributing it to an exercise of will power. His wife, however, stated that he still begged for drugs constantly. For the first 5 of these 10 years he had been a travelling salesman, and would visit physicians in the towns he passed through to get prescriptions, succeeding to some extent despite her practice of writing to all of these physicians, explaining that he was under medical care and they should not prescribe narcotics. For the last 5 years, however, he was confined to a wheel chair in his home, and during that time she kept him completely abstinent until the last 6 months, during which the family physician prescribed occasional narcotics for him. This was confirmed in detail by the physician.

There were also cases in which abstinence was attributed to the disappearance of illegal supplies of narcotics. Indeed, among those subjects whose major source of narcotics had been the illicit market, there was general agreement that illicit narcotics have disappeared from Kentucky, except the occasional drugs stolen from drugstores.[2]

One subject (Case 170) used narcotics steadily from 1925 to 1945, several years after his one hospitalization in Lexington. He quit in 1945 because his supplier, who regularly came to his county from New York City *via* Cincinnati, was incarcerated, and his supply was cut off.

In the final group of cases, there is a combination of what subjects described as will power and unavailability of narcotics. This was found especially among subjects with a history of alcoholism.

> One subject (Case 078), who had not used narcotics for 12 years, but was almost continually drunk during that time, explains his abstinence as follows: "More or less, it's will power. An addict devotes his entire life just to get more, and the more he gets, the more he takes. Anyone with any sense realizes that, and if he finally gets off, he quits. You go a day or two with it, then a day or two sick. It's not worth your time, your effort, what you have to go through to get it."

> Another subject (Case 076) originally used morphine to sober up after drunks, and in recent years has again been alcoholic, after quitting narcotics. "I didn't quit because I felt like I couldn't get it, I mean I hadn't come to that point, although I had it in mind that the time would come. I had been short several times and seen how I felt, how I had to go to substitutes, so I just—actually, I started back to the hospital." When he gets drunk now he does not seek narcotics to sober up because "I just set my foot down against it, it would be too much trouble to obtain the stuff. In other words, I can get over a drunk before I can get the narcotics. I don't even try, I don't even think of it . . . The only thing that worried me when I was on narcotics is if you had a wheelbarrow full, you wouldn't have enough, so even with money, you get to the point where you can't get it."

There are a few analogous cases in which subjects deliberately placed themselves in situations where narcotics would not be available to them.

> One woman subject (Case 020) and her husband (not an addict) had been entertainers, and fairly successful ones, travelling through metropolitan areas of the midwest where she could get narcotics to maintain her addiction. When she decided to quit using narcotics they left this work and moved back to a farm in Kentucky. Later they left this for an even more isolated farm, because there had been occasional visits from addicts she had met in Lexington, and they wanted to avoid these.

Other subjects achieved this end by telling their physicians of their history of addiction, and asking the physicians not to prescribe narcotics unless absolutely necessary. One subject even took the extreme, but successful, step of telling his physician that he was not to be given narcotics for any reason whatsoever. If the physician ever did give him a shot, he would shoot the physician.

Agreement Among Informants

There was universal agreement among informants that there is now less addiction, and that it is now much more difficult to obtain narcotics in Kentucky, than was the case 20 or 30 years ago. This statement applies not only to informants who gave unavailability of narcotics as a reason for abstinence in some specific case; the same change was noted by those who assigned their own abstinence, or that of some specific subject, to other reasons. It was also noted by those subjects who were themselves addicted when interviewed, and by informants on subjects who had been addicted until death. When subjects had shifted to barbiturates or alcohol they sometimes pictured this as a choice (narcotics involved too much trouble) but more commonly explained that the barbiturates or alcohol were a substitute when narcotics became too difficult to obtain. Their relatives, without exception, chose the latter explanation.

The police, narcotics agents and physicians who were interviewed also were unanimous in saying that there were fewer addicts today, and that it was more difficult for an addict to maintain his habit.

This unanimity among informants with respect to narcotics was in sharp contrast with their views on the extent and seriousness of problems of abuse of barbiturates, amphetamines and tranquilizers. Some knew of few cases and believed that concern about these problems was unwarranted, while others perceived them as extremely serious problems. It is this diversity of opinion on analagous problems which makes their agreement on narcotic addiction impressive.

Evidence From Currently Addicted Subjects

The evidence for a decrease in availability of narcotics in the first sections of this chapter is based on the experience of those subjects who did have a period of abstinence from narcotics. The third section reports that this decrease was confirmed also in the cases of those who continued to use narcotics. But if it is true that the latter subjects had increasing difficulty in obtaining narcotics, it should be possible to present some statistical evidence of this.

One group in which some indications should be found is that of the 21 subjects who were classified as currently addicted to narcotics in the followup study. Three of these cases cannot be used; two denied or minimized their drug use, and one user of cough syrup could not estimate how much he used. The others reported on the amount of narcotics they were using, and this amount was confirmed in most cases by the physician who was prescribing. It is therefore possible to compare their addiction in the early 1960s with their earlier addiction histories; the points of comparison are the drug used, and the average daily dosage.

At first admission, one was using meperidine, one methadon and all of the others morphine. When located, 12 of the 18 were using these three drugs, while two used paregoric, two codeine, one cough syrups containing codeine or dihydrocodeinone, and one laudanum. Six of the 18, in short, had shifted to narcotics less potent than those they originally used. This change is all the more striking if one recalls that 15 of these subjects were obtaining their narcotics by prescription, and these include all of the cases of morphine and meperidine use. The three who did not have a physician as their source of narcotics were all using the less powerful exempt narcotic preparations.

Translating the dosages of other drugs into their equivalent in morphine, at time of first admission these 18 subjects were using from 2 to 25 grains of morphine per day, with a mean of 7.9 grains per day. When interviewed, the range was from 1 to 12 grains per day, and the mean 4.0 grains. Four were using the same dosage as at first admission, two were using a higher dosage, and 12 were using smaller dosages. These facts might be explained as due to increasing age or other factors which made subjects satisfied with a lower dosage than at the time of their first admission, and satisfied with less powerful narcotics. This alternative can be ruled out. The only sense in which some were satisfied was that they had accepted as a fact that they could not get larger quantities. Several contrasted the present dosage with their old habits somewhat wistfully; what they get now keeps them going, while the dosage of decades ago had been something enjoyable.

> One subject (Case 033) has been receiving two grains of morphine per day in recent years, and has been described in a previous chapter as making a better social adjustment during those years than ever before in his life. When asked about his present dosage (already confirmed by his physician to be two grains a day) he said it was two grains; then he remarked he understood it had been scientifically established that two and a half grains per day was the correct dosage for an old addict.

Another subject, an addict for over 40 years, was using cough syrup regularly, and morphine on infrequent occasions "if I can get it and if I have money for it."

Evidence From Multiple Admissions

Another group of subjects on whom the hypothesized decrease in availability can be tested is that with multiple admissions to Lexington. Not only can the drug and dosage be compared from early to late admissions, but these subjects can also be compared on the number of days required for withdrawal from narcotics, an objective and fairly direct measure of the degree of physical dependence on narcotics which was shown on each admission.

Twenty-seven men had six or more admissions to Lexington. It was planned to compare the data from their first and second admissions with data from the last and next-to-last, but the first 10 cases showed such a clear pattern that it was not necessary to go further.

> A typical subject (Case 029) had seven admissions, the first in 1942 and the most recent in 1958. On his first admission, he was using six to seven grains of morphine daily, by the IV route, and 10 days were required for withdrawal. On his second, it was five grains of morphine,

still IV, and 5 days of withdrawal. On the sixth admission he was drinking four ounces of paregoric daily, with some use of barbiturates, and it was not necessary to give him any narcotics on withdrawal. On the seventh admission he was drinking four ounces of paregoric, was also using barbiturates and alcohol, and withdrawal required three days.

All ten subjects used morphine, plus heroin in one case, on their first two admissions. On the next-to-last admissions, one used only paregoric and one only alcohol. The other eight still used morphine, but in seven cases in combination with barbiturates and/or alcohol, or with other narcotics, mostly paregoric. Their pattern of use is summed up by one subject, who said he used morphine and anything he could get when morphine was not available. On the last admissions, five still used morphine, but all five supplemented it with other drugs. Four used only paregoric, and one only alcohol.

Comparison on average daily dosage cannot be made for one case, because data on the early admissions are missing. All of the other nine had clearly smaller dosages on the last two admissions than on the first two.

In two cases, data for comparison on the time required for withdrawal of narcotics are not available. In seven, the withdrawal time for the last two admissions is clearly less than for the first two. In the tenth case, the withdrawal period on the last admission is shorter, and on the next-to-last longer, than on the first two admissions.

There has been a tendency toward a shorter withdrawal period in the hospital in recent years. But this decrease is small, compared to that described above. Hospital staff responsible for withdrawal account for the decrease by the smaller habits which patients have had in recent years. It would be desirable to compare average length of withdrawal over time, for groups equated on average daily dosage at admission, on age, on general physical condition and other factors which would affect the speed of withdrawal. Such comparisons were not possible within this sample, not because of its small number, but because few subjects admitted in recent years reported dosages as high as those which were common in the early years of the hospital.

Alternative explanations of the findings therefore cannot be completely ruled out. But it remains true that in two groups of subjects, those who were currently addicted and those with multiple admissions, there are clear indications of less drug use in recent years, in that the average daily dose is less, many have shifted to less potent narcotics, and the average time required for withdrawal from narcotics is less. Further, the only explanation for these facts given by subjects themselves is that narcotics have become more difficult to obtain.

The Concept of Availability

While each of the above sets of facts falls short of proving it beyond doubt, because of alternative explanations which cannot be ruled out, the improbability of these alternatives and the consistent direction in which the facts point seem to the writer to justify the conclusion that narcotics have become less available in Kentucky, and that this decrease in availability explains some large part of the abstinence found in this study. If this conclusion is accepted, it is one of the major findings of the study. But other findings require that the concept of availability be clarified.

The importance of availability of narcotics in the onset and continuation of addiction has long been recognized in the literature. The concept has been used, for example, to explain why addiction rates are higher in two markedly diverse groups, among persons from the most underprivileged districts of metropolitan areas, and second among physicians and other health professionals. The former have narcotics available because the underworld, including the illicit heroin traffic, is closely associated with slum districts. The latter have narcotics available because they use them professionally. The implication is that other persons, in middle or upper-class areas, and in other occupations, are much less likely to have access to narcotics, and therefore are much less likely to use them. Another implication is that in any group of people some proportion are potential addicts, and once drugs become available, or to the extent that they become available, the potential addicts begin to use them.

These implications are plausible, and probably correct. But they present availability as something to be predicated on the drug alone, and the user as a passive recipient of the drug. An essential fact about the addict is that his is an active role. He does something to get his drug, even if the act be as simple as a physician's reaching into a cabinet. There is always some element of drug-seeking behavior on the part of those consumers of narcotics who are labelled addicts. The findings of this study suggest that all factors which determine individual behavior must be considered in the concept of availability. The concept does not apply to the drug alone, nor to the situation alone, but to both of these and to the characteristics of the potential user in what can be a complex interaction.

This can be exemplified by considering the methods by which subjects did and did not obtain narcotics. If availability refers only to the drug, or to the situation of the potential addict, narcotics can be said to be available in almost every town in Kentucky, in the United States, and indeed almost everywhere in the world. Wherever a physician is in practice, or a drugstore exists, there are narcotics. If one knows how to break into the store, or into a doctor's office, he can obtain narcotics. A successful career of burglary requires some skills, which are probably best learned from professional thieves, but single attempts at burglary can be conceived and carried out by almost anyone. Several cases in this study show that some addicts were able to see the possibility, and commit the burglary, even though it might have led to quick detection. Others were able to do it repeatedly, and to avoid detection in most of their offenses. But most subjects never attempted to burglarize drugstores or physicians' offices, even when they were using substitutes because morphine was "not available."

Similarly, forged prescriptions require some skills, but they can be acquired without formal teaching by a fair number of addicts. This method requires a close observation of the manner in which prescriptions are written, and stealing a pad of prescription blanks, which almost anyone could do in a physician's office, if the physician's attention was distracted for a few moments. Ability to imitate the physician's handwriting is not necessary, unless the prescription must be "cashed" in pharmacies where it is likely to be recognized. Besides these skills, certain personal attitudes and other qualities like coolness and self-confidence may be needed to take the prescription to a pharmacist, but these qualities are not rare. Yet only a small minority ever used this method of obtaining narcotics.

If such approaches are beyond him, the addict has other alternatives. He can try "making" doctors. The successful simulation of an illness for which narcotics would be indicated calls for qualifications as an actor which may be infrequent. But the methods of simply asking for narcotics because one is addicted and needs the drug, or begging for it, or making one's self so obnoxious in a crowded office that the physician may write a prescription just to get rid of the addict, have worked for some addicts, and would not be beyond anyone's capacity. Yet only about one-third of subjects used these methods.

During the years when narcotics became less available in Kentucky, they continued to be available in cities like New York, Chicago and Los Angeles. This fact was presumably known to all subjects. A few had lived for some years in such cities, and had used illicit drugs there. A few more had travelled widely, and knew from their own experience that heroin could be bought in these cities. The other subjects could scarcely have avoided the knowledge, either from the mass media or from their own observations and conversations when they were patients in the Lexington hospital. Why did they not move to these cities when narcotics were hard to obtain in Kentucky? Some did move to these cities; was the search for narcotics their reason?

If subjects had moved to the metropolitan centers of addiction in order to obtain narcotics, there is little doubt they would have been successful. In general, subjects who left Kentucky tended to be those

Table 13.2. Posthospital drug pattern by sex and by residence in or out of Kentucky at death or time located

Posthospital Drug Pattern	Male		Female	
	In Kentucky	Out of Kentucky	In Kentucky	Out of Kentucky
Addicted, Narcotics----------percent--	35	21	29	15
Addicted, Substitutes---------percent--	21	27	3	--
Some Abstinence------------percent--	25	34	13	54
Much Abstinence------------percent--	10	7	24	31
Complete Abstinence---------percent--	8	10	32	--
Total---------------percent--	100 [1]	100 [1]	100 [1]	100
Number of Subjects-----------------	154 [2]	41 [2]	38 [2]	13

[1] Figures do not total to 100 due to rounding.
[2] Subjects who had no post-hospital time, or who are unknown on post-hospital drug pattern, are not included.

who began drug use for pleasure, who had more arrests before and after addiction, and who were more involved in the drug subculture. Their aptitude in obtaining narcotics, and their readiness to use illicit means to obtain illicit drugs, had been demonstrated.

One would therefore expect that their posthospital drug pattern would be one of addiction to narcotics more often than for those who remained in Kentucky. But table 13.2 shows the reverse. Among both men and women, those who were living out of the State showed less addiction than those who remained. The differences are close to statistical significance, but in the direction opposite to that predicted by the hypothesis that they moved to get drugs.

Any prediction from residence to current addiction status, for those subjects still alive, would be less persuasive, because the prediction would be for a specific point in time, and accidental factors could cause current status to differ from the overall pattern of drug use. For what it is worth, however, table 13.3 shows that findings on current addiction status for living men closely parallel the findings on posthospital pattern for all men. This is not true of the women, but the number of women living out of the State is so small that no inference is justified.

There is, therefore, no statistical support for the hypothesis that subjects left Kentucky in order to go to places where narcotics would be available. There is also no support for this hypothesis in the interview material on the 30 living subjects now residing out of Kentucky, even when the move was to cities where illicit markets in heroin have existed

Table 13.3. Current addiction status of living subjects, by sex and by residence in or out of Kentucky at time located

	Male		Female	
	In Kentucky	Out of Kentucky	In Kentucky	Out of Kentucky
In institutions----------------percent--	14	18	--	12
Addicted, Narcotics----------percent--	20	9	15	25
Addicted, Barbiturates or alcohol percent--	20	32	4	--
Occasional Use--------------percent--	12	18	4	--
Abstinent-------------------percent--	34	23	77	63
Total-------------------percent--	100	100	100	100
Number of Subjects------------------	65 [1]	22 [1]	26	8

[1] Three subjects were not interviewed. Two were known to be living out of Kentucky, and could be classified on addiction status (both alcoholics), so these are included. It is only an assumption that the third was alive, and neither his address nor current addiction status are known, so he is omitted.

throughout the followup period. Three claimed to have moved away from Kentucky specifically to get away from narcotics. Of these, one has been an alcoholic ever since the move, one has used both alcohol and paregoric, and one has been completely abstinent. Four more stated they moved away for other reasons, but attributed their abstinence from narcotics to the fact that they were away from the sources of narcotics and the addicts they had known. But in general, the move away from Kentucky seemed to be motivated not by any seeking or avoiding of narcotics, but by other goals. The major one was better employment possibilities, for the men, and this or marriage for the women.

Several subjects who were still Kentucky residents also attributed their abstinence to moving away from their community—either within or outside of Kentucky—for a few years, after which they could return and remain abstinent. Among the subjects living in Kentucky who were found to be addicted, and who had been addicted most of their post-hospital time, those who claimed periods of abstinence often dated these to a time when they had moved away from home.

It is possible that a few subjects went to metropolitan areas so that they could continue to use drugs. These few were all among the deceased, and therefore among those who could not discuss why they had moved. As an example, one woman had obtained her narcotics from the physician whose employee and mistress she was, and left Kentucky when he was sent to prison. She went to Detroit where, up until recently, it was

335-199—69——15

easy to buy large quantities of exempt narcotics. She remained addicted to paregoric in Detroit until her death. These facts permit the interpretation that she moved there in order to obtain paregoric, but fall far short of proving it.

A more usual pattern is exemplified by a man who, when he decided to quit drug use, decided to go to another city to kick his habit. He chose Los Angeles because he had visited that city and thought he would like living there. He succeeded in abstaining from narcotics, but has been an alcoholic since the move. An especially suggestive pattern appears in another case history.

> This man (Case 034) became addicted in 1932, when morphine was administered after he suffered an injury. He continued using narcotics until his first admission to Lexington in 1947, obtaining the drug sometimes from other addicts, but mainly by making doctors. He had seven admissions to Lexington in 1947–1950. Then it was eleven years before his eighth admission.
>
> For eighteen years, up to 1950, he had been living in Kentucky, and with the exception of one 2-year period of abstinence and his periods of hospitalization had been addicted. Then a manufacturing company in Detroit sent recruiters to his community in Kentucky, and offered him a job. He went to Lexington, on his seventh admission, remained in the hospital 2 weeks for withdrawal to be completed, and left immediately for Detroit where he remained for the next nine years. During these years he worked fairly steadily, despite alcoholism and the illnesses and hospitalizations it led to, and did not use any narcotics, except once.
>
> This exception occurred several years after he had gone to Detroit. One day he happened to meet on the street an addict he had met in the Lexington hospital.
>
> "He asked me, he said 'how are you doing?' I said, 'I'm as clean as a whistle, and I'm going to stay that way.' He said 'that's good.' He said 'where do you live?' I said 'right down here.' I said 'where do you live?' He said 'on the west side.' Well, I was living on the east side. I said 'look, I come up here to get away from it, and I don't want anything to do with it.' He said, 'well, I don't blame you for that. I'm not pushing it, I just thought if you was hooked or wanted a bang, I could fix you.' I don't know whether he was pushing it or not, but anyway, I say 'well, I'm through with it.'
>
> "He said, 'I never come out in this neighborhood, hardly ever, I just come out here to see a friend.' Well . . . he went on and started up the street. I started down the street and I walked about ten steps, and I hollered at him, I said 'come on down to the room.' He has some pills, he gave me half a grain . . ."
>
> After this single shot, he did not happen to meet this addict friend again, and made no effort to locate him or others. He continued to work and drink, until years later layoffs at work and illness made him decide to return home. There he immediately met old addict friends, relapsed, and continued to be addicted until his death, with two more admissions to the Lexington hospital.

When narcotics became more difficult to obtain in Kentucky, then, very few moved to other places because narcotics could be obtained there. Similarly, most did not resort to other methods of obtaining narcotics which were feasible, like drugstore burglaries, forging prescriptions, or "making" doctors. Such facts do not fit the stereotype of the addict as one who is so dependent on the drug, so totally committed to obtaining it, that he "will do anything" to get it. Rather, the impression which emerges from observing the actual behavior of addicts is that there are many ways of obtaining narcotics, some of which are acceptable to all or to most addicts, while others are acceptable to and used by only a few.

If the frequency with which ways of obtaining narcotics are known to have been used by this sample is taken as a crude index of the general acceptability of these ways, it appears that most—probably all—would use narcotics prescribed by a physician. Many, but probably not all, would buy from peddlers. Many, but certainly not all, would go from physician to physician to see if they could get prescriptions; and among these most would base their request on the fact of their addiction, some would fake or claim an illness, and only a few would beg and threaten the physician for drugs. Only a minority would resort to drugstore break-ins or to forging prescriptions. It seems that, for this sample, an even smaller minority go to the trouble of moving to where narcotics would be available. At any level down this ladder of preferred methods, if the more preferred methods are blocked, some addicts use the less preferred, but some shift to substitutes for narcotics or become abstinent.

Sometimes this refusal to use methods lower on the ladder of preference was attributed to pride. Several in this study, for example, specifically stated they would never try begging for narcotics, though they knew other addicts who successfully obtained narcotics in this way. This was beneath them. Similarly, it has been relatively easy in most places, at least until very recent years, to obtain appreciable amounts of paregoric or cough syrups, by visiting enough drugstores. Some addicts do this, and maintain small but real habits. Others have never done it, and look down on those who do. For such persons, "availability" of narcotics clearly is related to self-concepts, to norms which specify what may be done and what may not. For them, narcotics were made unavailable, in the last analysis, by something within them, not by external forces.

The reasons why most subjects have never tried forgery or burglary to obtain narcotics may be identical with those which explain why most non-addicts do not use these or similar methods to obtain the things they desire. Some said it was because they considered it illegal, or wrong. Others, including some who had used these methods in the past, said they stopped because they were likely to be caught, and feared punishment. Several subjects referred to not daring to risk another sentence because, due to their long records, under present law it would have been a long sentence, in effect a life sentence. There seems to be no reason why such explanations should not be accepted as operating in some cases.

Another factor seemed to be operating in a large number of cases, and was clearly spelled out in a few. This was the recognition that most illegal methods were likely to be successful only for a short time, and eventually would be detected and punished. The addiction that could be so maintained, in short, would be fraught with constant anxiety, subject to frequent interruptions and failures, each producing the distress of withdrawal symptoms, and probably would be brief at best. In the face of these probabilities, many subjects in effect, and a few in specific words, decided "it's not worth it," and either shifted to substitutes or became completely abstinent.

The stereotype of the addict as valuing narcotics above everything else, in other words, is incorrect for many addicts and probably is accurate for very few. The findings are not consistent with an assumption that the addict's psychic economy is dominated by an obsession to obtain narcotics by any possible means. Rather, they indicate that the addict is much like other men, that what he wants can be foregone if he wants something else, or a combination of other things, more.

Such considerations suggest another look at table 13.1 where "will power" or one of its more specific variants is given as a reason for abstinence even more often than unavailability of narcotics. Some of these claims can certainly be dismissed as mere rationalizations, or as downright lies, but it would be wrong to discount these claims completely.

Some findings of this study have been described before. When a high rate of abstinence was reported, and attributed largely to unavailability of narcotics, the latter interpretation was normally accepted by smiles and nods from the audience. Since long before Freud, men have had a tendency to believe that the "true" or "real" explanation of behavior has been reached when the behavior is attributed to causes outside of or discreditable to the actor. One's readiness to accept unavailability and to ignore will power as an explanation may be due more to his beliefs about addicts and about human nature than to the relative weight of the evidence.

In at least a few cases, there can be little doubt that some choice of the subject enters into the explanation of his abstinence. The woman who moved to a farm because she could not get narcotics there (by the methods she had used), and those who moved away from home to avoid the addicts they had known, made narcotics unavailable, but their acts and not external circumstances alone caused the drug to become unavailable. In a few cases, subjects attributed their abstinence to religious conversion.

> One of these (Case 002) was a man who was floridly psychotic, with many religious delusions, during most of the 5-year sentence imposed in 1938 for sale of narcotics. His complete abstinence for more than 20 years after discharge was one of the best-documented in the study, with almost every informant in his community spontaneously mentioning him as one addict who was certainly cured. Among the facts mentioned was that he had attended church and Sunday School for over 300 consecutive Sundays, with several informants suggesting he had "too much religion," that his interest in it was abnormal. The taped interview with him reads like a disjointed revival sermon, and the interviewer saw the subject as a schizophrenic in not quite complete remission. But, however a psychiatrist might diagnose him, the facts indicate that it was an act of choice, even though psychotic rather than rational, which explains his abstinence.

On balance, the writer sees the increasing difficulty of obtaining narcotics in Kentucky as the major explanation for the decrease in addiction in the State, and for the abstinence in this sample. In some cases, unavailability is the only explanation needed; physical disabilities made it impossible for subjects to seek narcotics, and the persons who could have brought narcotics to them refused to do so. But in most cases an additional explanation is needed. The drug became unavailable because the usual method of obtaining it was blocked. Since some subjects then began to use other methods, abstinence in others cannot be explained by unavailability alone. There is no evidence in the study to deny, and some to suggest, that the additional explanation lies in personal qualities and characteristics of the subjects, or in their motivation.

How Availability Was Reduced

Most addiction in Kentucky was maintained on narcotics obtained directly from physicians, or from pharmacies on prescriptions supplied by physicians. The increasing difficulty of obtaining narcotics in Kentucky arose mainly from changes which greatly reduced the quantity of narcotics obtainable from physicians, and these changes are described in the next chapter.

But illicit narcotics were also, up to the 1930s or early 1940s, imported into the State, or into neighboring cities to which Kentuckians could easily travel. The information on this illicit traffic is less precise, and naturally less well documented, than that obtained on other sources. But the general agreement of informants is such that the following description of the illicit traffic and its decline can be presented as probably accurate in its major outlines.

While heroin was occasionally available, this illicit traffic was always primarily in morphine, suggesting that at some point the drug had been diverted from legal channels. There seem to have been at least three independent routes by which morphine was imported into Kentucky. One was from New York, through eastern Ohio and Kentucky, into Tennessee, West Virginia, North Carolina, and probably further south. A few Kentucky addicts, like the case cited above, bought directly from the couriers who travelled across the State. More often, subjects in the eastern part of the State described travelling to centers of distribution in Ohio or Tennessee to buy narcotics, or one local addict would go to these centers and return with enough to supply up to five or ten others.

Another route originated in Chicago, and went through Indianapolis, Evansville, and central and western Kentucky. The third originated somewhere to the southwest, perhaps New Orleans or Kansas City, and made smaller amounts of morphine available in a few towns of southwestern Kentucky. In the 1960s no remnant of these sources was found, except for the occasional importation of heroin from Chicago into Louisville, available to Negroes only. The routes seem to have been closed, for whites, by the mid-1940s.

Informants agree that the greatly increased efforts at law enforcement which began in the 1930s explain the decline, almost to the point of disappearance, of the illegal market. Some of these efforts took place out of Kentucky, as in the case of the subject whose supplier travelled through his town regularly, until the supplier was imprisoned in another State. As drug rings were broken up in several different cities outside of Kentucky, the channels to Kentucky were broken, and for various reasons were never renewed.

Part of the decline was due to efforts of local police, and Federal and later State narcotic agents in Kentucky. Most of the known sellers in the State were sentenced and removed from their communities for long periods of time, and most of these did not resume selling after release, both because they could not obtain drugs to sell and because they feared the increasingly long sentences for sales. The effective demand had also been reduced. In rural areas and small cities, in particular, it seems to have been impossible to conceal drug use from the community, so when officials began serious efforts to enforce the laws there was little chance to avoid prosecution, or at least an interruption of addiction by a period of treatment. The pattern seems not to have been, except in a few counties, one sharp break into the channels of supply, after which addiction did not appear again. Rather it seems to have been one in which small systems of a supplier and his customers were broken up on several occasions, after each of which the system was more difficult to reconstitute, and smaller.

Eventually they were too small to be viable, and the remaining addiction was one of individual addicts, each with a separate connection with one or more sources, almost all medical, while others gave up the use of narcotics, or used them only occasionally.

Law enforcement also seems to explain the reduction in the use of forged prescriptions for narcotics. The early indictments on this charge normally specify a large number of separate offenses, indicating that subjects had been able to cash many prescriptions before they were apprehended. Later ones show only a few specifications. As the system of checking prescription records grew, and as pharmacists and physicians became more aware of the practice and reported it more quickly, forgeries became uneconomical. The addict might obtain only a few grains of morphine before the inevitable happened, and then might have to serve several years for the offense.

The increasingly negative public attitudes towards addiction also played a role. The pressures from family members on the subject to quit drug use became stronger, in some cases to the point of reporting the addiction and the suspected source of supply to officials. It is also probably more than a coincidence that the illicit traffic finally ended during the years of the second World War. The reduction during the war may have been due, in part, to the shipping restrictions of the war years, as well as to the other factors mentioned. By the end of the war the established routes were broken, many of the middlemen had been frightened out of the business, and the declining prevalence of addiction in Kentucky made the effective demand for narcotics smaller. There is no apparent reason why communications could not have been reestablished, but the narcotics wholesalers certainly had no need to seek a market in Kentucky, and Kentucky addicts had made their adjustment, either by finding a stable medical source or by shifting to substitutes, or by complete abstinence. Whatever the relative weight of the reasons, communications were never reestablished.

Summary

A decrease in the availability of narcotics in Kentucky is the major factor which explains the abstinence of subjects in this study. Evidence for this decrease was found in several facts.

1. Subjects, their relatives and physicians attributed abstinence to unavailability of narcotics in over half of the cases where a reason was given.
2. The detailed descriptions of how narcotics became unavailable for specific subjects are plausible and convincing.
3. There is universal agreement among informants, including subjects, their relatives, physicians, law enforcement and health officials, that narcotics have become difficult to obtain for everyone, not just for

the individual subjects whose cases they discussed. This agreement contrasts with a wide range of opinion among the same informants on the availability of other drugs, and the prevalence of abuse of these drugs.

4. Those subjects found to be currently addicted were using less potent drugs, and smaller dosages, than at the time of their first admission to Lexington.
5. Subjects with multiple admissions were using less potent drugs, smaller dosages, and their habits were smaller, as measured by the time required for withdrawal, on their recent admissions, than on their early admissions to Lexington. Many currently addicted and multiple-admission subjects attributed these smaller habits to the fact that they could not get more narcotics.

But the decrease in availability of narcotics is a complete explanation of abstinence for only some subjects. In most cases, the usual source of narcotics was blocked, but alternative methods of obtaining drugs existed, and some used these. The fact that most did not, that to most subjects only some methods were acceptable and others were not, indicates that availability of narcotics cannot be conceived in terms of the drug alone, nor of the situation in which the potential addict finds himself. It must be conceived as a relationship between the potential user and the drug, in which his personal characteristics, his norms of what may and may not be done to obtain narcotics, are as important as the quantities of drugs at hand and the methods by which they may be secured.

That this conceptualization is correct is argued by the facts that most subjects never tried to obtain narcotics by burglary, by forged prescriptions, or by begging from or threatening physicians. Very few even used the expedient, available to most of them, of moving to cities where narcotics continued to be sold. Few addicts in this sample, and probably only a minority in any addict population, fit the stereotype of a person who "will do anything" to get narcotics. If this conceptualization is correct, one would expect measures of personality characteristics and attitudes to predict which addicts would become abstinent, which would shift to substitutes, and which would turn to new methods of obtaining narcotics, when the usual sources are blocked. Such measures were not available in this study, but case material strongly suggests that personality factors, subsumed by most subjects under the rubric of "will power," were operating.

The major reduction in the availability of narcotics is attributable to the reduction in the amount available from physicians. As for other sources of narcotics, there is no apparent reason to question the agreement of informants that the increased law enforcement efforts of the 1930s and later broke up the channels by which illicit narcotics were imported into the State, and made subjects less ready to risk other illegal means of obtaining narcotics, as by forging prescriptions. Other factors almost certainly having some effect include World War II, when the general decrease in narcotics probably helped to break up the illicit channels and made their reestablishment more difficult. The decrease in demand for narcotics, when these and the factors to be described in the next chapter reduced the prevalence of addiction, may also explain the failure to rebuild the illicit traffic, in that it would not pay enough to justify the risks involved.

Footnotes, Chapter 13

[1] The table shows that 122 men and 37 women, 58 percent and 68 percent of subjects, had periods of abstinence. These percentages are slightly below those reported in sub-table B–1 of Table 3.5, 59 percent and 73 percent. The reason is that Table 13.1 includes only periods of abstinence from last discharge to interview or death, while Table 3.5 included a few additional cases with periods of abstinence between admissions to Lexington. These few cases are omitted in Table 13.1 because information was not collected on reasons for the earlier abstinence.

[2] One possible exception to this might be the suburban areas of Kentucky in the Cincinnati metropolitan area, which were not included in the sample. Another exception seems to be that heroin from Chicago has been occasionally available in Louisville, but only among Negro addicts. Some subjects knew of this, and had tried to obtain some, but had been unsuccessful, probably due to fear that they were acting as informants for Narcotic Agents.

CHAPTER 14

Physicians and Addicts

Findings in previous chapters have repeatedly indicated the important role of physicians in the history of addiction in Kentucky. This chapter will summarize these findings, introduce new data on the changing relationship between medical practice and addiction, and examine the role relationship between physicians and addicts.

The reader should keep in mind that the physicians who produced and maintained much of the addiction in Kentucky were a small fraction of the physicians in practice. Other *caveats* will be noted in the sections to which they are appropriate.

Physicians as a Source of Narcotics

It was seen in chapter 6 that a sizeable minority in this sample—over one-fourth—obtained narcotics only from one physician at a time. Others obtained narcotics by travelling from one physician to another. Fourteen subjects were themselves physicians, who are known or reasonably suspected to have used narcotics from their own supply. Most subjects received at least some of their narcotics from physicians. In recent years, when addiction has been much less prevalent in the State, to maintain addiction steadily has required finding a physician who would prescribe regularly. But even in earlier decades, most of the subjects who were addicted at any given time were obtaining all or most of their drugs from physicians. Drugs sold on the illicit market were, in large part, supplied by local physicians.

There is agreement among all informants that this is a generally accurate picture. With respect to physicians as a source for individual subjects, there are a few cases in which the only evidence is hearsay, someone's statement that a certain physician prescribed for a given subject. Even in these cases there usually is multiplication of such hearsay, as when the same physician is independently named, by different informants, as having been the source of narcotics.

In most cases there was at least partial confirmation of the statements made by subjects and other informants. For example, a physician would be said to have prescribed for a subject over a period of 5 or 6 years. A court record, or an investigation by narcotics agents of pharmacy files, would then show that he had prescribed over the period covered by the investigation, usually from 6 months to perhaps 2 years. Frequently letters of referral or case histories from a physician at the time of a subject's admission to Lexington would confirm that he had prescribed for some length of time prior to the admission. Similar statements sometimes were found in the files of other hospitals.

Full confirmation was sometimes obtained from the physician himself. When subjects denied or minimized drug use, field staff sometimes found evidence that this was untrue. But normally when a subject said a physician had prescribed for him for some length of time, the physician confirmed this, and the drug and dosage the subject had described. This was the more true as the drug use was more recent, so exceptions are explainable as lapses of memory. For example, the physician who prescribed for 13 subjects in one county confirmed this in all cases but two. In these he did not deny prescribing, but said he did not remember the names, which is credible because both subjects had left town almost twenty years before. In other older cases, he remembered he had prescribed for long periods of time, but could not specify the number of years. In the current and recent cases, however, his description tallied exactly with the accounts given by subjects.

In short, where confirmation was conceivable it was normally found, and was as specific and detailed as one could expect in records which were kept for other purposes or from normal memories. In some cases, where the physician was long dead, and the records located contained no letters from him, not even partial confirmation was possible. But such cases were few. The general pattern described was identical with that of the confirmed cases, and there was no specific reason to doubt that the physician had been a source of narcotics. While it is conceivable that the data magnify the role physicians played as a source of narcotics, it seems beyond doubt that physicians once prescribed and dispensed narcotics much more freely than they do today.

The reasons why this was so fall into five groups, not mutually exclusive.

1. The explanation favored by subjects, and mentioned by some other informants, was purely economic. A number of physicians used to dispense narcotics for the money they could get.

> One subject (Case 123) said his usual source of supply was a physician in his community who would prescribe up to 50 grains of morphine per week under a false diagnosis. His "diagnosis" was tuberculosis of the hip, which the physician jocularly referred to as tuberculosis of the pocketbook. The subject stated he secured the 50 grains per week for a few years, until the Federal narcotics agents put an end to the practice.

> The widow and daughter of another subject (Case 254) blamed his addiction on a physician who got him addicted, and then kept raising the price of prescriptions. When, on his last visit to the physician, the latter asked $50 for a vial of morphine, the subject went back to his car, wrote a note, and killed himself.

> The widow of another subject (Case 035) attributed the beginning and continuation of her husband's addiction to a physician. She quoted the pharmacist for whom she had once worked as describing how this physician had built up the biggest practice in the county. When a new patient came to him, his first few prescriptions "would be some kind of medicine that made you feel real bad, and then he'd switch over and give them morphine to make them feel real good, and they thought he was a wonderful doctor." This was not described as an attempt to addict people, but merely to make them want to continue as his patients. In most cases, presumably, the illness was temporary and the narcotics were discontinued before any harm was done. But in some cases it lasted long enough to produce physical dependence, and the physician then continued to maintain the addiction.

The economic explanation is not implausible. While the population of Kentucky has been steadily rising, the number of physicians steadily declined for the first half of the twentieth century. The ratio of physicians to population was almost twice as high in 1909 as it was in 1958. Some practiced in villages with populations under 100. The less successful physicians in the earlier decades may therefore have been tempted to increase their income by what in some cases was no more than peddling drugs to addicts, and in other cases by keeping their patients satisfied through prescribing narcotics whose medical justification was questionable. The economic explanation is also supported by several accounts of how pharmacists, in the depression years, tried to secure the regular patronage of known addicts by offering to fill prescriptions at a lower price.

2. A second factor, frequently mentioned, was that the older and less well-trained physicians were those who prescribed morphine freely.

There were 114 physicians named as having prescribed narcotics for subjects at one time or another. Thirteen had prescribed in treatment which, by today's laws, would be clearly illicit; they were convicted of sale of narcotics or sold narcotics with little or no pretense of medical treatment. At the other extreme, 25 had been clearly within the bounds of normal and ethical treatment; there was evidence of careful efforts to administer minimal doses for minimal periods, or narcotics had been prescribed only when subjects were terminally ill. The remaining 76 fall into a middle group, without sufficient information to classify them at either extreme.

Of the physicians whose treatment was clearly illicit, 92 percent were graduated from medical school before 1920. This was true for only 28 percent of those whose treatment had been clearly licit. These facts alone would not prove that the older physicians prescribed morphine more freely, because it cannot be established that the 114 physicians identified are a representative sample of all physicians who prescribed narcotics. But the only known bias in determining which physicians were named is that field staff made a special effort to identify the current or the last physician who treated the subject, which would make more recent graduates from medical school more likely to be named.

Over half of the 114 physicians who had prescribed had been graduated from medical school before 1920, and about 40 percent before 1910. For 1910, Flexner's study of medical education established that the quality of medical training then was poor, and it may be presumed that by 1920 only minor progress had been made toward the great improvements in medical education initiated by his study. In 1910 Flexner stated that ". . . Kentucky is one of the largest producers of low grade doctors in the entire Union . . .",[1] and most of the pre-1910 physicians were graduates of medical schools in Kentucky.

That the quality of training was related to the use of narcotics is also suggested by the fact that only five of the 114 named physicians were Board certified, and all of these classed as giving clearly licit treatment. Another relevant factor is that it was only in the 1920s that medicine's first clear ideas about addiction, such as the nature of physical dependence, were formulated.

3. Another factor mentioned was that in the early decades of the century morphine was medically indicated more often than it is now. Most of the specific medications available today had not yet been discovered, so there were more patients for whom even the best physician could do no more than relieve pain. It may also be that some of the illnesses for which opiates had traditionally been used, such as dysentery, were more frequent before the relatively recent emphasis on sanitation and preventive health measures.

4. One factor, mentioned in only a few cases, was that the physician who prescribed or used narcotics did not know, or did not believe, that meperidine was an addicting drug.

5. A final factor frequently mentioned was that those physicians who addicted several persons in their communities were themselves addicts. Two kinds of evidence suggest that this was true. First, those physicians who were named as a source of narcotics in several cases were also named, frequently by different informants, as having been addicts, far more often than chance would explain. Second, of the fourteen subjects who were physicians and addicts, at least five had supplied narcotics to other addicts.

Just how this factor operated, however, is not clear. It is likely that several of the previous factors were also operative. The practice of the addicted physician often deteriorated (but not always—some addicted physicians were described as "the best doctor in town") so making money from drug sales may have been important. The addicted physicians were also among the older, less well-trained men, and it may have been their lack of professional skill rather than their addiction that explained their frequent use of narcotics.

But in a few cases there are hints that the addiction itself was a factor. One subject, about to marry the daughter of an addicted physician, was introduced to narcotics by her father, seemingly as a friendly sharing of a pleasant sensation. One may speculate that generous impulses to give to others the pleasure one enjoyed, or hostile desires to see others as enslaved as oneself, may have explained the physician addict's introduction of narcotics to others as much as they now explain why one metropolitan addict "turns on" another.

The Decrease in Availability of Narcotics From Physicians

The explanations advanced for the fact that physicians no longer so freely prescribe or dispense narcotics relate to the above factors.

First, Federal narcotic agents in cooperation with local police and later with State agents have put an end to the large-scale selling of narcotics by physicians. One physician, for example, was convicted of having sold on one day 400 grains of morphine for $120.00 to a subject, and this was only one of repeated sales, though he was not formally charged with the others. In such cases the physician was prosecuted and imprisoned. In other cases, during the course of an investigation the physician would "voluntarily" surrender his narcotic tax stamp, which authorized him to order and stock narcotics.

While the staffs of the Federal and State agencies have never been large enough to check all records of pharmacies and physicians regularly, they have permitted a system of spot checks, and checks of narcotics ordered, so that if a physician or pharmacist sold an unusually large quantity of narcotics he was likely to be detected quickly. The worst offenders, in short, were put out of business, and it may be presumed that the few other physicians who might be tempted to sell narcotics became fearful of doing so.

These checks also ensured that the physician addict was likely to be detected soon. In recent years, large narcotic orders by a physician, or an unusually large number of prescriptions written by him, have been more likely to indicate that he was using the drug than that he was selling it. When he was detected prosecution was usually avoided, but he was under pressure to seek treatment for his addiction, and was required to surrender his narcotics tax stamp, so that even when he returned to practice he could not supply narcotics to others.

In several different ways, therefore, the system of Federal and State supervision over the legitimate channels of narcotics distribution contributed to reducing the possibility of obtaining narcotics from physicians, just as these agents were seen in the previous chapter to have contributed to the closing of illicit channels.

Of equal or more importance has been the steady improvement in medical practice. The older and less well-trained physicians have been dying off. There are still a few left in Kentucky, and in other States, who prescribe narcotics more freely than their colleagues, but they are known to the narcotic agents. Checks on their dispensing and prescribing are especially frequent, which probably makes them more careful than they would otherwise be. But the bulk of physicians in practice today are more recently trained, better trained, have at hand more effective and less dangerous medications, and are more aware of the dangers of administering narcotics. Prescribing narcotics for alcoholics, for example, has become rare. To perhaps a lesser extent, physicians today are also more aware of the dangers of giving narcotics to patients with vague neurotic or psychosomatic complaints. There are, however, some indications that some physicians today may be as careless about prescribing barbiturates and tranquilizers as others once were careless with narcotics.

Physicians and Addicts

In the following section, the reader should keep in mind that there was no formal research design to study the relationship between physicians and addicts. The subjects constitute a random sample of Kentucky patients treated at the Lexington hospital, and may be regarded as representative of all Kentucky addicts within the limitations discussed in chapter 11, but there was no effort to sample Kentucky physicians. The data to be presented represent a by-product of the study, and inferences from them are not more than suggestive. The discussion of the physician-addict role relationship should be regarded as the writer's interpretation of the available data. It is included because if the interpretation is correct it carries important implications for policies on handling the addition problem.

Studies of social status and prestige in this country regularly report medicine as one of the most esteemed occupations. But if there is any group which fails to give it this high regard, it is addicts.

It is significant that of the reasons given above why physicians no longer prescribe narcotics, the subjects suggest only the two which show least respect for the profession. For subjects, the only reasons why physicians do not supply them with narcotics are that they no longer need the money, or they are afraid of the narcotic agents, or both. The attitudes of many were expressed by one subject who said there used to be many physicians who prescribed freely, and added:

> Yeah, but they were scared up. If a doctor gives you something now, he has to know that you need it, or you're not going to get it. He'll run you out of his office, right now. These narcotic men, they come around, you know, and they check all the places, and if they think a doctor's putting out a little too much drugs, they'll call his hand on it, and scare him up. These doctors, you know, spent a lot of money to make (become) a doctor, and they just make all kinds of money at anything now, a doctor does. He ain't going to take a chance on losing his license . . . Most any doctor now, if he is any kind of a doctor at all, you have to go up there and sit half a day, maybe all day, in his office. They just sit in droves there. He just takes in all kinds of money. With all other kinds of medicine except narcotics.

Another subject claimed he was able to purchase morphine from any physician he ever approached. He regarded physicians as the most greedy people on earth, and stated that in his experience it was usually the doctor's wife who made him stop dispensing narcotics. "The wives always get afraid that something is going to happen to their means of support."

Some physicians still write an occasional prescription, for an exorbitant fee, for a transient addict who will have the prescription filled and leave town. These are seen by addicts as venal. A few more can be duped into thinking the addict has an illness which requires narcotics, or can be persuaded to write a prescription to prevent withdrawal distress. The addict sees them as fools, as easily "conned," as "marks." The vast majority, from whom no drugs can be obtained, are seen as businessmen who refuse narcotics only because they make money in other ways with less risk.

The physicians who were interviewed, in turn, have no high opinion of addicts. A few perceive addicts as weak, ineffectual misfits who cannot help their craving for drugs. A few more feel guilty that they ought to perceive them so. But with few exceptions their basic attitude is summed up in the description many used; the addict is simply "a damn nuisance."

These mutually derogatory opinions should not be seen as arising from personal characteristics of addicts and physicians, or as attitudes the two groups happen to have learned. There is reason, rather, to see these as produced by discrepancies between the usual physician-addict relationship and socially structured expectations of what the physician-patient relationship should be.

Parsons has pointed out that the sick person is temporarily absolved of his normal responsibilities not only because of his temporary incapacity, but also on the assumption that the illness is not his fault; the sick person "can't help it." Furthermore, the illness is assumed to be undesirable and the sick person is expected to want to get well. He is not expected to possess the technical expertness required to treat the illness, so he should

335-199—69——16

seek the technically competent help of a physician, and cooperate with him in the process of getting well.

A primary expectation of the physician is that he will possess the technical competence his patient lacks. He is the expert who certifies that the patient is ill and unable to meet his normal obligations, and whose skills will bring the illness to an end, if the patient follows his instructions. Among his rewards are the respect and deference paid him by the patient and his family.[2]

These expectations are almost inevitably belied in most relationships between addicts and physicians.

The addict may feel that he "can't help" his addiction, that the narcotic is needed for some illness, or that after a person has been addicted for years it is impossible for him to do without the drug. Even addicts, however, talk of addiction and abstinence in terms of "will power," implying some free choice in the decision to use drugs. The general public, including most of the physicians who were interviewed, share this attitude. The usual assumption is that even if the addict "can't help" his addiction now, at some past time he could have. The addict is regarded as being at fault, and addiction does not exempt him from responsibilities as a physical illness does.

Physicians and society regard addiction as undesirable, and feel the addict should do something to end it. Many addicts do not see it as undesirable; their interest is in continuing it. Or, if they do feel it is undesirable, they may feel it is impossible to end it, and the sincerity of statements that they want to end it is likely to be doubted.

The physician is likely to feel that if any treatment can cure addiction, it would be psychiatric treatment, requiring frequent sessions with the addict over a long period of time. The general practitioner has little interest in this kind of treatment, has not had the specialized training for it, and does not feel he possesses any special competence in it. Even when the addict feels he "can't help" being addicted, he usually has little faith that psychotherapy can change this. Neither addict nor physician, in short, regard the latter as technically competent in the treatment of addiction.

But these considerations are not relevant in most cases. The addict goes to the physician not as a professionally skilled expert who will treat him, but as a person who has been given exclusive rights by society to dispense the narcotics the addict wants. The only fact relevant to the addict is that he will suffer the distress of withdrawal in a few hours if he does not get his usual dosage of narcotics. His competence in judging how much and what drug he needs equals or exceeds that of the average physician.

Even when the addict and the physician agree that narcotics are needed for some physical illness, the relationship between them eventually deviates from the ideal. In chronic illnesses for which medications other than narcotics are regularly prescribed, the professional role of the physician is protected by the infrequency of appointments. The physician sees the patient often enough to check on his progress and on possible side-effects of the medication, and in each meeting clearly exercises his skills as an expert. Between meetings, if the patient needs more of his medication he has the prescription renewed.

But narcotic prescriptions are not renewable, and the patient on narcotics must see the physician frequently to get new prescriptions. Most of their meetings consist of a few casual questions and the writing of a prescription identical with the last one. It not only appears but is true that the prescription is the only purpose of the meeting. When such a pattern is repeated over years, the addict sees no difference between it and that of an unethical physician who regularly sells prescriptions to an otherwise healthy addict. In each case, the addict does not go to the physician to find out and receive what he needs, but to get what he knows he needs. The transaction is easily perceived as purely commercial, and the physician as exploiting the addict.

The rare unethical physician may be satisfied with the fees he collects, but for most there is little satisfaction in such a relationship. The physician cannot feel he is exercising his highest skills, and must become aware that he is regarded by the patient and his family as a source of narcotics rather than as an expert in medicine. If there is any question about the medical justification for the narcotics—and there usually is when narcotics are used for 10 or 20 years—he risks the disdain of his colleagues and possible embarrassment, or more serious trouble, from an investigation by narcotics agents.

Once a pattern of regular prescriptions has been established, it may be difficult or impossible for the physician to break it. Physicians are aware of this, and most are therefore careful not to let it start. The easiest preventive is to refuse to accept an addict as a patient, and many make this a rule.

The problem arises most often when the physician who has been prescribing for an addict dies, retires, or refuses to continue prescribing. The addict then goes to another physician. In small cities the latter is likely to know of the addiction, and already to be of the opinion that it is not medically justified. If he does not know of it, he quickly learns, because the addict must tell him in order to get the prescription he needs, and the physician is likely to suspect or determine that no medical justification exists, outside of the physical dependence itself.

The physicians interviewed followed four courses of action in such cases. Some simply refused to accept such a patient. Others required that the patient be hospitalized for withdrawal, after which the physician would accept the patient, with the understanding that no narcotics would be prescribed. A few consulted with colleagues and narcotics agents, after which they maintained the patient on small doses of narcotics, with regular checks by the agents to ensure that the patient was not also obtaining narcotics from other sources. These were usually cases of elderly patients who had been addicted for decades. Finally, a few followed this last procedure without the consultations described. This, however, has been much less frequent in recent years than it was 10 or 20 years earlier.

If a continuing relationship with an addict is not rewarding to the average physician, a single contact is even less so. When an addict appears in a physician's office to ask for a prescription because he will suffer withdrawal symptoms without it, the vast majority of physicians today will refuse to prescribe. A few will prescribe, for humanitarian reasons, and many more will be troubled by the necessity to refuse. But they do regard it as a necessity. They know that compliance with one request is likely to lead to more, from the same addict and from others when the grapevine communicates that they did prescribe. They doubt their ethical and legal right to write such a prescription, and recognize that in most cases a prescription would achieve no more than to postpone the withdrawal distress for a day.

"*Authorized*" *Addiction*

There is a widespread belief, particularly among older addicts, that at some given age the Federal Bureau of Narcotics will approve a physician's prescribing narcotics for an addict on no other basis than his age and the fact that he has been addicted for years. One subject, asked if the physician who had been prescribing for him would continue, said:

> Oh yes, he'll just supply me right on. I'm 72 years old, and the narcotics authorities allow any addict if he is over 70, they allow doctors to prescribe for you . . . Mr. ______________ [the Federal narcotics agent] told me that when I become 70, and when I come back there, why he would clear it. The doctor must have thought he was in the clear because he wrote down everything and was careful.

The perception of this subject is not correct. Current laws and regulations would not permit prescriptions based on age alone. One subject correctly perceived current policy, quoting agents as having told him that in view of his physical condition, they would not advise a physician against prescribing narcotics for him, but equally would not recommend that a physician prescribe. In this case, the subject then went to a number of physicians to see if he could find one who would agree that he needed narcotics. None would agree, and he was addicted to cough medicines.

But in general, elderly addicts will have acquired some physical complaints. If such an addict in Kentucky found a physician who would prescribe narcotics for the physical complaint, the narcotics agents did not question the need. In one sense, therefore, the addict's belief is correct; if he can maintain his addiction long enough, eventually a sufficient medical reason to justify it may appear, and his use of narcotics will no longer be questioned. But he always faces the risk that if his physician dies or retires, it may be impossible for him to find another who will regard the drug as medically justified.

Summary

Addiction in Kentucky a generation ago was maintained for the most part on narcotics dispensed or prescribed by physicians. A few sold large quantities of narcotics for profit, but in many cases it was the poor training of physicians, their lack of understanding of the addiction process, and the lack of specific medications available today, which explain their dispensing of narcotics. Addiction was spread largely by physicians who were themselves addicts, and in a few cases addiction arose from the fact that physicians did not know meperidine was addicting.

In recent years physicians have supplied narcotics much less freely. The reduction can be traced in part to the prosecution of the unethical large-scale sellers, but even more to the better training of physicians and the more effective medications available in place of morphine. Physicians and addicts were found to have low opinions of each other, and this is interpreted as arising from factors which make it difficult or impossible for the relationship between physician and addict to approach the ideal physician-patient relationship. Among these factors is the fact that the addict tends to see the physician not as a technically competent expert, but simply as a source of narcotics, and frequently as exploiting the patient's need for narcotics. There are few satisfactions for the physician who treats an addict, and many prefer not to accept the addict as a patient.

Footnotes, Chapter 14

[1] Flexner, Abraham. *Medical Education in the United States and Canada.* Boston: The Merrymount Press, 1910. p. 17.

[2] Parsons, Talcott. *The Social System.* Glencoe, Ill.: The Free Press, 1951. pp. 428–479.

CHAPTER 15

History of Narcotic Addiction in Kentucky

Prevalence and Incidence

Data on the decrease in addiction have been presented in several chapters, and it may be well to bring these together in summarized form, so that the picture can be seen as a whole. An attempt can then be made to estimate the size of the decrease.

That there has been a decrease is shown by the following facts:

1. The physicians, county Health Departments, local police, Federal and State narcotics agents, and addicts in Kentucky are the persons in the best positions to have knowledge of the extent of the addiction problem. Without exception, they agree that it has greatly declined, that the number of addicts today is much smaller than it was 20 or 30 years earlier.
2. In chapter 12 one rural county was described in detail; where there used to be some 20 or more addicts in the 1920s and early 1930s, there were only two addicts in the early 1960s.

   In this respect, almost all non-metropolitan counties and the smaller metropolitan counties resembled the county described. There were several counties in which all addicts had been maintained by one or a few physicians; since these physicians died no new addicts were produced, and the old addicts have died or become abstinent. The only counties in which there has been no decrease are two in each of which only one addict has been known, and these are still alive and addicted.

   The decrease was not equally documented in the two most populous counties of the State, since in them most physicians were not interviewed. But all of the available information points to a similar decrease in these counties too. Unless physicians there are maintaining addicts to a much greater extent than in the rest of the State, which there is no reason to suspect, they too have many fewer addicts than they had 20 or 30 years ago.
3. First admissions of white patients to the Lexington hospital from Kentucky averaged about 45 per year for the first 20 years of the hospital's existence. In 1955–59 this average dropped to 21, and remained at that level in 1960–64. Since it was shown in chapter 11 that admissions to the hospital have represented an increasing proportion of the addicts in the State, from about half around 1940 to all or almost all around 1960, the steady rate of admissions for 20 years, and the drop in the next 10 years, indicate a decreasing number of addicts.

It remains to be seen if the extent of the decrease can be estimated.

Prior to the passage of the Harrison Narcotic Act the number of addicts in Kentucky is unknown. There is reason to believe, however, that the State had at least its fair share of the then numerous addicts in the United States. In Adams' famous magazine series on the nostrum evil and quackery, he noted the high content of opiates and cocaine in patent medicines between 1905 and 1912. Adams examined hundreds of testimonials sent to the patent medicine companies, noted that most of them were from illiterate and obviously ignorant people and that the vast majority were from small, remote hamlets. He asks, "Is it only coincidence that the mountain districts of Kentucky, West Virginia and Tennessee, recognized as being the least civilized parts of the country, should furnish a number of testimonials . . . out of all proportion to their population?" [1]

If it be assumed that the prevalence of addiction in Kentucky in 1914 was reasonably close to that in Tennessee, a study done that year in Tennessee furnishes a basis for an estimate for Kentucky. There were then 2,370 known addicts in Tennessee, two-thirds of them women, and at least 90 percent of them white.[2] These were registered under a law which permitted addicts to be furnished narcotics. The investigator estimated that not over one-half of the addicts were registered, and that the total number of addicts in Tennessee was about 5,000. In the censuses of 1890 through 1920, the population of Kentucky was slightly higher than that of Tennessee; in the same years, Kentucky's population was about 90 percent white, against Tennessee's 80 percent. On the assumption that the States were otherwise similar, it would therefore be reasonable to estimate a minimum of some 2,500 addicts in Kentucky in 1914, and perhaps as many as 5,000.

In 1918 a special committee of investigation, appointed by the Secretary of the Treasury, estimated the number of addicts in the United States on the basis of a questionnaire addressed to all physicians registered under the Harrison Narcotic Act. Kentucky physicians reported 1,612 addicts, and since the percentage of returns was only 42, the committee estimated the total at 3,972 addicts.[3] It may be noted that 5,366 addicts were reported from Tennessee, by 66 percent of its physicians, and a total of 8,180 addicts was estimated for Tennessee.[4] If these estimates are accepted as accurate, the prevalence in Kentucky was only half that in Tennessee, and the assumption of similarity between the States in the paragraph above was incorrect.

Kolb and DuMez estimated about 110,000 addicts in the United States in 1924.[5] Kentucky's population was then about 2.3 percent of the total population. If it had a similar proportion of all addicts, the estimate would be about 2,500.

The three estimates, based on 1914, 1918 and 1924 data, are clearly inaccurate to some degree, but are consistent in indicating that addicts in Kentucky numbered in the thousands.

If there were as many as 2,500 addicts in Kentucky in 1914 or 1924, the number had certainly dropped by the late 1930s and early 1940s. Judging from the findings of this study, the addicts admitted to Lexington in those years probably were about half of the addicts then living in the State. This is a rough estimate, but the percentage admitted would have to drop to 17 percent before the 420 admissions in 1935–44 could represent 2,500 addicts. This seems to be highly unlikely; one would then have expected some five addicts to have been named for each subject, rather than the 1: 1 ratio actually observed.

It would seem more probable that the number of Kentucky addicts in the late 1930s was approximately 800 to 1,000.

The estimate of 2,500 for 1914–1924 is speculative, though not unreasonable. The estimate of 800 to 1,000 for the late 1930s is still speculative, but more firmly based. For more recent decades, estimates are still firmer, because admissions to the Lexington hospital have come to represent almost all addicts in the State.

Of the 21 subjects classified in this study as currently addicted, and the 11 who would have been addicted if they had not been institutionalized when interviewed, 26 were still residents of Kentucky. The sample in this study represented about one-fourth of all Kentucky admissions, so it might be estimated that in the early 1960s there were about 100 Kentuckians, treated at Lexington between 1935 and 1959, who were still addicts. To this figure must be added the number of first admissions of Kentuckians in 1960–64, which was 110. Also to be added would be some figure, probably small, of recent addicts who had not yet had time to be admitted to the hospital.

An estimate of 250 to 300 white addicts in Kentucky in the early 1960s thus seems reasonable. There could not have been many less than 250. The upper limit is less certain, but it must be far short of the 800 to 1,000 of the 1930s unless there is a large number of addicts completely concealed from officials, physicians and other addicts.

All of the above estimates concerned whites. But the very small number of Negro admissions from Kentucky in 1935–59 has continued to run about one or two a year in 1960–64. The information available on Negro addicts in Kentucky suggests that there are very few who use narcotics regularly, though perhaps there are now a score or more who use them occasionally.

In summary, one can reasonably estimate that as of 1963 there were about 300 addicts in Kentucky, plus or minus perhaps 75. Around 1935–39 there were probably some 900, and the lesser certainty of this figure may be indicated by saying it was 900 plus or minus 300. In 1914–24 there were probably some 2,500. The prevalence of addiction now may therefore be estimated to be no more than one-eighth to one-tenth of its prevalence 50 years earlier. Since the population of the State has increased by more than 25 percent in these 50 years, the rate of prevalence has decreased to less than 10 percent of the rate around 1914. If one prefers to avoid the inevitable uncertainties of such estimates, the conservative conclusion would be that there has been a large decrease in prevalence, whatever the actual size of the decrease.

Estimates of incidence—the number of new cases of addiction each year—are necessarily less accurate, since they must be based mainly on the prevalence figures, with additional assumptions.

All of the available information suggests that those persons who became addicted in the earlier decades of the past 50 years were able to, and did, continue to be addicted without interruption for many years. Addiction histories of 20 to 50 years were common. In the 1914 Tennessee study the average length of addiction was slightly more than 11 years, for both men and women. The average length of addiction, at time of first admission, for subjects in this Kentucky study was almost as high. If it is assumed that the average addict continued to be addicted for about 20 years in 1914–24, a prevalence of 2,500 addicts would suggest about 125 new cases per year.

That the total length of addiction has steadily decreased in the past 50 years, that addiction is now interrupted earlier and more often, seems certain. But the extent of this decrease is not clear. It might be assumed that the average length of addiction dropped to about 15 years by 1935–39, and to about 10 years by 1963. If so, the 900 cases in 1935–39 would suggest an incidence of 60 new cases per year, and the 300 in 1963 about 30 new cases per year. It may be recalled that the data for one rural county in chapter 12 suggested that incidence in that county dropped from about one case per year in 1917–32 to one case every three years in 1933–62.

The estimate for the decrease in incidence is less certain than for the decrease in prevalence. The major point suggested, however, is almost certainly correct—that the decrease in incidence, while large, has been less than the decrease in prevalence. The major reason for this difference is that the average length of addiction has decreased, and this in turn is due to several factors: (1) the decrease in availability of narcotics; (2) the fact that age at onset of addiction has been increasing in recent decades; and (3) the fact that there has been more medical justification for the first use of narcotics in recent decades. The latter two relate to life expectancy at the time addiction begins; those who are older or more ill, or both, have fewer years to live and to be addicted, even if narcotics continue to be available to them.

The Changing Pattern of Addiction

As the incidence and prevalance of narcotic addiction decreased in Kentucky, there were parallel changes in the pattern of addiction. One variable in this study which was found to be associated with changes in many other variables was the year in which addiction began.

The rate of change itself changed noticeably about 1940, due to a complex of factors: the opening of the Lexington hospital, which provided a treatment facility for addicts; a drive to enforce the narcotic laws; a change in public attitudes due to the new definition of addicts as criminals; and, though probably to a lesser extent in Kentucky than in States where addiction was based more on an illicit market in heroin, the fact that World War II was blocking the illegal import of narcotics.

Another change can be presumed to have occurred around 1914, when the Harrison Narcotic Act became law. At the minimum, this indicated a public and nation-wide judgment that narcotic addiction was undesirable, and was to be suppressed. As the culmination of increasingly negative public attitudes toward addiction, it crystallized and almost certainly reinforced those attitudes. Some prosecutions followed, and public opinion came to equate addiction and crime more closely than before. There was concern over what would happen to addicts, as evidenced by the establishment of clinics or legal procedures to supply them with drugs, mainly after World War I, but as early as 1914 in Tennessee.[6] While many of the effects of the Harrison Act did not become fully apparent until years later, the existing addicts must have been more aware than others that change was in the offing, and that they would have to adjust to it.

The years 1914 and 1940 therefore can be taken as dividing points. No great violence will be done to the facts by taking three fairly equal time periods, say 1890 to 1914, 1914 to 1940, and 1940 to 1963, as the framework for discussion. The changes in pattern were not as abrupt or discrete as will appear from the following description, but were gradual and continuous. Still, the three periods will illustrate changes in central tendencies over time.

1. *Addiction Before 1914*. The earliest period is least well documented in this study, but one subject was addicted as early as 1897, and five percent of the sample before 1914. The memory of some informants went back to this period, and the patterns of addiction described in other States around this time almost certainly apply to Kentucky.

There were at least 2,500, and possibly as many as 5,000 addicts in the State, and almost certainly as many women as men, or more. It may be doubted that addicts were ever a representative sample of the population, but they came closer to this before 1914 than after; all classes of the population were represented among addicts, including some successful and locally prominent men and women.

Most were introduced to narcotics in the course of medical treatment or self-treatment, highly questionable by today's standards, but some of it excusable in terms of the knowledge and alternatives then available.[7] Alcoholism and pleasure-seeking were also roads to addiction, as in later periods. Once he began to use narcotics regularly, the addict had no difficulty in obtaining drugs. They could be bought over the counter in drug stores or general stores, by mail as patent medicines, or it would have been easy to find a physician to prescribe or dispense them.

Few of these early addicts had criminal records before addiction, and probably few acquired such records later, unless the addiction continued long after 1914.

It is likely that addicts were spread fairly evenly over the State, roughly in proportion to population.[8] There may have been more self-medication and more unwise prescribing of narcotics by physicians in isolated rural areas, but this was probably balanced by more use for pleasure in towns and cities.

It is not known to what extent the social performance of these addicts suffered, in the then-existing climate of easy and cheap access to drugs, and only mildly negative attitudes towards its use. It is likely that some showed no deterioration, or so little as to be imperceptible. But there were undesirable aspects to addiction, as evidenced by the demand for patent medicines advertised as cures, and by sanitaria supported by addicts seeking cures as much as by alcoholics. Some unknown, but fairly large, proportion of addicts before 1914 tried to end their addiction, and some completely unknown proportion may have succeeded.

There were many addicts; few had any powerful reason to conceal addiction, and the knowledge of neighbors in small communities meant that most addicts knew each other. But there was no advantage in being in contact with other addicts, and there is no indication that these contacts deserved the name of subculture.

2. *Addiction Between 1914 and 1940.* The pattern in this period is much better documented, since 127 subjects became addicted during it, and the 14 earlier subjects continued using narcotics for most of it. These were not representative of all Kentucky addicts in the period, in that young men were more likely than women or older men to enter the U.S. Public Health Service Hospital. Further, those who used illegal drugs or stole to get money for drugs were more likely to be sent to the hospital than addicts who used only drugs obtained from a physician. Findings must be evaluated with these limitations in mind, but since the limitations are known, generalizations made with caution can be accepted as probably correct.

This period witnessed a large decrease in the prevalence of addiction in the State, from over 2,500 before 1914 to about 800 or 1,000 in 1940. Some who had been addicted before 1914 may have given up their drug use. Among those who were relatively well-adjusted and conforming members of society, and especially among those who had been addicted only a few years, public disapproval of addiction and even slight difficulty in obtaining drugs may have been sufficient to produce abstinence. The fact that most study subjects found it difficult to achieve abstinence should not be generalized to earlier addicts; it may have been this difficulty which made it possible for them to be selected as subjects. Subjects did become abstinent when it became more difficult to obtain narcotics, so slight difficulty may have sufficed for others.

The decrease in prevalence was also due to a decrease in incidence. There were fewer new addicts to replace those who died or became abstinent. Narcotics could no longer be bought over the counter or by mail, so self-medication produced fewer addicts. Physicians were becoming more careful with narcotics. It may be that fear of prosecution kept some physicians from prescribing, though if so, their fear was unrealistic, as evidenced by the fact that a small minority of Kentucky physicians continued to dispense narcotics for several decades more, and very few were troubled by legal action. The more important factor was that most physicians fully subscribed to the position of the American Medical Association on the undesirability of maintaining addicts on drugs. They regarded supplying addicts as abhorrent, looked down on their colleagues who did dispense, and most would have nothing to do with addicts.

A third factor was that public attitudes kept some persons from using narcotics who would have used them in the earlier period. This is partly speculation, based on the assumption that there is some complex of personality factors which might be called "addiction-proneness." Those who scored low on this hypothetical measure presumably refused opportunities to use narcotics as the threshold of disapproval of use mounted higher. But it is not only speculation. New addicts were more often recruited from the ranks of men who had criminal records prior to addiction; 95 percent of subjects addicted before 1920 had no prior record, and this percentage dropped steadily each decade until, in the 1950s, only 53 percent of new addicts had no such record. New addicts, in short, came from a group which had already exhibited readiness to transgress.

Not only did incidence decrease, but it decreased differentially for diverse population groups. Addicts came increasingly from the lower socioeconomic classes. The ratio of male to female addicts began to increase, until by the 1930s it reached a 3:1 ratio. Incidence also began to differ geographically. It was still widespread—106 of the State's 120 counties sent at least one addict to the hospital after 1935—but now in small clusters of addicts in certain villages, towns, and cities. Access to drugs was possible only for those who lived where a physician dispensed drugs freely, or where older addicts could introduce new ones to drugs.

The three roads to addiction were medical treatment, alcoholism, and pleasure seeking, and men took these roads in the ratio of 4:5:3. Allowing for the selective factors in hospital admissions, medical treatment was probably first rather than second in importance. These roads were of almost equal importance in large cities; 35 percent medical, 34 percent alcoholism, and 31 percent for pleasure. In smaller towns the percentages were 48, 33, and 18; in still smaller villages, 51, 42, and 7. These percentages apply only to men; women began in the course of medical treatment, with only 8 of 54 women starting by the other routes.

Cohen says that "the crucial condition for the emergence of new cultural forms is the existence, *in effective interaction with one another, of a number of actors with similar problems of adjustment*." The new and similar problem many addicts faced in this period was maintaining a regular supply of narcotics. Knowing other addicts acquired new functional values. When drugs were in short supply, they could be obtained from others. Information could be traded on where and how drugs could be obtained. Skills which before had been unnecessary were now needed, and could be transmitted from one addict to another. These included criminal skills; how to commit burglaries, forge prescriptions, and "make" doctors. They also included addiction skills; how to inject narcotics, and how to process paregoric so the residue could be injected. Addicts could support each other in the attitudes and values needed to maintain addiction in the face of mounting public disapproval.

The extent of involvement in the drug subculture varied. Men became more involved than women, younger men more than older, those who began for pleasure more than the alcoholics, and the latter more than those who began drug use in medical treatment. An important determinant of involvement was the source of narcotics; an addict for whom a physician prescribed regularly had little need for other addicts, and was less involved with them. But as such physicians became increasingly rare, some addicts turned to alternative sources, and to the subculture. Most men became somewhat involved in this subculture, even when there were few other addicts in their immediate vicinity. Some had no contact with addicts in Kentucky, but had contacts outside of the State.

Narcotics could be obtained from a physician, or from an illicit market. The latter appeared soon after 1914 in some parts of the State, and much later in others. Some heroin was imported, but most of the supply was morphine, suggesting that the drug had been diverted from legal channels, rather than being smuggled into the country. But, though some came from outside the State, most illegal drugs in Kentucky, and all in some areas, were supplied by a few unethical physicians to a small number of addicts, who in turn sold them to others.

Addicts were more often recruited from the ranks of criminals, and partly for this reason, an increasing proportion had criminal records after the onset of addiction. But even among men with no prior record, in this period there was an increase in crime after addiction. Most men committed offenses against the drug laws, though only about one-third were arrested or sentenced for such offenses. There was also an increase in money-producing crimes; this was greatest among men who obtained most or all of their drugs from illicit sources, and was directly associated with the degree of involvement in the drug subculture.

Addicts were also recruited from among men who had showed other signs of poor social adjustment, though it is not known that this represents a change from the pre-1914 pattern. Most had used alcohol to excess, many had poor work records, many of those with military service had other than honorable discharges, and a sizeable minority had never achieved independence from their parental families. As drugs became more difficult to obtain, and as more addicts used expensive illicit drugs, role-performance deteriorated to a marked degree after the onset of addiction. Being an addict became almost a full-time occupation, and other roles were necessarily neglected. Marriages ended by divorce or separation, employment became less steady, and crimes became more frequent.

In short, those who became addicted between 1914 and 1940, and those whose addiction began earlier but continued after 1914, differed in many ways from earlier addicts. A drug subculture emerged, they became involved in it, and with this was associated an illicit market in narcotics and more crime. But most drugs were still supplied by physicians; a few were little more than licensed drug peddlers, but more often these physicians were addicts themselves, or simply less well-trained and less competent than the physicians of today. Most had graduated from medical school before the modern improvements in medical education, and as they did not have the scientific knowledge, they also did not have the specific medications available today.

This situation was changing slowly, as attitudes against addiction stiffened, and as better trained physicians replaced the older ones. A major change occurred between 1935 and 1940, and it is likely that this was triggered by the opening of the Lexington hospital. Addicts had been known to law enforcement officials before 1935, but few were charged with an offense, perhaps because this could only lead to imprisonment, which was not perceived as an appropriate step. But after 1935 they could be sent to a hospital, and in the next 5 years there was a drive over much of the State to force the younger male addicts into treatment, by sending them to Lexington as prisoners.

But the usual connotations of imprisonment applied. Addiction, in effect, was redefined as criminal, and as leading to severe punishment. The sudden removal of many addicts from their communities disrupted the channels of drug distribution, and some of the physicians who had supplied them were also sentenced. Other physicians "voluntarily" surrendered their narcotics tax stamps in the course of investigations, and still others suddenly became unwilling to supply narcotics on a regular basis. The source from legal channels was thus markedly restricted, and simultaneously illegal channels were broken up, both in Kentucky and other States. The shipping restrictions of World War II may have contributed to this. Perhaps as important as any of the other factors, public attitudes, which before had regarded addiction as mildly deviant behavior, harmful to the individual and his family, now regarded it as one of the worst of evils, and as a threat to the community. Achieving abstinence was regarded as requiring only an act of will, so when addicts relapsed after treatment they were regarded as hopeless weaklings, or as having chosen evil in place of good.

3. *Addiction Between 1940 and 1963.* The recent period is the best documented, because after 1940 almost all addicts in the State had at least one admission to the Lexington hospital. In addition, more of them were still alive and were interviewed, and memory was better for these recent decades.

Of the older men and the women who had been addicted before 1940, and were obtaining drugs from a physician, most were tacitly allowed to continue their addiction. In these groups, admission to the hospital usually meant that their physicians died or refused to continue prescribing. There was, however, a concerted effort to coerce younger men, and new addicts, into treatment.

The illicit market disappeared, at least in the sense of a market where drugs were always available. For brief periods, narcotics stolen from physicians or in drugstore burglaries might be for sale, or occasional shipments of heroin might enter one or two cities. Even in these cities addiction could not be maintained regularly on illicit drugs, and in most of the State these had completely disappeared. Exempt narcotics, like paregoric or cough syrups, were still used by some addicts, but these too became harder to obtain, and many addicts preferred alcohol to these. For practical purposes, the only remaining source of narcotics that could be regular was physicians.

But the number of physicians willing to prescribe was greatly reduced, by factors already described. The few who were willing would prescribe for only one or two, not for five or ten or more addicts, so those who were already addicted found it more and more difficult to continue. A few found physicians who would prescribe, and continued to be addicted.

Others shifted to substitutes for narcotics, mainly alcohol and barbiturates. Still others became completely abstinent.

Medical treatment, alcoholism, and pleasure-seeking had been the reasons for addiction, in 1914–1940, in 4:5:3 ratio; after 1940 it was a 5:2:1 ratio, among a much smaller number. New addicts were more likely to begin in the context of medical treatment, and this treatment was less questionable than earlier. This is not to say that the use of narcotics represented the best medical judgment, but at least it was no longer obvious even to a layman that it represented poor judgment. Physicians became much less likely to prescribe narcotics in the treatment of alcoholic excesses, and even those who were willing to maintain older addicts on drugs were careful not to produce new addicts. Addicts had difficulty in getting sufficient drugs for their own needs, and were less likely to give some to friends.

The age at onset of addiction continued to increase after 1940, a corollary of the above change in ratio; pleasure-seekers had always been the youngest at onset, alcoholics some 10 years older, and those who began through illness another 10 years older.

But the most striking change was that after 1940 new addicts were much less involved in the drug subculture. Even for those who became involved, the degree of involvement was less. At least five factors help to explain this change.

First, recent addicts began less often through alcoholism and pleasure-seeking, the reasons for addiction most closely associated with later involvement in the drug subculture. Second, they were less often from cities, and city dwellers had been the most involved. Third, they were older at onset, and it was younger subjects who became more involved. Fourth was the further decrease in prevalence; the number of addicts had dropped, and at any given time many were away from their communities, in hospitals or prisons. There were not many addicts left among whom interaction could take place.

Finally, many of the advantages of being in contact with other addicts had disappeared. They were no longer a source of narcotics, nor of information on how drugs could be obtained. If the addict had a physician who would prescribe, the drug was inexpensive enough; if no physician would prescribe, money would not help, because there were no illicit narcotics to be bought. The need for criminal skills, and the subculture's function of teaching them, had disappeared.

After 1940 even more new addicts had criminal records prior to addiction, but the increase in crime after addiction was less, and less serious. Much of their postaddiction crime can be seen as the continuation of an earlier pattern, rather than as the result of addiction. Many postaddiction offenses, indeed, were associated with alcoholism during periods of abstinence from narcotics rather than with narcotics use.

335-199—69——17

New addicts after 1940 continued to be persons who had shown earlier signs of poor social adjustment, as in the 1914–1940 period. There are indications that they were even more inadequate, including many passive, clinging, dependent individuals. Earlier addicts had been active, ingenious seekers after large doses of drugs, who could have been successful in many ways, had it not been for their alcoholism and addiction. Recent addicts were more often described as poor, miserable, useless individuals who would have been failures in any situation, and were less of a nuisance when maintained on small doses of narcotics.

Sex Differences

Throughout this report, on one variable after another it was found that men addicts differed from women addicts. It may be asked if these differences explain why prevalence and incidence have decreased even more for women than for men. If they do, it may also be asked how this explanation fits with the changing patterns of addiction described in the previous section, much of which was based on findings for men alone.

The women began their addiction in the treatment of illness much more often than did men. Only eight women began through the alcohol and pleasure routes; 15 percent as against 53 percent of the men. A larger percentage of women first received narcotics from a physician.

Once they became addicted, the women did not become as involved in the drug subculture as did the men. But there is a further difference here which is even more significant. The eight women who began through alcoholism or pleasure-seeking all became involved in the drug subculture, and seven of them to the highest degree measured in this study; their involvement exceeded that of the corresponding men. But the women who began addiction in the course of medical treatment became less involved than did the men who began in this way. The women, in short, tend to fall at one of the extremes, with no involvement or with much, depending on the way addiction began, while the men cover the entire range of involvement. Almost all showed some, even though the proportion involved also varied for men with the way addiction began.

To some extent, it may be that official eyes were closed to behavior of women which, in men, would have led to a record which in turn would have been coded as a sign of involvement. Thus the smaller increase in crime after addiction, for women, probably reflects in part the fact that they were less likely to be arrested and acquire a record even when they committed as many offenses as men. It is probably also in part due to the fact that when men and women were together involved in addiction, men took greater risks and were more likely to be arrested than their women partners.

But even in criminal activity, if one looks at the offenses subjects admitted having committed rather than at official records, fewer women committed offenses. In other respects, the lesser involvement of women is clear beyond question. Fewer—21 percent against 43 percent of men—obtained all or most of their drugs from illegal sources (this includes friends and relatives as well as peddlers, and a woman was counted as using illegal sources if her husband bought the drug and gave it to her). Women got drugs from fewer sources; 53 percent, against 24 percent of men, got drugs only from one physician at a time. Only 23 percent of women, against 54 percent of men, used the intravenous route of administration.

On each variable in the index of involvement, and on other related variables like the number of sources and the major source of narcotics, the eight women who began addiction for alcoholism or pleasure show a disproportionate number of positive scores. Further, these eight women had more than their share of deviant spouses. Involvement in the drug subculture was more closely associated with having deviant spouses for women than for men. Similarly, involvement was more closely associated with posthospital drug pattern for women than for men; those women with no involvement or with some involvement showed much more abstinence than the corresponding men, but women with much involvement showed just as little abstinence as did the men who were much involved.

The importance of self-concept, and its relative importance for the sexes, may be seen in one explanation of abstinence—that drug use ended when the medical need for which the drug had been given ceased to exist. This explanation was given for nine of 33 women and nine of 88 men.

With only slight over-simplification, it can be said that male addicts show a wide range of patterns of involvement and addiction, but the women fall mainly at the two extremes. At one, the larger number of women had some medical pretext for drug use, obtained drugs from one physician, maintained the self-concept of a patient taking medicine, avoided drug-seeking behavior which would destroy this definition, and either continued to be addicted, if the physician continued to prescribe, or became completely abstinent. At the other extreme, a small number of women began addiction for hedonistic reasons, which they recognized to be such, became even more enmeshed in the drug subculture than most men, obtained drugs from any source, including illegal sources, exhibited much drug-seeking behavior, and continued to be addicted—to narcotics if possible, or to substitutes if necessary.

For both sexes, those addicts who fit the first pattern were likely to become abstinent when physicians ceased prescribing. Most women fit it, and relatively few men. This difference therefore explains one of the striking findings of the followup study, that women became abstinent much more often than men. Those subjects who fit the second pattern were likely to be addicted to narcotics or substitutes and many more men than women fit it, so more men continued to be addicted to some drug. But the few women who fit the second pattern are just as likely as the similar men to continue addiction.

The findings suggest that women are less likely to become deviant, but that those women who do are likely to go the whole distance, and become more deviant than men. Alternatively, the norm for women is higher than for men, so women who become deviant are more visible, and seem more deviant to the observer. It may also be that more serious pathology is required to produce in women than in men behavior as deviant as addiction. The women subjects in this study came from broken homes more often than did the men, and the difference was especially marked in homes broken before subjects were six years old. Possibly relevant to the same point is the fact that psychoneurosis was diagnosed in women subjects more often than in men.

In earlier decades, all the evidence suggests that as many or more women than men became addicted, at a time when attitudes toward addiction were only mildly negative. Kolb long ago attributed the larger decrease in prevalence among women to the fact that women are more ready to conform than men, and therefore gave up their addiction, or resisted becoming addicted, more easily when the norms condemned it more strongly.[9] This seems plausible enough. In addition, another factor seems to be that medical reasons for addiction were always more important for women, so the improvement in medical skills, even if of equal importance for the sexes, would have reduced prevalence more among women.

There may be factors with opposite effect. First, western culture accepts dependence in women more readily than in men, and there is no apparent reason why this acceptance should not extend to dependence on drugs. There are suggestions in this study that once a woman was addicted, physicians were somewhat more willing to maintain her on small doses of narcotics than they were to maintain men, and law enforcement officials were less ready to question this for women than for men. Second, the deterioration in role performance which accompanies addiction under the present control system is less for women, because they exhibit less drug-seeking behavior, and it is less visible, because their primary roles are still within the family. The male addict who does not work, or works much less steadily, is seen as unemployed or operating at a less desirable level; the similar woman addict, in the eyes of most, is still a housewife. Her family may know that she is much less effective than before, but this is easily concealed from others.

It may be guessed, then, that if present trends continue, and new addicts are produced primarily in the course of medical treatment, the incidence of new cases of addiction in Kentucky may again become approximately equal for the sexes. But the number and rate of new cases, for both sexes, will be far below what they were before 1914.

Summary

This study, together with available data and estimates on the extent of narcotic addiction in earlier periods, furnishes strong evidence for the conclusion that prevalence and incidence have greatly decreased in Kentucky over the past 50 years. The exact size of the decrease can only be estimated, but it seems likely that the prevalence in the mid-1960s is on the order of one-tenth the prevalence of 50 years earlier. The decrease in the annual number of new cases of addiction is smaller, but probably the present rate is about one-fifth of the rate around 1914.

Associated with the decrease in the extent of addiction have been changes in the patterns of addiction. Before the passage of the Harrison Act most addicts began drug use in the course of medical treatment, by physicians or self-medication, though treatment of alcoholism and pleasure-seeking were probably also frequent reasons. Few addicts had criminal records before addiction, and there is no reason to believe that many acquired such records after addiction. Addiction posed problems to addicts and their families, as evidenced by the fact that many tried to end their addiction, but was not perceived as posing a direct problem for society.

In the period 1914–1940 there was mounting disapproval of addiction. Some sources of narcotics were cut off: direct purchases of legal narcotics early in the period, illicit narcotics late in the period. The major source was physicians, and this was gradually reduced throughout these years, and markedly reduced in the last 5 years of the period. Fewer persons were becoming addicts, and their characteristics changed. Addiction then tended to occur only in those places where a physician was careless with narcotics, or where there were old addicts to introduce new ones to drug use. More addicts had criminal records before addiction, and the alcohol and pleasure routes to addiction became relatively more important.

The major change, however, was that the contacts between addicts, which had existed before 1914, now came to have functional value, and the characteristics of a drug subculture emerged. This was both effect and cause of other changes; it was associated with an illicit market in narcotics, drug-seeking behavior, teaching and learning of attitudes and skills, an increase in criminal behavior, and with increased pressures toward relapse after treatment for addiction. The existence and even the effectiveness of the subculture in making drugs available to its members eventually contributed to a reduction in the availability of drugs. As drug-seeking behavior was more visible, and addicts were increasingly seen as members of a group wanting narcotics, rather than as individuals asking for medication, physicians, who by 1940 were the only possible regular source of narcotics, became less and less willing to supply narcotics.

After 1940 the addiction pattern began again to resemble what it had been before 1914, except in size. Addiction began more often in the context of medical treatment, and the first drug was less often supplied by an older addict. This was due in part to the fact that there were fewer addicts to recruit new ones, and these few had no narcotics to spare, and probably in part to the fact that inhibitions against experimenting with drugs were stronger, as evidenced by the fact that the proportion of addicts recruited from those with criminal records continued to increase.

Since addiction could be maintained steadily only if a physician would prescribe, involvement with other addicts served fewer practical purposes, and was potentially a threat to the source of narcotics, since it would define the individual to the physician as an addict rather than as a patient. Partly for this reason, and partly because by the 1950s there were few addicts with whom interaction was possible, involvement in the drug subculture decreased. It would be debatable whether what remains of the subculture in Kentucky deserves the name. The trend has certainly been toward the pre-1914 picture, of a number of individual addicts each in contact with his source of supply, but with few significant contacts among the addicts themselves. This number, however, is much smaller in the 1960s than it was before 1914.

The changes in recent decades have had similar effects on men and women, but these effects add up to much more abstinence and a lower incidence for women. The reasons for this are that among women addiction has always been more closely associated with some medical need, with physicians as the source of narcotics, with self-concept as a patient taking medicine rather than a hedonist seeking kicks, and possibly because women are more likely to avoid behavior frowned on by society than are men. Relatively few women began addiction through the alcohol and pleasure routes, and these few became even more involved in the drug subculture, even more deviant than most of the men.

Prevalence and incidence rates of narcotic addiction could, theoretically, approach zero, with the only cases being those of terminally ill patients, an essentially irrelevant group. In practice, given the fact that standards of medical practice will never be uniform, and some patients with questionable need for narcotics will be demanding and difficult for a physician to manage, it seems likely that there will always be a few addicts. There are some elderly addicts in Kentucky who will die within the next decade or two. The number of addicts will therefore decrease slowly for some years, if present trends continue and then will level off, probably at some figure between 100 and 200. These will constitute no particular problem to society, though they will be problems for themselves, their families, and their physicians.

Footnotes, Chapter 15

[1] ADAMS, SAMUEL HOPKINS. *The Great American Fraud.* Chicago: American Medical Association, 1912. p. 66.

[2] BROWN, LUCIUS P. Enforcement of the Tennessee Anti-Narcotics Law. *American Journal of Public Health,* 5:323–333, April 1915. Reprinted in O'DONNELL, JOHN A., and BALL, JOHN C. eds. *Narcotic Addiction.* New York: Harper and Row. 1966, pp. 34–45.

[3] TERRY, CHARLES E., and PELLENS, MILDRED. *The Opium Problem.* New York: Committee on Drug Addiction and Bureau of Social Hygiene, 1928. p. 31.

[4] *Ibid.*

[5] KOLB, LAWRENCE, and DUMEZ, A. G. The prevalence and trend of drug addiction in the United States and factors influencing it. *Public Health Reports,* May 23, 1924. Cited in: Terry and Pellens, *op. cit.* pp. 41–48.

[6] See ISBELL, HARRIS. Historical development of attitudes toward opiate addiction in the United States. In: FARBER, SEYMOUR M., and WILSON, ROGER H. L., eds. *Conflict and Creativity.* New York: McGraw-Hill, 1963. pp. 154–170.

[7] Terry and Pellens, *op. cit.* p. 135.

[8] Brown, *op. cit.* See also: MARSHALL, O. The opium habit in Michigan. Reprinted in: O'DONNELL and BALL, *op. cit.* pp. 45–54.

[9] KOLB, LAWRENCE. Drug addiction among women. *Proceedings of American Prison Association,* 1938. p. 349.

CHAPTER 16

Implications

The findings of this study, and the interpretations which have been given them, seem on the whole to fit into the growing consensus among those social scientists who have studied addiction. There are, however, a few points on which the present data add to earlier formulations, and a few which suggest modifications. This chapter will examine the implications, for theory and for public policy, of the study's findings.

Implications for Theory

1. *Ecology.* Chein, Clausen, Dai, Faris and Dunham and Finestone have emphasized the ecological distribution of addiction. In general, addiction in metropolitan areas has been highly localized in only a few sections, those characterized by poverty, poor housing, low education, crime and delinquency, and other indices of social deprivation and disorganization.[1] In this study no geographical clustering of addicts was observed within villages and towns. In the larger cities of the State there was some clustering, particularly among subjects who began using narcotics for pleasure, in the 1914–40 period, but seemingly not before 1914, and none was evident among the relatively few addicts with onset after 1940.

On the other hand, looking at the State as a whole, addiction has clustered in its urban places. It seems plausible that this was due to the fact that physicians and older addicts, the two major sources of introduction to narcotics use, were more numerous in urban places. The explanation is availability of narcotics, and is analogous to the explanation for the ecological distribution of addicts in metropolitan areas, that addiction is most frequent in the slum areas where underworld connections, including the illicit heroin traffic, exist. But there are signs that this pattern in Kentucky is changing; now addiction begins almost exclusively in the context of medical treatment, and few physicians allow it to begin. The future distribution of addicts is likely to depend on the location of these few, and no data are available to predict where they will be located.

2. *Becoming An Addict.* In Kentucky subjects were introduced to addiction through treatment of illness, treatment of alcoholic excesses, and pleasure-seeking. The last group, and in the writer's opinion the second, resemble fairly closely the white addicts in the metropolitan areas of their day, and in many respects even the minority-group metropolitan addicts of today. The first group, those who began in the context of medical treatment, was the largest in this study, but such addicts are

rare or unrecognized among metropolitan addicts of recent decades. This difference in the relative proportions of subtypes among addicts in Kentucky and those in metropolitan areas is important, and probably explains many of the other differences between subjects in this study and in others. The case descriptions in Lindesmith and Dai, whose subjects had largely been addicted before 1930, suggest that their distribution of subtypes was intermediate between the Kentucky and current metropolitan addicts.

More important than the specific differences between these samples is that the same general processual development applies to all of them. The natural history of the individual addict—his "moral career," in Goffman's term—is similar in all samples, and can be described in terms of the learning processes associated with continued drug use, as these have been outlined by Becker and Lindesmith.[2]

This study would place more weight than do most of the others on personality predispositions. Kentucky addicts had histories of deviant behavior in parents and siblings, of broken homes, and of inability to achieve independence from the parental family, often enough to suggest that some kind of later pathology was to be expected. There were clear signs of social inadequacy, in alcoholism, poor work performance, and poor adjustment in military service, prior to addiction.

3. *The Drug Subculture*. Once addiction began, it led to involvement in the drug subculture and to further deterioration. Here the similarities with and differences from other samples are particularly instructive. Metropolitan addicts are pictured as moving into the drug subculture inevitably,[3] because they need contact with other addicts and pushers to obtain drugs. The Kentucky findings are consistent with this explanation, despite the fact that some avoided, and others had only minimal, involvement with the subculture, because it was the source of drugs that determined the degree of involvement. Those subjects who were able to obtain narcotics regularly from a physician did not need to, and did not, become involved. Those who had no such stable source did become involved, or they became abstinent.

The findings in Kentucky support Cohen's suggestion that "a subculture owes its existence to the fact that it provides a solution to certain problems of adjustment shared among a community of individuals."[4] Before 1914, when addicts had no difficulty in obtaining narcotics, there were no indications that a drug subculture existed. After 1914, when drugs became more difficult to obtain, the subculture emerged, presumably because addicts could supply drugs to each other, or share knowledge about ways of obtaining them. The subculture began to wither away after 1940, partly because there were fewer addicts left to form a group. But a major reason seems to have been that the subculture was no longer effective in solving the common problem, that of obtaining drugs. Narcotics could not be obtained regularly from any source except a physician, and this was easier if the subject was perceived by the physician as an individual patient who needed medication, not as a member of a drug-seeking group.

If this interpretation is correct, the subculture came into existence to solve a common problem, obtaining drugs, and declined when it was no longer an effective solution to that problem. It is to be noted that addicts share other problems, for example the disapproval of their drug use by family and community, and a possible function of a subculture would be to supply the support of a group for maintaining addiction in the face of this disapproval. But this was not sufficient to bring the subculture into existence before 1914, nor to maintain it in recent years. In Kentucky, at least, the subculture was a highly utilitarian one, with the specific function of maintaining access to narcotics.

4. *Definition of Addiction.* There are some differences, which seem to the writer minor ones of viewpoint, between the approach used in this study and that used in others. Lindesmith, for example, defines an addict in terms of his craving for the drug, his tendency to relapse, and his way of life.[5] Chein would define addicts in terms of craving and "total personal involvement . . . the emergence of a personality structure built on narcotics, an associated self-image, and a related way of life." [6] This study has defined an addict in terms of daily use of narcotics, and the other factors emphasized by Lindesmith and Chein as separate variables whose association with that use was to be studied.

The Kentucky data fully support their emphasis on involvement, but show that its degree varies with the social structure within which narcotics are used, the standards of medical practice and the existence or nonexistence of an illicit drug market being the most important aspects of that social structure. It had been hoped that a measure of craving could be developed, but the study failed in this; no data were secured which seemed to be an adequate indication of the absence of craving. Further attempts to develop such a measure, and to study the conditions under which craving wanes and disappears, would contribute much to the understanding of addiction.

That the Kentucky subjects, as much as the group Lindesmith studied, showed a tendency to relapse, is evident. But the useful information about the group seems to be exhausted by giving the percentage who relapsed, or the percentage of time in addicted and other statuses. As applied to a group, in short, tendency to relapse is a statistical measure, an estimate of the probability of relapse. It cannot have such a meaning for the individual addict. It would seem necessary to conceive of an individual's tendency to relapse as a summation (or other combination) of all the individual factors found to be predictive of relapse. Those found to have an association with relapse in this study include degree of involvement in the drug subculture, self-concept as an addict seeking kicks or a patient using medicine, criminal record, preaddiction employment record, and preaddiction alcoholic excesses. Since these associations were significant despite the overwhelming importance of drug availability in explaining abstinence, it is likely that they would be useful predictors of abstinence where availability is held constant, as it may in effect have been constant in those cities with an illicit heroin market.

Lindesmith assigns central importance, in the process of becoming an addict and in the definition of a person as an addict, to the experience of withdrawal illness and learning that it is caused by the absence, and can be ended by the administration, of the usual dose of narcotics.[7] The histories of Kentucky addicts attest the importance of this, but there were also cases in which its importance seemed secondary. Subjects would describe their first shot of narcotics, and their recognition of it as "what I'd been looking for all my life." These were invariably subjects who had experimented with and developed dependence on other drugs, mainly alcohol. They were at least intellectually aware of the characteristics of narcotic addiction, including physical dependence and withdrawal, prior to their first use of narcotics, because they knew addicts well, and received their first shot from addicts.

This is not to deny that their later experience with withdrawal gave new meaning to their awareness, and thus involved new learning, but to suggest that their essential commitment to addiction predated their withdrawal experience. This conception expands, rather than contradicts, Lindesmith's formulation; it suggests that the history to be explained is not the narrow one of narcotics use, but the broader one of drug abuse, in which the specific drug used at different times may be of relatively minor importance. This broader conception may be needed in the future if, as some present information suggests, it is becoming a frequent pattern to use narcotics, alcohol, the barbiturates, amphetamines, hallucinogens and tranquilizers almost interchangeably, with drug preference of some importance, but the relative availability of drugs at different times even more important.[8]

5. *The Crime-Disease Controversy.* The findings in Kentucky are consistent with those of earlier studies in that, once addiction began, the performance of subjects in major roles deteriorated. They had multiple marriages, with frequent divorces and separations. They worked less steadily, or not at all. They became more involved in crime, but here again the details permit some expansion and modification of earlier formulations.

As in earlier studies, there was no indication that drug effects led to crime. Before 1914, when drugs were obtained easily, legally, and inexpensively, crime probably increased little or not at all after addiction. Between 1914 and 1940 it increased only slightly for those who had stable and legal supplies of narcotics, and much more for those who depended largely or entirely on illegal supplies. Some part of this increase is explained by the fact that addicts were increasingly being recruited from the ranks of criminals; more had criminal records before addiction, and to some extent their postaddiction crimes were merely a continuation of an established pattern, not attributable to addiction.

After 1940 the latter explanation became more important. Since narcotics had to be obtained from physicians on some medical basis or pretext, crime did not help in obtaining them. There was still some increase in postaddiction over preaddiction crime, but lesser in extent and in the gravity of offenses than for earlier addicts. More of the postaddiction crime could be seen as a continuation of established patterns—the proportion with preaddiction criminal records had increased to about one-half—and much of it was associated with alcoholism when narcotics were unobtainable, rather than with addiction.

To ask if the addict is a criminal or a sick person, therefore, confuses the issue; [9] the plain fact is that he is often both. In some cases subjects committed no criminal offenses, obtaining both drugs and money for drugs legally. In others, the only offenses were against the drug laws, and these could range from only illegal possession to obtaining drugs on false pretenses or forging prescriptions. In still other cases subjects committed larcenies, burglaries and robberies; these could be attributed to the addiction, but some subjects probably would have been guilty of some of these offenses whether or not they were addicted. Finally, some were professional criminals before the onset of addiction, and probably would have continued even if they had never used narcotics. The real question is not whether all addicts should be handled as criminals, or all as patients. It rather should relate to what can be done for the various subtypes of addicts. To some extent this is a question of public policy, which will be discussed below, but the major importance of so framing the question is to point to the need of experimental studies of treatment methods, and their effectiveness not for addicts in general, but for specified types of addicts.

6. *Anomie.* The most general sociological theory that has been advanced to explain addiction is Merton's theory of anomie. Anomie can arise from a disparity between cultural emphasis on goals that all should achieve, and norms governing the means by which they may be achieved. When paths to success are blocked, one possible role adaptation is retreatism, and addicts are given as one example of retreatists.[10] Cloward and Ohlin have expanded the idea, and suggested that addiction is most likely when both legitimate and illegitimate paths to success are blocked; it is those who fail twice who are most likely to become addicts.[11]

Lindesmith and Gagnon argue that the theory, in either form, cannot be reconciled with the known facts about addiction,[12] and the Kentucky findings support their argument rather than the theory.

Addicts in Kentucky had at least as much opportunity to achieve success as did their nonaddict contemporaries. Their parents were above average in education, their fathers in occupational level, and subjects themselves were above average in education. Some achieved occupational success, in professions or business, despite addiction. Others were on their way to it when addiction began, and their later failure is more easily seen as the result than the cause of addiction. Still others were successful in criminal careers before addiction, and they and others were successful criminals during addiction.

The rates of incidence and prevalence of addiction have dropped in Kentucky over the past 50 years, but no evidence known to the writer suggests that there was a corresponding decrease in anomie. The decrease in addiction did seem to be attributable to aspects of the social structure, but these were specific factors like advances in the standards of medical practice, increased efforts at enforcement of drug laws, and increasing public disapproval of drug use. It could be argued that these reflect a decrease in anomie, not necessarily general but in the areas that would affect drug use, but such a *post hoc* explanation is not persuasive. It seems more conservative to conclude that the anomie theory finds no support in Kentucky addiction.

This, of course, does not disprove the theory, or even weaken it to any appreciable extent. Here the differences between addicts in Kentucky and elsewhere may be important. Anomie and blocked opportunities may explain the addiction among minority groups, and in the slum areas of large cities. The latter were the addicts Cloward and Ohlin seem to have had in mind.[13]

7. *Maturing Out of Addiction.* Finally, the Kentucky data furnish no support for a specific theory of addiction, Winick's explanation of how addicts "mature out" of addiction. The explanation notes that addiction frequently begins in the late teens and early twenties, when the person faces problems of sex, aggressiveness, and vocation. If it ends in the thirties, this may be because, "as a result of some process of emotional homeostasis, the stresses and strains of life are becoming sufficiently stabilized for the typical addict so that he can face them without the support provided by narcotics."[14] The fact to be explained was that many addicts disappeared from the files of the Federal Bureau of Narcotics, around the age of 35.

Since 1953, addicts have been reported to the Bureau on a standard form. When reported, the person is counted as an "Active Addict," and remains in this classification for a minimum of 5 years. If reported again, a new 5-year period begins in the active file for him. But if he is not reported within 5 years he is shifted from the active to the inactive file, on the assumption, supported by Bureau experience, that "it is practically impossible for an addict who has reverted to drug use to avoid coming to the attention of the authorities . . ."[15]

Winick analyzed data on 7,234 addicts who were originally reported during 1955, and who were removed from the active file at the end of 1960 because they had not been reported again. Winick treated the transfer to the inactive file as equivalent to the cessation of addiction, and concluded that about two-thirds of addicts eventually cease using narcotics, many of them in their thirties.

The Kentucky data indicate more abstinence with age, and in this sense are consistent with Winick's findings. But detailed analysis suggests that maturation does not explain the abstinence. In the summer of 1963 subjects in the Kentucky study were checked against both a master file on all individuals ever known to the Bureau of Narcotics, and the separate file of those reported under the procedure established in 1953. Of the 21 subjects who were classified as addicted to narcotics when they were interviewed for this study, two had never been known to the Bureau. Of the 19 known, though their addiction had been steady, for decades in most cases, only one was reported and counted as an active addict between 1953 and 1963. Five were mentioned in the Bureau's master file after 1953, in connection with investigations in which they were suspected of narcotics use or sales, but the evidence was not strong enough so that they were formally reported as addicted. Seven more were reported to the Bureau as addicted, in or after 1953, but they were reported as receiving their narcotics from one physician each, were regarded as medical addicts, and therefore were not counted as active addicts.

For these 21 subjects, therefore, eight were never reported to the Bureau between 1953 and 1963. Addiction was known in seven more cases, and reasonably suspected in five others, but these were not counted as active addicts. Though all 21 were addicted, only one was counted as an active addict.

This points up one problem in equating absence from the active file with abstinence, but is not a fair test of Winick's conclusions. He dealt only with those addicts who once were in the active file and were dropped from it. The best comparison, therefore, would be restricted to those subjects who had been reported under the new procedure.

Seventeen male subjects and one female had been reported to the Bureau under the new procedure since 1953. The woman and five of the men were reported in recent years, less than five years before the records were checked. Twelve of the men, however, were last reported between 1953 and 1958; at least 5 years had elapsed for 11 of them, and almost 5 years for the twelfth.

In this group of 12 subjects, the situation is exactly that studied by Winick, in that they were reported under the current procedure of the Bureau, and were transferred to the inactive file after 5 years had passed during which they were not reported again. Five of the 12 died within the 5-year period. One was in prison throughout this period and after it. Three were using narcotics during and after the period except when institutionalized. Two spent part of the period in prison, then were abstinent from narcotics, but were alcoholics. Only one, the man seen just before his 5-year period ended, was completely abstinent for most of the period.

In only one case of the 12, therefore, were there both a cessation of addiction and a possibility that this was due to maturation. Two more ceased to be addicted, but their use of alcohol suggests this was due to inability to obtain narcotics. One ceased because he was in prison, five died, and the remaining three were still addicted, but were not so reported.

These facts do not destroy Winick's thesis. The Kentucky addicts used narcotics obtained legally, and were not likely to be arrested and reported to the Bureau. They were middle-aged or elderly, and if their use was reported, they were likely to be seen as "medical addicts," who are not included in the Bureau's count of active addicts. Heroin users, on the other hand, who make frequent purchases of the drug from peddlers, using money they have obtained by crimes, are clearly more likely to come to the attention of law enforcement agencies, and to be reported to the Bureau. Winick's conclusions may, therefore, be correct for illicit heroin users, who form the bulk of addicts today. But it is clear that it would be desirable to study a sample dropped from the Bureau's active file, to see to what extent the absence of a new report indicates maturing out of addiction.

The absence of a report within 5 years may be due to inadequacies in the reporting system, and some unknown number who are transferred to the inactive file may be continuing to use drugs illegally. Others have been redefined as medical addicts, but are still addicted. Some others—and this study suggests that the number may be fairly large—are dead. Still others may not be reported again because the first report was based on an arrest which led to a long sentence, and they are still in prison. Finally, of those who are still alive, not institutionalized, and not using narcotics, some are abstinent only or mainly because they cannot obtain narcotics, and of these many may be alcoholics or addicted to other kinds of drugs. Only when these are sorted out can it be possible to test the hypothesis that maturation accounts for the abstinence of the remainder.

Implications for Policy

What public policy should be toward the addiction problem is fundamentally a moral question, and the social scientist has no special competence in answering it. But the answer must depend on judgments about the harm done by addiction to addicts and to others, and about the probable benefits and costs of different programs. Social science studies can throw light on these, and on the basis of such studies some students have advocated radical changes from current policies. Schur, for example, described present drug laws as unenforceable.

> What have these legal policies accomplished? Law enforcement officials often assert that addiction is being kept under control, yet even government estimates have placed the number of addicts between 45,000 and 60,000, and almost all nongovernmental experts feel these figures greatly understate the problem. In any case, it is certain that these laws have not come anywhere close to eliminating addiction . . .[16] basically, it is the supply-and-demand element and the lack of a complaining victim, rather than the cleverness of the law violators, that render the drug laws so largely unenforceable.[17]

But it cannot be said that the laws were unenforceable in Kentucky. Even if the estimate of the size of the decrease in prevalence, made in the previous chapter, is incorrect, there can hardly be any doubt that there was a large decrease. Enforcement of the drug laws was only one factor in causing it, and perhaps not the most important; improvements in medical practice, mounting public disapproval of drug use, and even such factors as the shipping restrictions during World War II also explain the decrease. It is impossible to sort out the effects of each, but it would also be impossible to deny that law enforcement had some effect.

But perhaps it was important only in Kentucky, and the findings of this study are irrelevant for the nation as a whole. To evaluate this possibility, it is necessary to distinguish between the effects of law enforcement on preventing the diversion of narcotics from legitimate channels of distribution, and its effects on the illicit distribution of heroin smuggled into the country. Law enforcement in Kentucky was effective in reducing the availability of narcotics from legitimate channels, and there is no apparent reason why similar efforts should not be, and no reason known to the writer to suggest that they have not been, equally successful in other States. The pattern of addiction that existed in Kentucky up to the late 1930s, the maintenance of addiction by physicians, used to be common in the South, and probably in all States.[18] But recent studies of addicts do not suggest it is now common anywhere in the United States. For this aspect of enforcement, it seems justified to generalize from the Kentucky experience to the whole country.

Law enforcement also succeeded in destroying the illicit drug traffic in Kentucky, and it would seem probable that it has succeeded, or could

335-199—69——18

succeed, in comparable situations—in towns and small cities where addicts are highly visible. The fact that many addicts used to come to the Lexington and Fort Worth hospitals from towns and small cities, while in recent decades almost all have come from large metropolitan areas,[19] suggests that the illicit traffic has disappeared, or has been greatly reduced, except for the large metropolitan areas. But it is clear that efforts which succeeded in smaller cities might not work in large ones, and indeed the persistence of the heroin traffic demonstrates that efforts have not been equally successful there.

Even this, however, does not show that such efforts have been completely ineffectual in metropolitan areas. It may be noted that Schur bases his judgment that the drug laws are unenforceable on three points. The first is that addiction, like the two other forms of deviant behavior he discusses, abortion and homosexuality, is a crime without a victim; that is, the addict, the woman who seeks an illegal abortion and the homosexual enter the illegal transaction voluntarily, and are not likely to complain to the police against the pusher who sells drugs, the abortionists, or the homosexual partner.

This is true, certainly makes the job of the police more difficult, and tempts police to use methods which approach or violate the limits our society will tolerate. But Schur does not distinguish differences which certainly exist among these three types of crimes. Most addicts today have records of arrests and sentences.[20] Probably only a small proportion of homosexuals do, and the percentage among women who have had abortions must be minute.

Some of the arrests of addicts are the result not of violations of drug laws, but of other crimes committed to get money. The victims of their larcenies do complain to the police. Many also result from illegal transfers of drugs. The fact that there is an illicit drug distribution system carries the usual connotations of a system; there must be some regularity, some predictable recurrent activities, for the system to work. These give the police opportunities to interfere, even though no participant in the system has complained. The addict normally must make his connection with the pusher several times a day, and the meeting places, while they vary, are relatively small in number.[21] If he can be kept under surveillance, he will lead detectives to the pusher. Similar methods are not available for the other crimes without victims. The woman who has had an abortion is not likely to need another until some time has elapsed. Homosexual activity falls somewhere between the others in this respect, probably much closer to abortion.

Schur's second reason for calling the drug laws unenforceable is that they have not eliminated addiction. By this standard all laws are unenforceable. In effect, Schur contrasts the existing number of addicts with the desirable number, zero. The best comparison would be with the expected number of addicts, if the present system of control were not in effect. In lieu of that, the comparison should be with the number of addicts at some past point in time, before the present system went into effect.

Schur gives a third reason why drug laws are unenforceable, the supply-and-demand element. Chein also argues that, barring an enormous and impractical increase in law enforcement efforts, such efforts "cannot possibly have much impact on the volume of the illegal narcotics traffic if there is not, independently, a great reduction in demand."[22] This is due to the fact

> that illegal narcotics are not in a normal commodity market. The customers have long since established themselves as individuals virtually immune to competing situations, so vital does this commodity seem to them . . . The higher the price, the more desperate the stratagems to which these consumers will resort . . .[23]

We are to take literally, in short, the statement that addiction involves a developing "bondage to the drug." [24] In Lindesmith's words, the addict's desire for the drug

> is not casual or vague, but is a powerful motive driving him to seek satisfaction in the face of almost insuperable obstacles and at the cost of unbelievable sacrifices. A universal aspect of the behavior of addicts is that they permit little or nothing to stand between them and the drug.[25]

These statements come close to describing the behavior of many addicts, in some stages of their addiction, but on the face of it such general statements are not likely to be true of all addicts at all times. They state that narcotics are exempt from the economic laws that govern all other goods, and addicts are unlike all other men. The statements certainly do not hold for addicts in Kentucky. When narcotics became more difficult to obtain, some resorted to more desperate stratagems, but other shifted to more available drugs, and still others became abstinent. There were many methods by which drugs could be obtained, and these could be roughly graded on a continuum from acceptability to nonacceptability. Subjects varied on where they drew the line, and a few might have used any means to continue their addiction, but it is certain that most refused to use some of the means open to them. Most did not take even the relatively simple step of moving from Kentucky to cities where illicit narcotics could be bought.

The possibility cannot be ruled out that the Kentucky subjects were different in this regard from other addicts. But the simpler explanation is that Schur, Chein and Lindesmith are exaggerating, and making an absolute of, the unquestioned tendency of addicts to continue their addiction if they can. It may be noted that Chein, for example, does not cite data to show that any specified sample of addicts used new and desperate means, but continued their addiction, as prices rose. His is an abstract economic argument, reminiscent of the iron law of wages, or other early economic analyses. Granting the assumption of economic man, or of the addict as someone who will do anything to get drugs, the conclusions are impeccable; but real people are found not to be economic men, and most addicts do draw the line somewhere.

A further point is that Chein studied adolescent addicts. Even if it were true, during their early stage of addiction, that nothing would make them give up drug use, this would not justify the inference that it would always be true of them. Similarly, Lindesmith's subjects were, for the most part, still using narcotics—though one was abstinent for fifteen years.[26] The relevant difference between these samples and the Kentucky sample may be that the latter was studied late enough for abstinence to appear, and thus to make it evident that some addicts do not continue addiction at the price of any behavior necessary. This must be true in New York City and elsewhere, because the followup studies cited in chapter 3 show that some addicts achieved abstinence there too.

The argument that the drug laws are unenforceable therefore rests on weak grounds: a comparison of present prevalence with the desirable zero rate, instead of with expected or past rates; an analogy between addiction and abortion and homosexuality which is partly revealing and partly misleading; and an exaggerated perception of the addict as a person who will do anything to obtain drugs. The present system of social control of addiction has worked reasonably well in Kentucky, and has not yet been demonstrated to be a complete failure in New York or elsewhere.

The belief that the present system has failed is one basis, but not the only one, for suggestions that it should be changed. Several, for example, have suggested that the addiction problem be taken away from the police and turned over to the medical profession. This is usually associated with the suggestion that narcotics be made available to addicts legally and cheaply. This would remove their need to commit crimes to get money for drugs; it would recognize the addict as a sick person, and put him in the hands of those who can, or can learn to, treat him.[27]

The findings of the Kentucky study do not, in the opinion of the writer, warrant taking sides on this controversy. But they do point to four problems that would arise if the suggestion were adopted. The problems are probably soluble, but the solutions should be sought before the change is made.

It does appear reasonable to assume that crimes by addicts to obtain narcotics would diminish if drugs were made available cheaply and legally. In Kentucky, the increase in criminal behavior after the onset of addiction was least for those who had a stable, legal source of narcotics, and greatest for those who depended on illicit sources. While there is no statistical justification to generalize from Kentucky addicts to present day metropolitan addicts, it is plausible that they are alike in that they would not steal to buy diluted and expensive drugs if they were given potent and cheap drugs. It is not likely that all crimes by addicts would end, as long as addicts are recruited largely from among criminals, but it is probable that a legal supply of drugs would reduce the number of crimes. What costs might have to be paid for this and other benefits of the proposal?

One would be the maintaining of addiction in some persons who otherwise would have become abstinent. It was clear in Kentucky that some subjects gave up their addiction when it became impossible, or even only difficult, to obtain narcotics. Most, almost certainly, would have continued to be addicted if the drugs had been furnished to them. Followup studies in New York and California have shown that a fairly large percentage of addicts there also eventually become abstinent; it is a guess, but a reasonable one, that many of them too would remain addicted if drugs were given to them.

The Kentucky study showed that while several variables distinguished, to a statistically significant degree, between subjects who became abstinent and those who did not, these variables did not efficiently predict which would, and which would not, become abstinent. Such predictors might be discovered, and if they are, a program for addicts could give drugs to one addict, because he would relapse anyway, and withhold drugs from another, because he can be abstinent. Until such predictors are established, it would be necessary to supply drugs to all, and the putative benefits some would receive would be balanced by the maintenance of unnecessary addiction in others. This would seem a high price to the families of those Kentucky subjects who achieved abstinence, and even to some of the subjects themselves; they did not become abstinent willingly, but most now profess thanks that they did.

A second problem is the question of whether such a program would lead to an increase in addiction. Chein feels sure this would not happen, and attacks the expectation of an increase by the following ironical presentation of its logic:

> The logic of the expectation of an increase is simple—childishly simple: A person who takes a narcotic must have got both the idea of taking it and the supply from someone else; therefore, addiction is contagious; therefore, every addict is the narcotics analogue of a "Typhoid Mary"; therefore, anything which makes it easier for addicts to get along in the open environment is bound to bring with it an epidemic; therefore, permitting physicians to use their own discretion about prescribing narcotics for addicts is bound to increase the number of addicts.[28]

The straw man Chein erects is demolished, but it is not the only logic which predicts more new addicts, though not necessarily an epidemic, under the proposed policy. An increase could be expected because similar causes and conditions are likely to produce similar results.

The proposal could not be put into effect unless public disapproval of addiction declined, or, if drugs were supplied to addicts under an approved program, people would come to believe that the use of drugs cannot be too bad. The new program would therefore operate in a climate like that of the 1920s, or earlier. It would also resemble that period in that there would be more addicts—those maintained on drugs who otherwise would have been forced into abstinence.

Under such conditions in the past, some addicts did introduce others to narcotics. In Kentucky, one male subject in four, and one out of six female subjects, were first given narcotics by addicted friends or relatives. In additional cases, where a physician supplied the first narcotic, the physician was an addict. It is not that every addict was a "Typhoid Mary," converting many others into addicts, but that some addicts did, in fact, introduce one or two others to drugs. The numbers were small, and never added up to an epidemic in Kentucky, but 30 or 40 years ago they added up to higher totals than today.

The logic, then, is that a return to old conditions is likely to mean a return to the old prevalence. The presumption could be rebutted by evidence that addicts have changed, or that motives which once led them to give drugs to friends no longer operate, or that the program or other factors will enforce different behavior in the future. In the absence of such evidence, it is not illogical to expect an increase in prevalence if drugs were made available to Kentucky addicts. The increase might be much short of an epidemic, but any increase would trouble many Kentuckians.

These first two problems relate to a general consideration. In any national program which deals with a highly localized problem, it is possible that its effects will differ in different places. The present complex of policies and attitudes has reduced the addiction problem in Kentucky, and probably in most parts of the country. If it has failed in New York City and other areas, and a new policy would ease their difficulties at the cost of some increase in Kentucky and elsewhere, it becomes an ethical problem to balance benefits and costs, and a political question whether Kentucky and other States will be willing to pay the price.

A third problem can be dismissed quickly. Addiction could not simply be handed over to the medical profession without supervision. Only a minute fraction of physicians would abuse their responsibility, but even a very small number could create and maintain a great deal of addiction. A policing mechanism might be established within the profession, but some social control would be needed. But the point does not require extended discussion; the solution would not be difficult.[29]

The final problem also relates to the medical profession. Clinics might be established in New York and other centers of addiction, as Chein and others have suggested, but they would be impractical in towns and small cities where there are only two or three addicts. There, the dispensing of drugs would have to be handled by the local physicians. In Kentucky, most of them want no part of it. As Schur has pointed out, one of the functions of the present policies on addiction may be to remove from physicians a responsibility that they are happy not to have.[30] The new policy would have to overcome the reluctance of physicians, and establish a structured relationship between addicts and physicians which would satisfy both. This study suggests two considerations which would facilitate this.

Clinics could aim to help addicts solve their manifold problems, and eventually, in many cases, to give up their addiction. But it would be a mistake to aim at a psychotherapeutic role for the individual physician who would be treating one or a few addicts. In general, he does not possess the needed skills, nor the time and interest required to learn and apply them. It would be necessary to define his role as simply maintaining the addiction by supplying narcotics. For this purpose it would be unnecessary and undesirable that he be required to see the addict frequently, to write a prescription or dispense narcotics every day or every few days. It would seem sufficient that he see the addict as frequently as his professional judgment requires, and that in the intervals the addict be supplied through other channels.

This could be through pharmacies, if narcotics prescriptions were made renewable. It would probably be desirable that the addict be required to have his prescription filled frequently, perhaps every day, so that he would not be able to increase his dosage beyond what the physician judges to be correct, and so that he would not have on hand quantities much greater than for his own immediate needs, which he might impulsively offer to others. Once again, there would be a role for an enforcement agency to see that the system is not abused.

In summary, the findings of this study would not suggest any major changes in the way addiction is handled in Kentucky. The complex of laws, policies, day-to-day applications of both, public attitudes, and standards of medical practice which has existed for some decades has succeeded in reducing the prevalence of narcotic addiction. Enforcement of law is, in practice, flexible and reasonable enough so that there is little reason for physicians to feel it interferes with their practice of medicine, and in fact few of those interviewed in the course of this study do feel this. This flexibility extends to the point that some addicts are being maintained on regular doses that most physicians would regard as medically unjustified. There is an element of unfairness in this, from the viewpoint of ex-addicts, who feel that others with no more need for narcotics receive drugs, while they cannnot find a physician who will prescribe. But almost certainly less harm is done in these cases than would be done by any approach effective enough to end all dubious maintenance on narcotics.

A reasonable approach might be to keep the present system in its major outlines, and make tentative and experimental approaches toward the new proposals, and toward current practices in Kentucky. Rather than aim at having physicians take over the entire problem of addiction at once, those individual physicians who are interested in it could be permitted and encouraged to experiment with a few addicts each. If they consult with colleagues before maintaining an addict on narcotics, thus obtaining support for the decision that narcotics should be administered, they would have nothing to fear from law enforcement officials. Indeed, it would be desirable to consult with these officials too. A few such experiments are already in existence.

The benefits of such an approach, assuming that its effects are carefully evaluated and communicated to the medical profession, would not be only in what would be learned, nor in the fact that such trials could be discontinued quickly and easily if unanticipated ill effects outweigh the good. If they succeed, or even if they only show that the benefits somewhat exceed the costs, they will simultaneously establish the grounds for expanding the program and interest other physicians in taking part in it. The latter may be the more important consideration.

Other Implications

This study also has implications for the operation of the Lexington hospital, and by a simple extension for the Fort Worth hospital too.

This is only the fourth follow-up study of Lexington patients in 30 years, and only the second which was undertaken by hospital staff. Since it was started, two additional studies have been done on Lexington patients and one on Fort Worth patients.[31] All of these studies have relevance for evaluation of the hospital programs, but none was designed specifically to measure their effects. It seems evident that a regular program of such studies, especially studies designed to test specific forms of treatment, with experimental and control groups, is needed.

When the two Federal hospitals were conceived, it was as much as institutions to do research on addiction as to offer treatment. But the need for discovering what kinds of treatment were effective, and for what types of patients, was soon forgotten, not by hospital staff, but somewhere along the budgetary chain on which support depended.

If the millions of dollars spent to operate the two hospitals had been accompanied by a few hundred thousand dollars for research, it is likely that some treatment approaches could by now have been dropped as worthless, more promising ones expanded, and perhaps more effective ones developed.

In the past five years a beginning toward clinical research was made, as small amounts of money were furnished to support it. In 1967 the hospitals became part of the National Institute of Mental Health, and research became their primary mission.

This will require changes in the hospital programs so that research designs can be implemented. It may mean, for example, construction or modification of buildings so that different treatment groups can be separated, or keeping the number of patients admitted enough below hospital capacity so that ward transfers dictated by research as well as treatment considerations can be made quickly and easily. This implies changes in budgetary procedures; the hospitals' budgets should be based on the missions assigned to them, not, as is partly true now, on the number of beds filled by patients. Indeed, effective treatment and competent research may require a marked reduction in the number of patients, with no decrease or even an increase in staff to serve and study them.

The hospitals cannot be expected to have much effect on patients who remain only a few days or weeks. At the other extreme, treatment will presumably be less effective if patients are required to remain months or years after the optimal release point, as judged by the treatment staff. This implies that voluntary patients should not be admitted unless they can be required to remain for some minimal period, and prisoners should be eligible for parole so that hospital staff and the Parole Board can exercise judgment in setting the date of release. The first need may be met by the Narcotic Addict Rehabilitation Act of 1966 which provides for civil commitment. The second would also require a new law, restoring parole eligibility where it is now denied.

Footnotes, Chapter 16

[1] CHEIN, ISIDOR; GERARD, DONALD L.; LEE, ROBERT S.; and ROSENFELD, EVA. *The Road to H*. New York: Basic Books, 1964. pp. 17–74.

CLAUSEN, JOHN A. Social patterns, personality and adolescent drug use. In: LEIGHTON, ALEXANDER H., *et al.* eds. *Explorations In Social Psychiatry.* New York: Basic Books, 1957. pp. 230–277.

DAI, BINGHAM. Opium Addiction in Chicago. Shanghai: The Commercial Press, 1937. pp. 88–89, 189.

FARIS, ROBERT E. L., and DUNHAM, H. WARREN. *Mental Disorders in Urban Areas.* Chicago: University of Chicago Press, 1939. p. 170.

FINESTONE, HAROLD. Narcotics and criminality. *Law and Contemporary Problems,* 22:12, Winter 1957.

[2] BECKER, HOWARD. *Outsiders.* New York: The Free Press, 1963. pp. 41–78.

LINDESMITH, ALFRED R. *Opiate Addiction.* Bloomington: Principia Press, 1947.

[3] SCHUR, EDWIN M. *Crimes Without Victims.* Englewood Cliffs, N.J.: Prentice-Hall, 1965. p. 140.

[4] COHEN, ALBERT K., *Delinquent Boys, The Culture of the Gang.* New York: The Free Press, 1955, p. 148.

[5] Lindesmith, *op. cit.* pp. 46–63.

[6] Chein, *op. cit.* p. 26.

[7] Lindesmith, *op. cit.* pp. 67–83.

[8] LUDWIG, ARNOLD M., and LEVINE, JEROME. Patterns of hallucinogenic drug abuse. *Journal of the American Medical Association,* 191:92–96, January 11, 1965.

HAMBURGER, ERNEST. Barbiturate use in narcotic addicts. *Journal of the American Medical Association,* 189: 365–368, August 3, 1963.

[9] The question is common in the literature, e.g. in Finestone, *op. cit.,* and Schur, *op. cit.* See also *Drug Addiction: Crime or Disease?* Bloomington, Indiana: Indiana University Press, 1961.

[10] MERTON, ROBERT K. *Social Theory and Social Structure.* New York: The Free Press, 1957, p. 153.

[11] CLOWARD, RICHARD A., and OHLIN, LLOYD *E. Delinquency and Opportunity.* New York: The Free Press, 1960. pp. 178–184.

[12] LINDESMITH, ALFRED R., and GAGNON, JOHN. Anomie and drug addiction. In: CLINARD, MARSHALL B. ed. *Anomie and Deviant Behavior.* New York: The Free Press, 1964. pp. 158–188.

[13] There are still serious difficulties in testing the anomie theory. Fundamentally, it holds that anomie is only one of the causes of deviant behavior; there are other causes, not all of which are specified. Further, anomie does not invariably produce deviant behavior; "countervailing mechanisms," not all of which are specified, can prevent the appearance of deviant behavior despite the existence of anomie. If both anomie and deviance are observed, the former may be seen as cause of the latter; if only anomie is observed, the countervailing mechanisms have prevented the deviant behavior; if only deviant behavior is seen, it must have been produced by one of the other causes. Any conceivable set of empirical findings, in short, fits the theory. What is needed is specification of some empirical findings which could disconfirm the theory.

[14] WINICK, CHARLES. Maturing out of narcotic addiction. *Bulletin on Narcotics,* 14:5, January-March 1962.

[15] *Ibid.* p. 2.

[16] Schur, *op. cit.* p. 134.

[17] *Ibid.* p. 135.

[18] BALL, JOHN C. Two patterns of narcotic drug addiction in the United States. *Journal of Criminal Law, Criminology and Police Science,* 56: 203–211, June 1965.

[19] BALL, JOHN C., *et al.* Characteristics of hospitalized narcotic addicts. *Health, Education and Welfare Indicators.* U.S. Department of Health, Education, and Welfare, March 1966. pp. 17–26.

[20] Almost all who are counted as active addicts by the Bureau of Narcotics are reported by law enforcement agencies, when they are charged with or sentenced for some law violation. Of close to 1,700 addict patients admitted to the Lexington hospital in 1965, four out of five of whom were voluntary admissions, 84 percent admitted a history of arrests.

[21] MILLS, JAMES. The World of Needle Park. *Life,* Volume 58, February 26, 1965.

[22] Chein, *op. cit.* p. 371.
[23] *Ibid.* p. 370.
[24] Schur, *op. cit.* p. 122.
[25] Lindesmith, *op. cit.* p. 46.
[26] *Ibid.* p. 127.
[27] Committee on Public Health, Subcommittee on Drug Addiction. Report on drug addiction. *Bulletin of the New York Academy of Medicine,* 31:592–607, August 1955. See also Chein, *op. cit.* pp. 369–386.
[28] Chein, *op. cit.* p. 376.
[29] Since this paragraph was written, the 1965 report of Great Britain's Drug Addiction Committee has been published. It notes a recent increase in heroin and cocaine addiction in Great Britain, and attributes this to "the activity of a very few doctors who have prescribed excessively for addicts." It recommends that addicts be "notified to a central authority," that special treatment centers be established, and that the prescribing of heroin and cocaine to addicts, by doctors other than those on the staffs of these treatment centers, be made a statutory offense. See Drug addiction: The second report of the interdepartmental committee, *International Journal of the Addictions,* 1: 131–146, January 1966.
[30] Schur, *op. cit.* p. 162. Schur also refers to a recent "apparent willingness to accept increased responsibility for the treatment and management of addicts" on the part of the medical profession. This writer questions the willingness; the proposal is usually that some other physicians, or an official agency like the U.S. Public Health Service, take the responsibility.
[31] These studies are identified in footnotes 2, 4, 5, 6, 7 and 8 of Chapter 1.

APPENDIX A

Selection of the Sample

The universe to be sampled was first defined as including all persons admitted to the Lexington hospital as addicts who had been residents of Kentucky at the time of their first admission, provided that there had been at least one discharge prior to 1960. Individual patients were identified as belonging to the universe by two independent procedures; names were listed from the hospital's register of admissions, and were also listed from a file which contains a card for each person ever admitted. In this way names missed by one procedure were found by the other, and errors inherent in identifying individuals from over 70,000 admissions were minimized.

The universe thus became a list of 1,063 individuals. Only 50 of these were Negro, and all the others white. The number of Negroes was too small for any useful comparisons, so the universe was redefined to include only whites.

It was decided that the sample size should be about 300, in the expectation that this number would provide at least 100 deaths, and at least 100 still living.

One or more patients had been admitted from 106 of Kentucky's 120 counties. Nineteen counties had furnished only one patient each, while one had sent 249 patients to the hospital. Five metropolitan counties included 39 percent of patients in the universe, while the 21 most rural counties included only 7 percent of the universe.

Sampling by random selection of individuals would therefore have meant that only a small proportion of subjects would be from the more rural counties, and from those counties which had furnished only one or a few addicts. The major goals of the study, however, required that such cases be well represented. This argued for sampling by counties. Further, it was planned to check official records, such as police and county court records, and such checks could be done almost as quickly on all subjects from a county as on a few of them. In addition, interest in the extent to which a drug subculture existed in counties with only a few admissions required that all subjects in such counties be interviewed. On the other hand, it would be impractical to interview all patients from the largest county, with its 249 patients.

Arbitrary decisions were used to solve these problems. While the five metropolitan counties included 39 percent of the universe, only one-third of the sample was to be selected from them. The remaining 200 cases would be selected from the rest of the State. Several steps were therefore used in the sample selection.

For the metropolitan part of the sample, the procedure was as follows. One-fifth of the patients were randomly selected from the county with most admissions, and one-fourth of patients from the county with the next largest number. Of the three remaining counties then classified by the Census as Standard Metropolitan Statistical Areas, one was randomly selected.

Table A1 shows how the remaining counties in the sample were selected. The upper half shows in a 4 x 5 table the 101 nonmetropolitan counties from which patients were admitted. One axis runs from the most urban to the most rural counties, and the other is based on the total number of patients admitted from the county. Placement of counties on the first axis is taken from Aurbach's study of the urban-rural continuum in Kentucky.[1] The cutting points on the other axis were chosen to make it possible to sample from counties with only one admission and from those with only a few admissions, and to equalize as much as possible the total number of patients in each row of the table. From the cells in the "total" column, it was evident that if approximately one-third of the counties in each row were selected, the total number of subjects would be close to the goal of 200 nonmetropolitan subjects.

Table A1. Counties in Kentucky, and counties in sample, by urban-rural status of counties and number of addict patients admitted (number of individuals in parentheses)

Number of patients, 1935–1959	Most Urban			Most Rural	Total
	Counties in Kentucky				
1	2 (2)	8 (8)	4 (4)	5 (5)	19 (19)
2–5	12 (43)	14 (43)	7 (28)	13 (39)	46 (153)
6–10	7 (48)	6 (45)	4 (28)	2 (12)	19 (133)
11–20	6 (101)	2 (23)	3 (43)	1 (16)	12 (183)
21–33	3 (84)	—	2 (49)	—	5 (133)
Total	30 (278)	30 (119)	20 (152)	21 (72)	101 (621)
	Counties in Sample				
1	1 (1)	2 (2)	1 (1)	2 (2)	6 (6)
2–5	4 (10)	5 (17)	2 (9)	4 (11)	15 (47)
6–10	3 (22)	2 (15)	1 (6)	1 (6)	7 (49)
11–20	1 (16)	1 (12)	1 (12)	1 (16)	4 (56)
21–33	1 (21)	—	1 (22)	—	2 (43)
Total	10 (70)	10 (46)	6 (50)	8 (35)	34 (201)

The procedure used for selecting counties can be exemplified by considering the third row of the upper table, the counties from which 6 to 10 patients had been admitted.

There were 19 such counties, so six or seven should be selected for the sample, with six having twice the chance of seven to be chosen. Using a random number table, seven happened to be selected as the number of counties to be chosen from this row. It had been ruled that if any cell was occupied, it should be represented in the sample, so selection began in the cell with the smallest number of counties. For the third row, this was the "most rural" cell, with two counties, and one of these two was randomly selected. In the second cell of the row there were six counties, of which two were randomly selected. There were then four counties to be selected from the first and third cells in the row, in either a 3:1 or 2:2 ratio. The ratio was randomly selected first, then the individual counties in the cells.

This procedure resulted in the sample distribution of counties and individuals shown in the bottom half of Table A1. Adding to this the three metropolitan counties, the sample consisted of slightly less than 300 individuals in 37 counties. It will be recalled, however, that this selection was based on the information contained in a card file and a register of admissions. When individual case records of sample subjects were abstracted, several subjects were removed because it was found that they had not been residents of Kentucky. In another case the address was an error, and its correction lost a one-patient county, adding the subject to a county in the 2–5 patient group. Such changes brought the sample size to 285 individuals in 36 counties.

During the field work, it was established that seven of these patients had not been residents of Kentucky, though they had given a Kentucky address. Twelve more had not been addicted to narcotics, but to other drugs. These 19 cases were removed, and the final sample size was 266 subjects.

No cases were selected to replace those so removed from the sample. The selection procedure justifies the inference that, if a different sample had been chosen by the same methods, approximately the same number of nonnarcotic addicts, and of nonresidents, would have been identified. No bias, therefore, is introduced by dropping these cases from the sample.

Footnotes, Appendix A

[1] AURBACH, HERBERT A., *An Empirical Study In The Application Of The Folk-Urban Typology to The Classification Of Social Systems.* Doctoral Dissertation, University of Kentucky, 1960.

APPENDIX B

Computation of Expected Deaths

The number of expected deaths in the sample was computed in the following manner.

Age-sex-race-specific death rates were computed for ten-year age groups as of 1940, 1950, and 1960. The number of deaths for each age group was taken from reports of the Kentucky Department of Health; Table 4, Total Resident Deaths, 1940, Bulletin of the Department of Health, Vol. XIV, No. 1, August, 1941, p. 51, and from similar tables in Kentucky Vital Statistics Reports for 1950 and 1960. The population in each age group was taken for 1940 and 1950 from Table 15, 1950 Census, Vol. II, Part 17, pp. 27–29; for 1960 from Table 37, 1960 Census Final Report PC (1)–19C, p. 145.

The rates for 1940 were assumed to apply to the period 1935–44; for 1950 to the period 1945–54; and for 1960 to the period 1955–63. For each individual in the sample a hypothetical group of 1000 individuals of the same sex and age, as of the year in which the subject was first admitted to the Lexington hospital, was used as a cohort to which the appropriate death rates were applied, year by year, to 1963. This procedure gave the expected number of deaths up to 1963, for the cohort corresponding to one sample subject. The sum of expected deaths for all cohorts, divided by 1000, is the number of expected deaths in the sample.

In the procedure described, some errors are introduced by the use of rates for 10-year age groups, and by using the rates for mid-points as those of 10-year periods, but these errors should cancel out. Kentucky rates are the most appropriate to use, since most subjects, even those who eventually moved from the State, had lived much of the time in Kentucky.

The procedure computes expected deaths for full years, to 1963. In effect, therefore, it computes deaths between the date of first admission and the 1963 anniversary of that admission. Since the anniversaries can be assumed to be spread evenly over 1963, the results of the procedure should be the same as if computations were to July 1, 1963 for each subject.

Status as alive or dead was checked as of July 1, 1963 for all subjects who were residents of Kentucky, and thus for the majority of the sample. The interviews with subjects living in other States were almost all conducted between January and October, 1963. It is conceivable that one or two of the latter, here treated as alive in July, 1963, had died by then, but the probability is small.

335-199—69——19

APPENDIX C

Causes of Death

Table 1. Causes of death, by sex

Code No.	Cause	Male	Female
1	Tuberculosis of respiratory system	11	0
2	Tuberculosis of meninges and central nervous system	0	1
5	Tuberculosis, all other forms	1	0
20	Septicemia and pyemia	0	1
43	All other diseases classified as infective and parasitic	1	0
47	Malignant neoplasms of intestine, except rectum	1	0
49	Malignant neoplasms of larynx	0	1
50	Malignant neoplasms of trachea, bronchus and lung, not specified as secondary	4	0
52	Malignant neoplasms of cervix uteri	0	1
57	Malignant neoplasms of all other and unspecified sites	1	0
60	Benign neoplasms and neoplasms of unspecified nature	0	1
63	Diabetes mellitus	4	1
66	Allergic disorders; all other endocrine, metabolic, and blood diseases	2	1
67	Psychoses	1	0
68	Psychoneuroses and disorders of personality	8	0
70	Vascular lesions affecting central nervous system	9	4
80	Chronic rheumatic heart disease	2	1
81	Arteriosclerotic and degenerative heart disease	26	3
82	Other diseases of the heart	6	0
83	Hypertension with heart disease	2	2
84	Hypertension without mention of heart	2	0
88	Influenza	0	1
89	Lobar pneumonia	1	0
90	Bronchopneumonia	1	0
91	Primary atypical, other, and unspecified pneumonia	2	0
97	All other respiratory diseases	1	0
99	Ulcer of stomach	1	0
100	Ulcer of duodenum	1	0
103	Intestinal obstruction and hernia	1	0
105	Cirrhosis of liver	7	0
107	Other diseases of digestive system	0	1
109	Chronic, other, and unspecified nephritis	5	0
112	Hyperplasia of prostate	1	0
122	Arthritis and spondylitis	1	0
137	Ill-defined and unknown causes of morbidity and mortality	2	0
138	Motor vehicle accidents	5	0
140	Accidental poisoning	5	0
141	Accidental falls	4	0
143	Accidents caused by fire and explosion of combustible material	1	0

Table 1. Causes of death, by sex—Continued

Code No.	Cause	Male	Female
147	All other accidental causes	1	1
148	Suicide and self-inflicted injury	7	0
149	Homicide and injury purposely inflicted by other persons (not in war)	2	0
	Total	130	20

Table 2. Male survival rates

Interval Following First Adm. Years	Persons Dying During Interval	Persons Withdrawing Alive During Interval	Persons Alive at Beginning of Interval	Person Years Exposed	Proportion Dying in Interval	Proportion Surviving	Cumulative Survival Rate
0–1	14	0	212	212	.0660	.9340	.9340
1–2	8	0	198	198	.0404	.9596	.8963
3	8	0	190	190	.0421	.9579	.8586
4	5	3	182	181	.0276	.9724	.8349
5	10	3	174	172	.0581	.9409	.7856
6	8	1	161	160	.0500	.9500	.7463
7	4	0	152	152	.0263	.9737	.7267
8	7	3	148	147	.0476	.9524	.6921
9	13	2	138	136	.0956	.9044	.6259
10	4	1	123	123	.0325	.9675	.6056
11	8	4	118	116	.0690	.9310	.5638
12	4	6	106	102	.0392	.9608	.5417
13	5	8	96	92	.0543	.9457	.5123
14	3	6	83	80	.0375	.9625	.4931
15	6	5	74	72	.0833	.9167	.4520
16	1	8	63	59	.0169	.9831	.4436
17	2	4	54	52	.0385	.9615	.4265
18	4	2	48	47	.0851	.9149	.3902
19	2	3	42	40	.0500	.9500	.3707
20	3	0	37	37	.0811	.9189	.3406
21	1	1	34	33	.0303	.9697	.3303
22	0	0	32	32	.0000	1.0000	.3303
23	4	5	32	30	.1333	.8667	.2863
24	5	2	23	22	.2273	.7727	.2212
25	0	8	16	11	.0000	1.0000	.2212
26	0	1	8	7	.0000	1.0000	.2212
27	0	2	7	5	.0000	1.0000	.2212
28	1	3	5	4	.2500	.7500	.1659
29	0	1	1	1	.0000	1.0000	

Table 3. Female survival rates

Interval Following First Adm. Years	Persons Dying During Interval	Persons Withdrawing Alive During Interval	Persons Alive at Beginning of Interval	Persons Years Exposed	Proportion Dying in Interval	Proportion Surviving	Cumulative Survival Rate
0–1	1	0	54	54	.0185	.9815	.9815
1–2	3	0	53	53	.0566	.9434	.9259
3	3	1	50	49	.0612	.9388	.8692
4	1	1	46	46	.0217	.9783	.8503
5	1	2	44	42	.0238	.9762	.8301
6	2	0	41	41	.0488	.9512	.7896
7	1	1	39	40	.0250	.9750	.7699
8	1	1	37	36	.0278	.9722	.7485
9	0	2	35	34	.0000	1.0000	.7485
10	0	5	33	30	.0000	1.0000	.7485
11	0	1	28	27	.0000	1.0000	.7485
12	0	3	27	25	.0000	1.0000	.7485
13	2	5	24	22	.0909	.9091	.6805
14	2	2	17	16	.1250	.8750	.5954
15	1	3	13	11	.0909	.9091	
16	0	3	9	8	.0000	1.0000	
17	1	0	6	6	.1667	.8333	
18	0	1	5	4	.0000	1.0000	
19	0	1	4	3	.0000	1.0000	
20	0	1	3	3	.0000	1.0000	
21	0	1	2	2	.0000	1.0000	
22	1	0	1	1	1.0000	.0000	

APPENDIX D

Construction of Table 11.3

The two tables of this Appendix contain the data from which Table 11.3 was derived. The tables are complex, and their construction must be understood before they become useful. This construction will be explained in terms of Table D.1, for male subjects.

In the left column, the figure is the upper limit of the time period; "1" means that the period begins with the date of first discharge and extends to its first anniversary, "2" that the period is that between the first and second anniversaries, and so on.

Columns 1 through 4 add horizontally to 212, the number of male subjects, on each line. The first three columns are cumulative counts of those removed from observation, who had a second admission, or who died. The fourth column therefore represents for each year the number of men still alive, still under observation, and without a second admission, who could have been using narcotics. In columns 5 through 8 the man-years represented by the number in column 4 are distributed, in four addiction statuses.

"Removed from observation," in column 1, arises from the date of discharge. The two men removed in the fourth year, for example, might be men who were discharged in 1958 and interviewed in 1962; information is available on them for three full years, but not for all of the fourth year, and not for later years. In the fifth year three more were removed from observation, so the total of five is shown in column 1 for that year.

Similarly, 43 men had a second admission to the hospital in the first year after their first discharge, and 11 more in the second year. These figures are cumulated in column 2, and the table notes only their second admission, paying no attention to whether or not they had more than two admissions.

Once they are listed as having had a second admission, their subsequent histories are not considered in the table, and their deaths are not included in column 3. It may be noted that the highest figure in column 2 is 97, though 98 men had a second admission. In one case the subject was admitted as a prisoner awaiting trial, and his change of status to prisoner was counted by the hospital as a second admission, though there was no free time between admissions. In this table the two admissions are counted as one.

Column 2 is of interest, since it clearly indicates that those second admissions which occur take place soon after first discharge. Fifty-six percent (54 subjects) of those second admissions which will occur have occurred by the end of the second year after first discharge. By the end of 4 years, 74 percent and by the end of 9 years, 90 percent of those patients who will be readmitted have been readmitted. Since only a few have been removed from observation at these points, these percentages could not be much reduced even if most of those removed were eventually readmitted.

Seventeen men died in the first year after their first discharge, and four more in the second, and these are shown in column 3. Column 4 shows the number of subjects not yet removed from observation, not yet readmitted, and not yet dead. It represents, therefore, the number of men who could be using narcotics, or who could be abstinent. This is also the number of man-years which can be distributed in such categories.

The four columns on the right of the table take these man-years, and assign them, in percentages, to four statuses—unknown, addicted, in institutions, and off narcotics. In this table, "off narcotics" is to be taken as meaning that the subjects were not addicted to narcotics. It includes those who were alcoholic or addicted to barbiturates, and even the small number who were using narcotics occasionally. This usage differs from that employed in most of this report. It is justified here by the assumption, which is almost but not completely accurate, that it is narcotic addiction, rather than alcoholism or other problems, which leads to readmissions.

Because columns one, two and three are cumulative, the number of man-years in the fourth column steadily decreases, so the percentages in the lower lines of the table are based on smaller numbers and presumably are less reliable than the percentages for earlier years.

For the first fifteen years column 5 shows that about five percent of the man-years could not be assigned to one of the meaningful categories. Column 6 shows that the percentage addicted is 45 in the first year, drops rapidly in the next two years to about 33, holds level for two years, and then drops again to between 20 and 25 percent for the sixth through thirteenth years. Then it drops again, to under ten percent, for about nine years, with an increase in the last two years. This increase means little, since the percentage reported represents only one subject for each of the last three years. The drop to under 10 percent in the 15th through 21st years is not based on much larger numbers, and should not be given much more weight, though the larger numbers and the stability of the pattern through these years lend somewhat more plausibility to the percentages reported.

The overall pattern of the column is clear. There is a steady decrease in the percentage of time spent addicted to narcotics. It is equally true, however, that this percentage never reaches zero. Of those subjects, still alive and under observation, who have not been readmitted to the hospital, some are still addicted to narcotics as long as 24 years after first discharge.

Column 7 shows more fluctuation, and a slower and smaller pattern of decrease. For about the first 8 years, about 10 to 12 percent of man-years are spent in institutions. Most of this is prison time, but it also includes hospitalizations and time spent in Veterans' domiciliaries. From the 9th to about the 16th year, the percentage of time in institutions drops below 10, but not much below. Then, in the 17th year there is a marked drop, remaining low through the 23rd year, and an increase in the past year. These, again, are the years in which the percentages are based on small numbers.

Finally, column 8 shows that the percentage of man-years off narcotics increases steadily for 18 years, then fluctuating and finally dropping when the number under observation becomes very small. At first, the percentage of man-years off narcotics is about 40, reaching 50 percent only in the 4th year and 60 percent in the 8th. The increase then is very slow, with small drops in the 12th and 13th years, until it reaches 80 percent in the 15th year. The later increases and fluctuations are less firm, but the percentage off narcotics is 85 or higher from the 16th through the 22nd year.

The general pattern of the table is clear, and indicates what one would intuitively regard as plausible—that the longer the subject remains out of the hospital the more probable it is that he is not addicted to narcotics. The table can, however, be used for more precise estimates, by being recast into the form of Table 11.3. Table 11.3 was constructed from Table D.1 in the following manner.

Since the hypothetical cohorts of Table 11.3 are assumed to have been discharged from the hospital a given number of years, and not to have had a second admission, columns 1 and 2 of Table D.1 become irrelevant; each cohort corresponds to the men included in columns 3 and 4. Since 17 died and 152 were under observation in the first year, 101 would be dead in the hypothetical cohort of 1000 in Table 11.3. The remaining columns in Table 11.3 show how the 899 men still alive would be distributed in the three addiction statuses shown, by multiplying 899 by the percentages shown in columns 5 through 8 of Table D.1.

Two minor points in this procedure require explanation. First, for Table 11.3 the "unknown" cases in column 5 of Table D.1 are assumed to fall into the other three statuses in proportion to the size of the percentage for each of these. The assumption may be wrong, but this would not change any of the figures in Table 11.3 to an appreciable degree. Second, there has been a shift from man-years to men. Table 11.3 implies that, in the first year after first discharge, 428 men were addicted to narcotics for twelve months each, 78 more spent the entire year in institutions,

Table D.1. Second admissions, deaths, and percentage of man-years addicted, in institutions, and off narcotics, for male subjects, by number of years after first discharge

	(1)	(2)	(3)	(4)	Percent of Man-Years			
Year After First Discharge	Cum. No. Removed From Observ.	Cum. No. Admitted	Cum. No. Dead	No. Under Observ.	(5) Unknown	(6) Addicted	(7) In Instits.	(8) Off Narcotics
1	--	43	17	152	4.6	45.4	8.3	41.7
2	--	54	21	137	3.6	39.0	13.1	44.2
3	--	62	28	122	4.9	31.4	15.1	48.6
4	2	72	30	108	3.7	33.0	12.0	51.3
5	5	77	34	96	3.1	33.1	11.7	52.1
6	6	84	39	83	7.2	25.9	9.8	57.0
7	6	84	44	78	6.4	25.4	10.6	57.6
8	8	86	48	70	5.7	21.3	10.5	62.5
9	10	87	55	60	6.7	20.0	8.5	64.9
10	10	87	58	57	3.5	22.2	8.0	66.2
11	13	87	59	53	3.8	23.0	6.8	66.5
12	18	89	62	43	4.6	25.4	9.5	60.5
13	21	91	64	36	5.6	22.2	10.0	62.3
14	23	94	65	30	3.3	13.3	8.6	74.7
15	25	95	67	25	4.0	8.0	6.0	82.0
16	29	95	68	20	---	6.2	7.1	86.7
17	29	97	68	18	---	5.6	0.9	93.5
18	30	97	68	17	---	5.9	---	94.1
19	30	97	70	15	---	6.7	1.1	92.2
20	30	97	70	15	---	6.7	4.4	88.9
21	30	97	71	14	---	7.1	3.0	89.9
22	32	97	72	11	---	9.1	4.5	86.4
23	33	97	75	7	---	14.3	2.4	83.3
24	35	97	75	5	---	20.0	13.3	66.7

and 393 were off narcotics the entire time. The more accurate reading would be that of 899 man-years, 428 were spent addicted to narcotics, though conceivably all of the 899 men contributed some months of addiction to this total, and similarly to the other totals. It would be justifiable, however—insofar as any inference from Table 11.3 is justified—to predict that at any given moment within the first year of discharge, of 899 living men 428 would be found to be addicted.

Table D.2 presents comparable data for the female subjects. While the general pattern roughly resembles that found in the table for men, it is much less marked, and fluctuates more. There is a decrease in the percentage of man-years addicted, but it never falls as low as it does for the men. There is also an increase in the percentage of time off narcotics, but it peaks earlier, and never rises as high as it does for the men. The initial impression one might gain is that the increase in abstinence for the women is less marked than for the men, which would be markedly at variance with the findings reported earlier.

Closer analysis will show that such an impression would not be justified. First, the numbers on which the percentages are computed are much smaller. By the end of the fifth year, the number of man-years falls to 25, a figure not reached until the 15th year for the men. It was pointed out in the discussion of the male subjects that the findings beyond the 15th year for men must, for this reason, be given less weight. For the same reason, findings beyond the 5th year for women must be treated with equal caution.

If the percentages in the last column of Table D.2 are compared with those in the last column of Table D.3, it will be observed that for the first seven years—and these are the most reliable years in both tables—the percentage off narcotics is higher for the women than for the men. It is only in the 11th year, when the number of man-years falls to 11 and below for the women, that the percentage of time off narcotics reported for the women falls appreciably below that reported for the men.

If a table like Table 11.3 were constructed for the women, it would show somewhat more abstinence for them. In the fifth year after discharge, for example, it would show 242 dead, as compared with 262 men; 243 addicted, against 252 men; 30 in institutions, against 89 men; and 485 off narcotics, against 397 men.

In the tables of this Appendix, the women do not show the marked superiority in abstinence over the men which is so clear through most of this report. The major factor explaining this is that in these tables "off narcotics" is to be taken literally, and includes those who were alcoholic or addicted to barbiturates. For the men, this makes for a large difference from tables in the body of the report, since so many were alcoholics or barbiturate addicts. Few of the women were addicted to substitutes, so adding these to the completely abstinent does not inflate the figure, as it does for men.

Table D.2. Second admissions, deaths, and percentage of man-years addicted, in institutions, and off narcotics, for female subjects, by number of years after first discharge

	(1)	(2)	(3)	(4)	Percent of Female Years		
Year After First Discharge	Cum. No. Removed From Observ.	Cum. No. Admitted	Cum. No. Dead	No. Under Observ.	(5) Addicted	(6) In Instits.	(7) Off Narcotics
1	--	14	2	38	48.7	5.5	45.8
2	--	16	4	34	39.7	3.9	56.4
3	1	16	6	31	40.6	3.2	56.2
4	1	17	7	29	37.1	4.6	58.3
5	2	19	8	25	32.0	4.0	64.0
6	3	19	9	23	37.0	----	63.0
7	3	19	10	22	40.9	0.4	58.7
8	4	19	11	20	41.2	2.5	56.3
9	6	19	11	18	33.3	0.9	65.7
10	10	19	11	14	35.7	----	64.3
11	13	19	11	11	50.0	----	50.0
12	14	19	11	10	50.0	----	50.0
13	16	19	12	7	33.3	1.2	65.5
14	16	19	13	6	33.3	----	66.7
15	17	20	14	3	33.3	----	66.7
16	17	20	14	3	33.3	33.3	33.3
17	18	20	14	2	50.0	----	50.0
18	18	20	14	2	50.0	----	50.0
19	19	20	14	1	100.0	----	----
20	19	20	14	1	100.0	----	----

INDEX OF NAMES

SUBJECT INDEX